Case Studies
in Mathematical Modeling

Case Studies
in Mathematical Modeling

Edited by
William E Boyce
Department of Mathematical Sciences,
Rensselaer Polytechnic Institute
Troy, New York, U.S.A.

Pitman Advanced Publishing Program
BOSTON · LONDON · MELBOURNE

PITMAN PUBLISHING LIMITED
39 Parker Street, London WC2B 5PB

PITMAN PUBLISHING INC.
1020 Plain Street, Marshfield, Massachusetts

Associated Companies
Pitman Publishing Pty Ltd, Melbourne
Pitman Publishing New Zealand Ltd, Wellington
Copp Clark Pitman, Toronto

First published 1981

AMS Subject Classifications: 69-XX General Applied Mathematics

Library of Congress Cataloging in Publication Data

Case studies in mathematical modeling.

  (Applicable mathematics)
  Includes bibliographies and index.
  1. Mathematical models. I. Boyce, William E. II. Series.
QA401.C35 511'8 80–14252
ISBN 0-273-08486-0

Filmset at The Universities Press, Belfast.
Printed and bound in Great Britain at The Pitman Press, Bath.

Contents

Christoph Witzgall, Judith F. Gilsinn
and Douglas R. Shier

List of contributors

Ronald A. Drew	Rensselaer Polytechnic Institute
Judith F. Gilsinn	National Bureau of Standards
Alan G. Konheim	IBM Thomas J. Watson Research Center
Jonathan K. Millen	MITRE Corporation
Bruce A. Powell	Westinghouse Research and Development Center
Lee A. Segal	Weizmann Institute for Science and Rensselaer Polytechnic Institute
Douglas R. Shier	National Bureau of Standards
Lynn O. Wilson	Bell Telephone Laboratories
Christoph Witzgall	National Bureau of Standards

The material was prepared with the support of National Science Foundation Grant No. SED75-03520. However, any opinions, findings, conclusions, or recommendations expressed herein are those of the Author(s) and do not necessarily reflect the views of NSF.

Preface

In 1976 the Department of Mathematical Sciences of Rensselaer Polytechnic Institute, with the help of a grant from the National Science Foundation, initiated a curriculum leading to the degree of Master of Science in Applied Mathematics. The purpose of this program is to provide suitable training for students who wish to prepare for careers in industry or government at the Master's level.

A new course on Advanced Mathematical Modeling was developed as a part of this degree program. A major part of this course each year are several series of lectures given by active practitioners of applied mathematics. Most of the lecturers are employed in government or industrial research laboratories, and speak with first-hand knowledge of the applications of mathematics in a nonacademic environment.

In this book we have collected the lecture notes prepared by several of the lecturers in the course. The chapters are independent of each other, and, as a group, provide a representative sample of contemporary applied mathematics in industrial and government research installations. The individual chapters vary considerably in the kind of mathematical background that is required. The level is approximately that of a senior or first-year graduate student.

It is a pleasure to express my thanks to the authors of each chapter, and to the National Science Foundation for their financial support of the program from which these lecture notes came. There is a rapidly growing body of literature at various levels on mathematical modeling. I hope that this volume will be a useful addition.

William E. Boyce
Troy, N.Y.
3 January, 1980

1 A mathematical model relating to herbicide resistance

LEE A SEGEL *Weizmann Institute for Science and Rensselaer Polytechnic Institute*

1.1 Introduction

Since correct attitudes are almost as important as professional skill in successful industrial applications of mathematics, I will depart somewhat from the usual impersonal scientific style in these notes, to insert appropriate advice and comments where it seems relevant. A conventional account of the research described here, less detailed in several respects but containing many more biological comments and some further mathematical modeling, can be found in [1].

My involvement with this project began when I was approached by a colleague at the Weizmann Institute, Dr Jonathan Gressel of the Plant Physiology Department. Dr Gressel asked if I could provide a mathematical model to underpin some of his ideas on why plants seem not to develop resistance to herbicides.

(*Comment:* Perhaps the single most important attribute of a successful *academic* researcher is the ability to discern important problems and to pursue them until a successful conclusion is reached, almost regardless of how long this takes. By contrast, an *industrial* researcher will usually operate as a 'problem solver'. He should love the challenge of an office door that is open to a diverse set of people who can describe, with varying degrees of comprehensibility, problems from many different fields on which they would like a mathematician's help, usually with temporal and economic constraints that mandate the goal of *better* understanding a phenomenon, not *fully* understanding it.)

Conversations with Dr Gressel resulted in the following general outline of the problem.

Repeated use of various antibiotics has resulted in the appearance of bacteria that are resistant to attack by these agents, and an analogous phenomenon has arisen with respect to insect resistance to insecticides. It appears, however, that little weed resistance to herbicides has been observed by farmers and agricultural specialists. The question is, why not?

Under normal conditions, without herbicide spraying, one expects a cycle of seed *germination* (some seeds pass from a dormant to a growing condition), *establishment* (tiny young plants or *shoots* appear), growth to maturity, and scattering of seeds from each mature plant at the end of the growing season.

(*Comment:* One or more of the italicized words may be new to the reader, although there is nothing difficult in their definitions. In general, mastering the jargon of a new field is fundamentally a trivial task, but one which must be undertaken at once. I have found it helpful on occasion to compile a little word-list, just like a vocabulary list that one prepares when studying a foreign language. But here the task is relatively easy, for mastery of just a dozen or two new terms is often enough to break the terminology barrier.)

Two facets of typical weed growth bear special mention. One is that whatever the vicissitudes suffered by the weeds during the year, there is approximately a uniform number of germinating seeds per unit area at the beginning of the next season. Gressel calls this the *Parkinson effect*, for it is reminiscent of 'Parkinson's law' that the amount of work expands to fill the available work-time.

A second special facet of weed growth, related to the first, is that far more dormant seeds can be found in the ground than will germinate in a given year, and that seeds retain their ability to germinate for a number of years. A typical finding concerning the slowly decaying viability of seeds is illustrated in Figure 1.1. Gressel felt that this 'seed bank' effect was an important factor in explaining the nonappearance of resistant strains. His reasoning began with the expectation that, in a large population of weed seeds or plants, there would be a few mutants that would be resistant to herbicide killing. Herbicide treatments are usually applied at the beginning of the growing season, when the weeds have just become established. These treatments should considerably increase the proportion of *resistant* shoots, compared to the *susceptibles* that are largely killed by the herbicide. (Typically, 10 percent or at best 1 percent, of the susceptibles remain after a spraying, and we can probably assume that the resistants are virtually unaffected.) But the effect of the resulting increase of resistant seeds will be markedly diminished by the presence in the ground of an overwhelming number of susceptible seeds in the seed bank.

A certain very small fraction of seeds each season is expected

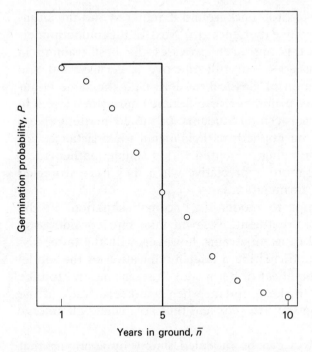

Fig. 1.1 Probability P that a seed will germinate (under optimal conditions) as a function of $\bar{n}$, its years in the ground. O, conjectured 'typical' experimental points; —, an approximation to the experimental results.

to mutate from susceptible to resistant or vice versa. This fraction could be as low as one in 10^{10}. Usually the mutants, while resistant to herbicides, will be 'less fit' in other respects, for example in the number of seeds produced per plant.

1.2 Formulation of a mathematical model

(*Pedagogical note:* At this point in the lectures I stopped and asked the class to tell me what to do next. I requested that they begin by telling me any possibly relevant mathematical or semi-mathematical statement to write on the blackboard.

It is my experience that this 'Socratic' approach to modeling is very successful. (a) With guidance of a greater or lesser extent, depending on how much time can be devoted to the exercise, students can collectively do most of the work necessary to form-ulate the desired model. Naturally, this is easier in problems like the present one where little background is required and the situation is close to everyday experience. (b) Next to a genuine model-making experience, this approach provides the best training in model-building. Less good but still effective is very careful and responsible examination of classical models, with the same equation being derived by a number of different approaches (*see* Lin and Segel [4], Section 14.1). (c) Students, or subject matter experts who have come to the applied mathematician for assistance, are often unimpressed on being presented with a simple mathematical model. They are far more appreciative when they have struggled themselves with the formulation.)

Let us first attempt to model the 'normal' situation, in the absence of herbicide treatment. We will take into consideration both susceptible and resistant strains, however, with the latter less fit than the former (anticipating a later modification of the model to take account of the effect of herbicide). It seems natural to take a discrete approach to the problem, when one keeps track of the various effects during the nth year and thus sees what will emerge during the $(n+1)$th.

The Parkinson effect can be modeled simply by assuming that the same number N seeds per unit area will germinate. Of these, in the nth year a percentage σ_n will be susceptibles and a percentage ρ_n will be resistants. These percentages will depend on the relative numbers of susceptible and resistant seeds in the seedbank, and on the relative viabilities of these seeds. In a first model, which should normally be the simplest reasonable description of the situation, let us assume that seeds in the bank retain their initial viability for $\bar{n}$ years and then cease altogether to be viable. This amounts to replacing the actual declining viability by a step function (*see* Figure 1.1).

We shall also assume (which is often the case) that only a relatively small number of the seeds in the bank ever actually germinate, so that in tallying the seeds in the bank one need only keep track of 'deposits'; withdrawals can be neglected in calculating σ_n and ρ_n.

Let $N_i^{(S)}$ and $N_i^{(R)}$ be the number of susceptible and resistant seeds deposited in the ground at the end of the ith growing season. To determine the percentage of the N annually germinating seeds that are of the two categories, we shall merely count the total seeds in the ground for the past $\bar{n}$ years and weight the count by a relative germination factor χ. This gives

$$\sigma_n = \frac{\sum_{i=n-\bar{n}}^{n-1} N_i^{(S)}}{\sum_{i=n-\bar{n}}^{n-1} [N_i^{(S)} + \chi N_i^{(R)}]}, \qquad \rho_n = \frac{\chi \sum_{i=n-\bar{n}}^{n-1} N_i^{(R)}}{\sum_{i=n-\bar{n}}^{n-1} [N_i^{(S)} + \chi N_i^{(R)}]}.$$

(1.1a,b)

The factor χ, $\chi > 0$, has been introduced here in such a way as to preserve the relationship

$$\sigma_n + \rho_n = 1,$$

(1.2)

necessitated by the fact that σ_n and ρ_n are essentially probabilities of mutually exclusive events. In most circumstances the number of resistant seeds will be very low, so that the term $\chi N_i^{(R)}$ can be neglected in the denominators of the expressions in (1.1). Then the meaning of χ is clear; it is the relative probability that a resistant seed will germinate. We shall assume that $\chi < 1$ reflects one aspect of the expected poor relative performance of the resistants in all respects except tolerance of herbicide.

Of the seeds that germinate, let β_S (β_R) be the proportion of susceptibles (resistants) that become established, ψ_S (ψ_R) the proportion of established plants that survive to the end of the season, and ν_S (ν_R) the number of seeds per survivor. Finally, let a fraction μ of each type of seed mutate to another type. With all this, the number of seeds deposited in the ground at the end of the nth growing season will be given by

$$N_n^{(S)} = \sigma_n N \phi_S (1 - \mu) + \mu \rho_n N \phi_R,$$
$$N_n^{(R)} = \rho_n N \phi_R (1 - \mu) + \mu \sigma_n N \phi_S,$$

(1.3a,b)

where

$$\phi_S \equiv \beta_S \psi_S \nu_S, \qquad \phi_R \equiv \beta_R \psi_R \nu_R.$$

(1.4a,b)

If we substitute into the above equations the expressions (1.1a) and (1.1b) for the probabilities σ_n and ρ_n, we find that the difference equations thus generated will describe the evolution of the weed population, providing that we prescribe an 'initial situation' of $\bar{n}$ years duration.

The boxed equations (1.1) and (1.3) provide what might be termed a 'basic mathematical model of the phenomenon under investigation. True, we have yet to incorporate the effect of herbicide spraying, but this only requires introduction of a factor α_S (α_R) to describe the proportion of newly established susceptibles (resistants) that survive the spray treatment.

Formulation of the basic model is often the most difficult step in the analysis. Once such a model is available, however, one begins to feel a measure of optimism that the analysis will eventually prove fruitful. The basic model may be rather intractable, so that simplifications will be mandated; additions and corrections may have to be made, but at least one has translated the essence of the given situation into a meaningful mathematical problem.

Before proceeding to consider the effect of herbicide, let us examine the normal situation. In so doing we shall take advantage of some intuition to simplify the equations considerably, so that calculations become very simple.

Under normal conditions we expect the resistants to be at a disadvantage, to be *less fit* in biological parlance. This we express by the inequalities

$$\chi < 1, \qquad \phi_R < \phi_S. \tag{1.5}$$

The first of these we have already postulated; it refers to seed viability. The second inequality establishes overall susceptible superiority in the combined areas of germination, establishment, and reproductivity.

In the absence of mutation it is fairly clear that the inferior fitness of the resistant will lead eventually to its extinction. In mathematical terms, one expects that, given (1.5), the solution of equations (1.1) and (1.3), with $\mu = 0$, regardless of initial conditions, will be such that

$$\lim_{n \to \infty} N_n^{(R)} = 0.$$

With mutations, a small number of resistants should remain in the population, for every year a few susceptible seeds mutate to resistants. The 'back mutation' of resistants to susceptibles should be negligible, for this is a very small fraction of a relatively tiny number. Thus for realistic values of the various variables and parameters we should be able to approximate (1.1) by $\sigma_n \approx 1$, $\rho_n \ll 1$ (nearly all germinating seeds will be resistant) and (1.3a) by

$$N_n^{(S)} \approx N\phi_S \equiv N_C^{(S)}. \tag{1.6}$$

To find the small number of resistants we have from (1.1b) and (1.3b) the approximate equation

$$N_n^{(R)} \approx \frac{f}{\bar{n}} \sum_{i=n-\bar{n}}^{n-1} N_i^{(R)} + \mu N \phi_S.$$
(1.7)

Here we have employed the parameter

$$f = \chi \phi_R / \phi_S, \qquad f < 1,$$
(1.8)

which we term the *preselection fitness factor*. Equation (1.7) has a steady-state solution that we shall denote by $N_C^{(R)}$; the subscript C refers to the control situation, in the absence of herbicide. We find from (1.7) that

$$N_C^{(R)} = \frac{\mu N \phi_S}{1 - f}.$$
(1.9)

As anticipated, the steady-state level is proportional to the mutation frequency. It is possible to show (*see* below) that the solution to (1.7) always approaches this steady-state value as $n \to \infty$.

We have assumed that the solution of our governing equations would tend to a state where the number of resistant plants is far less than the number of susceptibles. After simplifying our equations accordingly, we found a solution of the anticipated character. This consistency gives us confidence that our answers are a good approximation to the truth. Lin and Segel [4] (Section 6.1) discuss instances wherein consistent approximations are nonetheless inaccurate, but it appears that here we can be fairly certain that there are no hidden ill-conditionings that can give rise to the 'wretched consistent approximations' illustrated by Lin and Segel [4].

Let us now suppose that application of herbicide began in year zero, after a long sequence of normal years in which susceptible and resistant numbers are given by the control steady-state levels of (1.6) and (1.9). It is quite possible that the herbicide will lead to an increase in the numbers of resistants, but the ratio of resistants to susceptibles should nevertheless remain low for some years. Thus the general spirit of our approximate equations can be retained in analyzing the growth of the resistant population, although we must now modify (1.7) to take account of the percentage α_S (α_R) of newly established susceptibles (resistants) that survive spraying. This is done by multiplying ϕ_S (ϕ_R) by α_S (α_R). Thus, in the presence of herbicide, the behavior of a relatively small resistant population is governed by

$$N_n^{(R)} \approx \frac{f\alpha}{\bar{n}} \sum_{i=n-\bar{n}}^{n-1} N_i^{(R)} + \mu N \phi_S \alpha_S, \qquad n = 0, 1, 2, \ldots . \tag{1.10}$$

Here the *selection coefficient* α is defined by

$$\alpha \equiv \alpha_R / \alpha_S. \tag{1.11}$$

To analyze (1.10) we first look for a steady-state solution

$$N_n^{(R)} = N_{SS}^{(R)}$$

for all n. We find that

$$N_{SS}^{(R)} = \mu N \phi_S / [1 - \alpha f]. \tag{1.12}$$

This solution is positive and thus makes biological sense when

$$\alpha f \equiv \frac{\chi \phi_R \alpha_R}{\phi_S \alpha_S} < 1. \tag{1.13}$$

Indeed, in this situation the resistant has an 'overall fitness' (including herbicide resistance) that is less than the susceptible. Thus it is no surprise that a new steady-state level of the resistant can exist. We expect that the resistant level tends to the new value from arbitrary initial conditions; evidence in favor of this view will be presented shortly. When $\alpha f > 1$, the solution (1.12) has no biological meaning, but it is still a particular solution of the governing difference equation (1.10).

A little familiarity with difference equations (for example from Levy and Lessman [3]) reveals many analogies with differential equations. Here we are faced with a linear inhomogeneous difference equation, so we expect (and can easily show) that the general solution will be the sum of a particular solution of the inhomogeneous equation plus the general solution of the homogeneous. Indeed, if we write

$$N_n^{(R)} = N_{SS}^{(R)} + R_n, \tag{1.14}$$

we find that R_n satisfies the homogeneous equation

$$R_n = \frac{\alpha f}{\bar{n}} \sum_{i=n-\bar{n}}^{n-1} R_i, \qquad i = 0, 1, 2, \ldots . \tag{1.15}$$

As mentioned, the initial situation will be taken to be the steady state attained in the absence of spraying:

$$N_n^{(R)} = N_C^{(R)}, \qquad n = -\bar{n}, -(\bar{n}-1), \ldots, -1. \qquad (1.16)$$

In the new variables, this gives

$$R_n = N_C^{(R)} - N_{SS}^{(R)} = \mu N \phi_S \left[\frac{1}{1-f} - \frac{1}{1-\alpha f} \right],$$

$$n = -\bar{n}, \ldots, -1. \qquad (1.17)$$

When $\alpha f \gg 1$, we can simplify the initial conditions to

$$\boxed{\begin{aligned} R_n &= N_C^{(R)}, \qquad n = -\bar{n}, \ldots, -1; \\ N_C^{(R)} &\equiv \frac{\mu N \phi_S}{(1-f)}. \end{aligned}} \qquad (1.18)$$

This simplification will not be valid if $\alpha f \approx 1$, i.e. if in the presence of herbicide the susceptible and resistant plants are very nearly equally fit. Such a situation is 'nongeneric' and can be ignored in a broad view of the phenomenon—but this exceptional case should at least be kept in the back of one's mind.

The boxed equations (1.15) and (1.18) comprise what we could term a 'core problem', a mathematical problem the solution of which would seem to describe the absolute essence of the phenomenon.

1.3 Solution

The solution of (1.18) can be written in the form

$$R_n = \sum_{i=1}^{\bar{n}} A_i m_i^n, \qquad (1.19)$$

where the constants A_i are determined by the initial conditions (1.18) and the m_i are the $\bar{n}$ roots (assumed distinct) of the algebraic equation

$$m^{\bar{n}} = \frac{\alpha f}{\bar{n}} [m^{\bar{n}-1} + m^{\bar{n}-2} + \cdots + m + 1]. \qquad (1.20)$$

The solution tends to zero or 'blows up', depending on whether $\max_i |m_i|$ is less than or greater than unity (Problem 4). The well-known Routh–Hurwitz criterion provides a necessary and sufficient condition for all roots of a polynomial to be in the left half-plane. By a simple bilinear transformation, the half-plane can be mapped into a circle; using this idea Jury [2] wrote out the relevant criteria for the first few cases. General formulae can be found, for example, in Lindorff [5]. Application of these formulae shows that the roots of (1.20) lie within the unit circle in the complex plane if and only if αf is less than unity. In this case R_n will tend to zero, so that the number of resistant seeds $N_n^{(R)}$ will tend to the new steady-state value $N_{SS}^{(R)}$. This bears out our conjecture that a new low level of resistants will be attained if the post-herbicide fitness of the resistants remains lower than the fitness of the susceptibles.

Of primary interest when $\alpha f > 1$ is the rate at which the resistant population grows. I thought it best to try to get a feel for the situation by performing a trial numerical calculation. I used the values

$$\bar{n} = 5, \qquad \alpha f = 10, \qquad N_C^{(R)} = 2,$$

and obtained the following results from (1.15) and (1.18):

$R_{-5} = 2,$	$R_{-1} = 2,$	$R_3 = 488,$
$R_{-4} = 2,$	$R_0 = 20,$	$R_4 = 1460,$
$R_{-3} = 2,$	$R_1 = 56,$	$R_5 = 4376,$
$R_{-2} = 2,$	$R_2 = 164,$	$R_6 = 13\,088.$

One notices at once that the relation $R_i = 3R_{i-1}$ is already a good approximation for $i = 1$ and gets increasingly better. This type of approximation can be obtained from the governing equation (1.15) by noticing that

$$R_{n+1} - R_n = \frac{\alpha f}{\bar{n}}\left[\sum_{i=n+1-\bar{n}}^{n} R_i - \sum_{i=n-\bar{n}}^{n-1} R_i\right] = \frac{\alpha f}{\bar{n}}[R_n - R_{n-\bar{n}}]. \qquad (1.21)$$

Since $R_{n-\bar{n}} > 0$ in the cases that interest us, we can write

$$R_{n+1} - R_n < \frac{\alpha f}{\bar{n}} R_n,$$

so that

$$R_{n+p} < \left(1 + \frac{\alpha f}{\bar{n}}\right)^p R_n. \qquad (1.22)$$

Moreover, the right-hand side of (1.22) is a good approximation to the left-hand side to the extent that $R_{n-\bar{n}} \ll R_n$. The cases of most interest to us are those wherein the resistant population grows rapidly, so that the approximation that the resistant population grows by a factor of $1 + (\alpha f/\bar{n})$ each year will be an excellent one for our purposes. We can sum up the situation, using (1.16), in the approximate formula

$$N_n^{(R)} = N_C^{(R)} \left(1 + \frac{\alpha f}{\bar{n}}\right)^n, \qquad n = 0, 1, 2, \ldots. \tag{1.23}$$

In our trial computation, $\alpha f/\bar{n}$ was equal to two, so in this special case we recover our approximation $R_i = 3R_{i-1}$. Note that even this very simple problem illustrates one of the roles of numerical computations for a specific case – possible revelation of insights that will permit simplification and hence, perhaps, a compact analytical approximation.

1.4 Discussion

From our analysis we can conclude that the nonappearance of resistance to herbicide would seem to derive from two related possibilities. (1) Resistant strains are still less fit even when the weeds are subject to herbicide spraying. In this case the herbicide treatment merely leads to an adjustment in the low steady state of the resistant population, a state where resistants appear only because of mutations of susceptibles. (2) Resistant strains are more fit than susceptibles when subject to herbicide spraying, but it takes many years for the resistant population to grow to noticeable proportions from its initial extremely small fraction of the susceptible population.

Situation (1) or (2) above holds depending on whether or not $\alpha f < 1$. Note that the duration of the seed bank $\bar{n}$ does not enter here. But $\bar{n}$ does appear in the approximate factor by which the departure of the resistants from their pre-herbicide steady state increases, namely $1 + \alpha f/\bar{n}$.

There remains the necessity of illustrating in a little more detail the interplay of the various parameters of the problem. Attention to the traditions of the subject matter field can be very important here, for the impact of good work may not be appreciated if results are presented in unfamiliar form. For example, applied mathematicians generally prefer to work with dimensionless variables but sometimes subject matter specialists find far more congenial the use of dimensional quantities measured in certain standard units.

The qualitative question that motivated our investigation was, 'Why don't herbicide-resistant strains appear?' More quantitatively we could ask, 'How long does it take for resistant strains to be noticeable?' 'Noticeable' is not a precise word. Somewhat arbitrarily, perhaps, but very reasonably (and here Dr Gressel's knowledge of farm practices was essential), we regard the resistants as noticeable when their number, after spraying, is equal to the usual number of remaining susceptibles. For then a farmer would see double the expected number of shoots at the conclusion of his spraying program.

The number of susceptibles after spraying is $\beta_S \alpha_S N$. The number of resistants after spraying in the nth season is $N_n^{(R)}/\psi_R \nu_R$. Let n^* be the value of n that will render those two numbers equal, i.e.

$$N_{n^*}^{(R)}/\psi_R \nu_R = \beta_S \alpha_S N.$$

Using (1.23) we have

$$N_C^{(R)} \left(1+\frac{\alpha f}{\bar{n}}\right)^{n^*} \Big/ \psi_R \nu_R = \beta_S \alpha_S N. \tag{1.24}$$

Substitution for $N_C^{(R)}$ from (1.9) finally yields

$$n^* = \frac{\log \dfrac{\alpha_S}{\mu} + \log \left[\dfrac{\nu_R}{\nu_S} \dfrac{\psi_R}{\psi_S}(1-f)\right]}{\log \left(1+\dfrac{\alpha f}{\bar{n}}\right)}. \tag{1.25}$$

(Of course, to be precise we should take the smallest integer greater than n^* as the season in which sprayed resistants first exceed susceptibles.)

To bring out the role of $\bar{n}$ we can calculate the ratio of the value of n^* for an $\bar{n}$-year seed bank to the value of n^* when there is no seed bank ($\bar{n} = 1$). This is

$$\frac{n^*(\bar{n})}{n^*(1)} = \frac{\log (1+\alpha f)}{\log (1+\alpha f/\bar{n})}. \tag{1.26}$$

As we pointed out, the product of the selection factor f and the fitness factor α must be greater than unity if the resistant population is to increase. Suppose that $\bar{n}$ is sufficiently large relative to αf, so that $\alpha f/\bar{n} \ll 1$. Then the approximation $\log x \sim x$ for x small (using natural logarithms) leads to

$$\frac{n^*(\bar{n})}{n^*(1)} \approx \bar{n} \frac{\log{(1+\alpha f)}}{\alpha f}. \tag{1.27}$$

On the other hand, if the spraying is so thorough that αf is large, it could be that $\alpha f / \bar{n} \gg 1$. In this case

$$\frac{n^*(\bar{n})}{n^*(1)} \approx \frac{\log{(1+\alpha f)}}{\log{(\alpha f)} - \log{\bar{n}}}. \tag{1.28}$$

Thus if resistants would not grow too fast in the absence of a seed bank then (1.27) will be a good approximation and the length of time until the appearance of resistants is proportional to $\bar{n}$; that is, in this case the seed bank has an important effect in delaying the advent of noticeable resistance. On the other hand, when spraying permits rapid multiplication of resistants, then $\alpha f / \bar{n}$ is large and the dependence on $\bar{n}$ is a weak logarithmic one. Figure 1.2 presents graphs showing the dependence on $\bar{n}$ for different values of the parameter αf.

In further considering the effect of parameters on n^* we note that the second term in the numerator of (1.25) depends only on

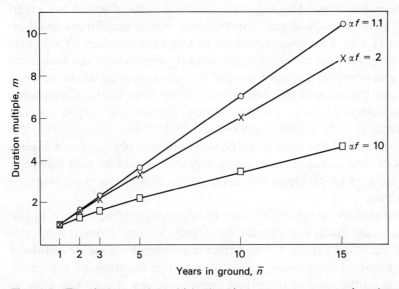

Fig. 1.2 The factor m by which the time to appearance of resistance is multiplied, when the assumed duration of a seed's viability in the seed bank is increased from one to $\bar{n}$ years. (These graphs are unaffected by approximations of the initial condition.)

the intrinsic properties of the plants and is not (in the short run) under the control of the experimenter or farmer. Note also that it is sufficient to consider the case $\bar{n} = 1$ (no seed bank), for the effect of the seed bank can be obtained from Figure 1.2. Moreover, let us write the denominator of (1.25) in the form

$$\log \left[1 + \frac{f}{\alpha_S(\bar{n}/\alpha_R)} \right].$$

We now see that in our principal calculations we can assume that the resistants are completely unaffected by herbicide ($\alpha_R = 1$ so $\alpha = 1/\alpha_S$); any effect of the herbicide on the resistants ($\alpha_R < 1$) can be determined by considering the seed bank duration to take an 'effective value' $\bar{n}/\alpha_R$.

These considerations lead us to the calculation of

$$n^* \Bigg|_{\substack{\bar{n}=1 \\ \alpha_R=1}} = \frac{\log \left(\dfrac{\alpha_S}{\mu}\right) + \log \left[\dfrac{\nu_R \psi_R}{\nu_S \psi_S} (1-f) \right]}{\log (1 + \alpha_S^{-1} f)}. \tag{1.29}$$

Figure 1.3 shows some typical results, emphasizing the role of the selection factor α_S. The calculations, the results of which are given here, have employed the approximate initial conditions used to obtain (1.18). The approximation in question requires $\alpha f \gg 1$, and thus is a good one in the most important cases, where the resistants have considerably superior overall fitness compared to the susceptibles; in these cases the calculation of the time to the appearance of resistance is most critical. When the overall fitness of the resistants is only slightly superior to that of the susceptibles, the overestimate of the time to resistance that one obtains from Figure 1.3 is of little consequence, for in any case it is clear that this time is so long as to preclude the appearance of resistance in practical situations.

Note that to calculate the time to appearance of resistance in the general case from the graphs, one finds a value from the appropriate curve on Figure 1.3 and then multiplies by a factor obtained from Figure 1.2 by using as an abcissa the duration of the seed-bank $\bar{n}$. In the case of imperfect resistance, one should use $\bar{n}/\alpha_R$ as an abcissa rather than $\bar{n}$.

Our conclusion is simple. The mathematical model presented here renders quantitative, albeit approximately so, the interplay of

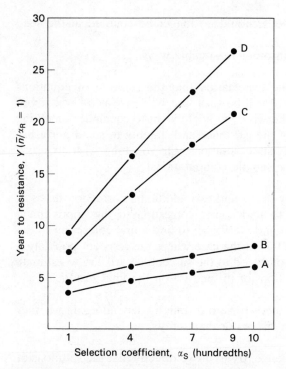

Fig. 1.3 Years Y_1 to the appearance of resistance as a function of the proportion of susceptible shoots that remain after spraying. Curve A: $f = 0.9$,
$(\nu_R\psi_R/\nu_S\psi_S) = 0.95$, $\mu = 10^{-6}$. Curve B: same as curve A except that $\mu = 10^{-8}$.
Curve C: $f = 0.1$, $(\nu_R\psi_R/\nu_S\psi_S) = 0.5$, $\mu = 10^{-6}$. Curve D: same as curve C except
that $\mu = 10^{-8}$. These graphs are appropriate for resistants that are unaffected by
herbicide ($\alpha_R = 1$), in the absence of a seedbank ($\bar{n} = 1$). See text for information
on how these restrictions can be removed.

various factors that affect the appearance of herbicide resistance.
(Further developments, and agronomic implications, can be found
in Gressel and Segel [1].) Experiments to test the importance of
these factors are now feasible; this is the next step.

Acknowledgement

The research reported on here was supported by the United
States–Israel Binational Science Foundation (BSF 5777).

Problems

(Some of the following problems are mini-projects.)

1. (a) Modify the basic model of (1.1) and (1.3) to take account of the

fact that germinated seeds should no longer be counted in the seed bank.

(b) Extend the model in other reasonable ways.

2. Provide evidence for the expectation that the solution of equations (1.1) and (1.3) with $\mu = 0$ will be such that $N_n^{(R)} \to 0$ as $n \to \infty$. If you can prove this, fine. Otherwise you might want to conclude something from an investigation of the existence and stability to small perturbations of possible steady-state solutions. Or you may wish to use a computer to make some sample computations.

3. Use perturbation theory (a) to find two additional correction terms in (1.27) and (1.28); (b) to find a first correction to the approximate solution (1.23) of (1.15) and (1.17); (c) to find a first correction to the approximate equation (1.7) in the case where the resistant population is not negligibly small compared to the susceptible. (d) Try to estimate the effect of the corrections of (b) and (c) on the final results.

4. Show that R_n of (1.19) tends to zero or infinity depending on whether $\lim_{n \to \infty} \max |m_i|$ is less than or greater than unity.

5. As a mathematical challenge, try to prove directly that the solutions of (1.20) satisfy $|m| < 1$ if and only if $\alpha f < 1$.

6. (a) Discuss existence and uniqueness theory for the solutions to (1.1) and (1.3).

   (b) On biological grounds one would expect the solutions to (1.1) and (1.3) to be positive. Try to prove this. Formulate and try to prove other general properties of the solution. (*Partial answer*: What about continuous dependence on parameters?)

7. What are the effects of stopping herbicide treatment? (After the student has attempted an answer, he or she can turn to Gressel and Segel [1] for one approach to this question.)

References

1 Gressel, J. and Segel, L. A. The paucity of plants evolving genetic resistance to herbicides: possible reasons and implications, *J. Theoret. Biol.*, **75**, 349–371, 1978.

2 Jury, E. I. *Sampled-Data Control Systems*, John Wiley, New York, 1958.

3 Levy, H. and Lessman, F. *Finite Difference Equations*, Macmillan, New York, 1961.
4 Lin, C. C. and Segel, L. A. *Mathematics Applied to Deterministic Problems in the Natural Sciences*, Macmillan, New York, 1973.
5 Lindorff, D. *Theory of Sampled-Data Control Systems*, John Wiley, New York, 1959.

2 Mathematical modeling of elevator systems

BRUCE A POWELL *Westinghouse Research and Development Center*

Summary

These notes are based on a series of lectures on the mathematical models of elevators developed by the author and Dr D. H. Shaffer since 1966. No material of a Westinghouse proprietary nature was discussed; all material has appeared in the public scientific literature or in US patents.

Most of the lecture time was spent on two distinct topics: (1) elevator banking optimization and (2) computer simulation of supervisory control strategies. The banking problem is one in which a building is split into two or more groups of contiguous floors, with each group of floors served by a different *bank* of elevators. A complete banking arrangement for a building is specified by the following parameters:

(a) number of banks,
(b) floors to be served by each bank,
(c) number of cars in each bank,
(d) speed and capacity of cars.

The process of determining optimum banking arrangements is formulated in terms of dynamic programming. Basic concepts of dynamic programming are explained in terms of a sample problem. Since the banking optimization assumes morning up-peak traffic, additional analysis of elevator service at other times of the day is required. Extensive use is made of computer simulation models of the supervisory strategy that governs the elevator's operation.

In addition to discussion of the formal mathematical models, two computer programs were run (via remote terminal to the Westinghouse Research and Development Center's Univac 1100 computer) to demonstrate that the finished product of a mathematician's work can be a useful tool to the elevator engineer and marketing representative. The programs run were the banking optimization program and the SMF2 simulator. To show the students' potential results of the use of models, a field trip was made to Agency

Building No. 2 of Albany's Empire State Plaza. The elevator system was observed, and the students participated in a small data-gathering exercise. The data were analyzed and used as input to the SMF2 simulator to show how traffic studies could be carried out.

2.1 Introduction

Before delving too deeply into the models, let me give you an idea of where I come from. Our mathematics group operates out of Westinghouse's Research and Development Center in surburban Pittsburgh. We have twelve mathematicians, all of whom have a PhD; my specialty is operations research. We do mathematical consulting for the entire corporation in areas of statistics, analysis, reliability, optimization, simulation, and operations research. A key element in all of our work is *usefulness*, because our consulting opportunities arise from the need of another Westinghouse employee to solve a mathematical problem. Our projects are typically funded from one man-week to a man-year, and no one mathematician spends full time on any single project.

In dealing with elevators, we will consider four basic points:

1. background of the problem area,
2. development of appropriate mathematical models,
3. outline and interpretation of the solution,
4. advantages and limitations of the models.

We will consider what a mathematician can bring to the party of vertical transportation. These lectures will be very applied and will be devoid of theorems.

Several threads run through all of our projects. These are

models
mathematical solutions
computers
dealing with people
implementation of results

We will see these threads via elevators. The models and solution will be demonstrated via remote terminal hook-up to Westinghouse. When these lectures were presented 'live', dealing with people and implementation was exemplified during a 'field trip' to an actual elevator installation.

2.2 General information about elevators

Our elevator modeling effort began in the mid-1960s when an engineer from Westinghouse's Jersey City elevator plant came to Dr D. H. Shaffer with a request: 'Can we develop a tool to estimate elevator service in high-rise buildings?' As a result of our projects, which at their peak were funded for one man-year per year, we developed a number of models and computer programs which ultimately have proved useful both to the design engineer in the development of new and improved systems and also to the marketing engineer as a sales tool.

The first task in any modeling project is to obtain background information about that which is being studied. A little background on elevators, while not directly applicable to the models, is in order.

An *elevator* is defined as a conveyance designed to lift people and/or material vertically. The British use the word 'lift'. There are several distinct uses of elevators, among them being

(a) commercial buildings,
(b) college classroom buildings,
(c) freight elevators,
(d) dumb-waiters.

In the 1800s, there was a legitimate concern for safety. These concerns were somewhat alleviated when Elisha Otis invented a braking mechanism. Initial elevators were hydraulic, in contrast to most modern elevators which are hoisted by a system of steel ropes. Even so, hydraulic elevators are still installed in buildings that are not too tall. The speeds of today's elevators vary from 'slow' to $1800 \, \text{ft} \, \text{min}^{-1}$, which is a little more than 20 miles h^{-1} or just under $10 \, \text{m} \, \text{s}^{-1}$. Maximum speeds are limited due to considerations for pressurization in the cab and aerodynamics in the hatchway.

The student might logically ask what a mathematician can contribute to elevators, since most problems involve engineering considerations. Consider the following statements that describe a mathematician:

> he deals with numbers
> he thinks logically
> he can take a verbally stated problem and put it into mathematical form
> he can solve the mathematical problem
> he can write computer programs and interpret the results

We can say the above things about a mathematician's contribution to any problem. The following pages will illustrate the contribution to elevator modeling.

2.3 Some simple models of elevator travel time

The modeling of any transportation system will eventually deal with the time required for the vehicle to travel a certain distance. The following hypothetical role-playing situation was carried out in order to illustrate the interaction between the mathematician (i.e. the consultant) and the elevator manufacturer (i.e. the person with the problem). The lecturer – playing the role of the elevator manufacturer – asks an ill-defined question of the class, which plays the role of the mathematician: 'I have this elevator. Do you have a computer program to figure out how long it takes to get to the top?' Now, it is the student's (i.e. the consultant's) job to ask enough questions to formulate a mathematical problem. The most obvious questions are 'How far is it to the top?' and 'How fast does the elevator go?' Assuming the distance is D and the speed is v, the mathematician writes a formula for T, the time to get to the top:

$$T = D/v. \tag{2.1}$$

If $D = 180$ feet and the speed was $500\,\text{ft}\,\text{min}^{-1}$, the value of $T = 21.6$ s. (The units of feet per minute for speed and seconds for travel time are common to the elevator industry.)

But the mathematician-student suddenly realized that the elevator in equation (2.1) would start out instantaneously at $500\,\text{ft}\,\text{min}^{-1}$ and would slam into the top at full speed. Acceleration must also be considered. Let a represent acceleration. Now, the elevator's speed will be a function of time, linearly increasing until it reaches full speed v (*see* Figure 2.1). He can show that the elevator will reach full speed in time

$$t_A = \frac{v}{a}.$$

If $a = 4 \text{ ft s}^{-2}$, then $t_A = 2.1 \text{ s}$. By symmetry, the elevator will also spend t_A time units decelerating at the top. During time t_A, the car traveled a certain distance which can be derived easily from the laws of motion:

$$v = \frac{ds}{dt} = at,$$

$$\int ds = \int_0^{t_A} at \, dt = \frac{v^2}{2a}.$$

Therefore, the distance traveled during both acceleration and deceleration is v^2/a. For $a = 4 \text{ ft s}^{-2}$, this distance is 17.4 ft. The remaining distance $(D - v^2/a) = 162.6 \text{ ft}$ requires time $(D - v^2/a)/v$ or 19.5 s. The total travel time is thus

$$T = \frac{D - v^2/a}{v} + 2\frac{v}{a} = \frac{D}{v} + \frac{v}{a} \tag{2.2}$$

and for this example is equal to 23.7 s. This answer is in contrast to the 21.6 s given by (2.1).

But the astute applied mathematician would know that the acceleration is not really constant either. If it were, the passengers would feel a sudden jerk upon starting and stopping. Thus, the mathematician-student could derive a third approximate formula

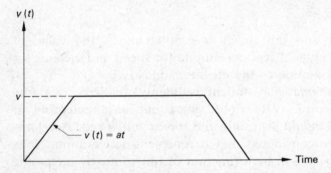

Fig. 2.1 Speed versus time.

for T which uses a J-factor:

$$\frac{da}{dt} = J \quad \text{(a constant)}.$$

The student can show that the time that the elevator takes to reach maximum acceleration is a/J and that the distance traveled during this time is

$$s = \frac{J(a/J)^3}{6}.$$

For our numerical example, with $J = 2 \text{ ft s}^{-3}$, we have $s = 2.7 \text{ ft}$.

Problems

1. Derive the formula for T, the time to reach the top, when the acceleration is not constant; that is, continue the above derivation. Call this formula (2.3).

2. With numerical examples, show how much difference there is in the three formulas (2.1), (2.2), and (2.3).

3. If your calculator could not compute powers of 3, what approximation would you make to calculate travel time?

4. What if D, the distance to the top, were small, so that the car never reached full speed? How would the formulas for T be different?

The point of these problems is to show the student how a vaguely stated question can be turned into a sequence of interesting mathematical problems. The problem is a meaningful one, because the optimization and simulation that will be discussed later requires such a formula.

2.4 Round-trip time and interval

A good way to conceptualize the motion of an elevator is to imagine a round-trip of a car† represented as motion in a circle. Figure 2.2 shows a car labeled A which begins a trip at the bottom

---

† The words car and elevator are commonly interchanged.

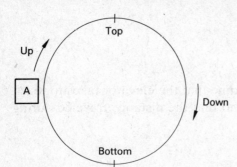

Fig. 2.2 Schematic representation of an elevator's round-trip.

of the building, goes to the top, and returns. Assuming this car requires 60 s to make the round-trip without any stops, the student can recognize that the car passes any given stop once each 60 s. The word 'stop' means a floor–direction pair; floor 5 UP is different from floor 5 DOWN. We will call this time-between-car-passings the *interval*. Now, if a passenger pushes a button at a floor, sometimes he will be so lucky that his wait will be zero. Another time, his call might just miss the car and he might have to wait 60 s. Assuming the arrival of the passenger is random in time, we can see that his average waiting time, denoted by AWT, is

$$\text{AWT} = \tfrac{1}{2} \text{ interval}$$
$$= 30 \text{ s}.$$

Now, say you have two cars, A and B, and you dispatched them together as in Figure 2.3(a). It is not difficult to see that the interval, and hence the average waiting time, has not changed. On the other hand, if the two cars were spaced 180° in time, as in Figure 2.3(b), then the interval and waiting time would be halved. This is because the interval is the time between passings of *any* car at a given stop. Figures 2.3(a) and (b) also illustrate that when 'bunching' of cars occurs, the average waiting time increases.

The task of a building's elevators in the morning up-peak is to fill the floors with its occupants. Clearly, the time required for the building to become full depends on the round-trip time of each elevator. Consider a realistic model for this round-trip of a car carrying a full load of passengers. Figure 2.4 shows schematically what happens: the car becomes loaded at the main floor, travels express to the lowest upper floor that it serves, makes a sequence of local runs, discharges passengers, and then returns empty to the

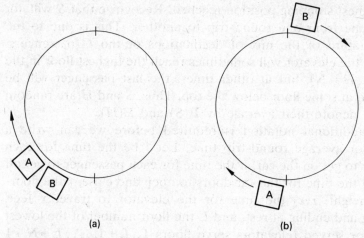

(a)   (b)

Fig. 2.3

main floor. (Note that we will have to make use of the formula for travel time which we considered earlier.)

To model the round-trip time, some notation will be necessary. Let C represent the number of passengers on a car, N the number of upper-floors served, S the number of stops actually made, and

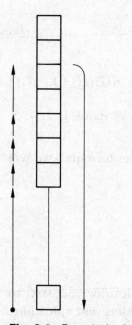

Fig. 2.4   Round-trip time.

H the highest stopping position reached. Recognize that S will not be the same from one round-trip to another. This is due to the random nature of the mix of destinations of the C passengers. Likewise, the elevator will sometimes reach the highest floor in the bank (i.e. $H = N$), but at other times, the last passenger will be discharged at some floor below the top. Thus, S and H are random variables; denote their average by $E(S)$ and $E(H)$.

Some additional notation is required before we can write a formula for average round-trip time. Let l be the time for each passenger to get on the car, u the time for each passenger to get off the car, d the time for the car doors to open and close, f the floor-to-floor height, $r(x)$ the time for the elevator to travel x feet, beginning and ending at rest, and L the floor number of the lowest upper floor served (elevators serve floors $L, L+1, \ldots, L+N-1$ for a total of N floors above the main floor). With this notation, we can write down nine separate time components of the round-trip of an elevator:

1. Time to load C passengers is lC.
2. Time to close doors at main entrance is $\frac{1}{2}d$.
3. Time to travel express to lowest stopping position is $r((L-1)f)$.
4. Time to open and close doors on local service is $dE(S)$.
5. Time to unload C passengers is uC.
6. Running time to highest stopping position is

$$r(f)(E(S)-2)+r[(E(H)-E(S)+1)f].$$

7. Running time express to main entrance is $r[(E(H)+L-1)f]$.
8. Time to open doors at main entrance is $\frac{1}{2}d$.
9. Other lost time is 10 per cent of the sum of items 1, 2, 4, 5, and 8 above.

Now, we know the running time (i.e. travel time) formula – we will use (2.2) from the previous discussion:

$$r(s) = \begin{cases} \dfrac{s}{v}+\dfrac{v}{a} & \text{if } s \geqslant v^2/a, \\[2ex] 2\sqrt{s/a} & \text{if } s < v^2/a. \end{cases}$$

Also, component 9 above is used by the elevator industry to account for random events occurring during loading and unloading. After all this notation, we know that the round trip time is the sum of the nine time components:

RDTRIP $= \sum$ Nine time components

$$= 1.1C(l+u)+1.1d(E(S)+1)$$
$$+[E(S)-2]r(f)+r((L-1)f)$$
$$+r((E(H)-E(S)+1)f)$$
$$+r((E(H)+L-1)f).$$

Consider a numerical example. Suppose we have a car that has a capacity of 19 passengers and goes 1000 ft min^{-1}. The car serves the main floor and upper floors 21–30. Floor-to-floor height of the building is 12 ft. Other parameter values are as follows: acceleration, $a = 4$ ft s^{-2}; door time, $d = 6$ s; load time, $l = 1.0$ s per passenger; unload time, $u = 0.8$ s per passenger.

The formula for RDTRIP can be used to compute round-trip time with the above parameter values and also $L = 21$, $N = 10$, $f = 12$, $v = 1000/60$, and $C = 19$. If for the moment we take it as given that

$E(S) =$ average number of stops

$= 8.65,$

$E(H) =$ Average highest stopping position reached

$= 9.85,$

then we can verify that

RDTRIP $= 170.7$ s.

The above value is for a single car. If we also know that a bank of six identical elevators serves floors 21–30, then the interval is

$$INT = \frac{RDTRIP}{Number\ of\ cars} = \frac{170.7}{6}$$

$= 28.5$ s

and the average waiting time is half the interval or

AWT $= 14.3$ s.

Let us now develop formulas for $E(S)$ and $E(H)$. First, assume that each of the C passengers chooses his floor of destination independent of every other passenger and that he is equally likely to choose any of the N floors. In probability terms, this means

Pr {any given passenger will have floor i as destination} $= 1/N$.

Define a random variable I_i as follows:

$$I_i = \begin{cases} 1 & \text{if a car stops at floor } i, \\ 0 & \text{otherwise.} \end{cases}$$

With C independent passengers, we have

$$\Pr\{I_i = 1\} = \Pr\{\text{at least one passenger's destination is } i\}$$
$$= 1 - \Pr\{\text{no passengers will have destination } i\}$$
$$= 1 - \left(1 - \frac{1}{N}\right)^C.$$

Since the random variable S (the number of stops) is the sum of I_i, we have the expected value of S given below:

$$E(S) = \sum_{i=1}^{N} E(I_i)$$
$$= \sum_{i=1}^{N} \left[1 - \left(1 - \frac{1}{N}\right)^C \right]$$
$$= N \left[1 - \left(1 - \frac{1}{N}\right)^C \right].$$

Intuitively, the average number of stops is a function of the number of floors served, N, and the number of passengers. We have already seen that for $N = 10$ and $C = 19$, $E(S) = 8.65$. Table 2.1 lists values of $E(S)$ for various combinations of N and C.

For the random variable, H, it should be clear by now why H *is* a random variable: the car does not always reach the same highest

Table 2.1 Values of $E(S)$ as function of N and C

| Number of passengers, C | Number of floors served, N | | |
	8	12	20
15	6.9	8.7	10.7
19	7.4	9.7	12.4
25	7.7	10.6	14.4

Table 2.2 Values of $E(H)$ as a function of N and C

Number of passengers, C	Number of floors served, N		
	8	12	20
15	7.9	11.7	19.2
25	8.0	11.9	19.6

stopping position. Note that

$$\text{Pr}\left\{\begin{matrix}\text{a single passenger gets off}\\ \text{the car at or before floor } k\end{matrix}\right\} = \frac{k}{N},$$

$$\text{Pr}\left\{\begin{matrix}\text{all } C \text{ passengers get off}\\ \text{at or before floor } k\end{matrix}\right\} = \left(\frac{k}{N}\right)^{C}.$$

The variable H is equivalent to the largest value in a sample of size C from a discrete uniform distribution with replacement. Therefore

$$\text{Pr}\{H = k\} = \text{Pr}\{\text{largest value} = k\}$$

$$= \text{Pr}\{\text{largest} \leq k\} - \text{Pr}\{\text{largest} \leq (k-1)\}$$

$$= \left(\frac{k}{N}\right)^{C} - \left(\frac{k-1}{N}\right)^{C}.$$

The expected value of H is therefore

$$E(H) = \sum_{k=1}^{N} k\left[\left(\frac{k}{N}\right)^{C} - \left(\frac{k-1}{N}\right)^{C}\right].$$

Table 2.2 above gives numerical examples.

2.5 Filling time for a bank of elevators

Of particular interest to a building owner is the length of time that a bank of elevators will require to carry the entire population of the floors to their destinations in the morning rush hour. With the formulas already developed, we can estimate the average *filling time*.

Denote by NCARS the number of cars in a bank of elevators. The interval has been shown to be INT = RDTRIP/NCARS. This means that every INT seconds, a car will leave the lobby fully loaded. Let TPOP be the total population of the floors served. We can see that the number of carloads of people necessary to fill the floors is TPOP/C. Therefore, it is not difficult to see that the filling time is approximately

$$FILLT \sim \frac{TPOP}{C} \cdot \frac{RDTRIP}{NCARS} .$$

As a numerical example, consider the six-car bank of 1000 ft min^{-1} elevators serving floors 21–30. The round trip time with $C = 19$ passengers was 170.7 s. If the population is equal to 125 people per upper floor, the filling time is

$$FILLT \sim \frac{1250}{19} \cdot \frac{170.7}{6}$$

$$= 1872 \text{ s},$$

which is approximately 31 min. This filling time is a measure of the ability of the elevators to move people.

Another measure of handling capacity (HC) is the number of people that the cars can move in a 5-min period, expressed as a percentage of the total population. This formula is easily derived:

$$HC = \frac{C/(RDTRIP/NCARS)}{TPOP} \times 300 \times 100.$$

For the six 1000 ft min^{-1} cars serving floors 21–30, this handling capacity is

$$HC = \frac{\frac{19}{(170.7/6)}}{1250} \times 300 \times 100$$

$$\sim 16.0 \text{ percent of the population in 5 min.}$$

The development of these measures of FILLT and HC are important in developing good banking arrangements in high-rise buildings, as will be seen in the following section.

2.6 Simple elevator banking optimization

Elevator service in high-rise buildings has been improved by the concept of banking. A building is split into two or more groups of contiguous floors, and each group of floors is served by a different

Table 2.3   Arrangement of three banks of elevators in a 30-storey building

	Floors served	Population	No. cars	Capacity, (lb)	Speed (ft min^{-1})
Bank 1	M, 2–14	2536	8	4000	700
Bank 2	M, 14–22	1841	6	4000	700
Bank 3	M, 22–30	1571	6	4000	1000

set of elevators. We will use the term bank to refer to a set of elevator cars serving common floors. A complete banking arrangements for a building is specified by the following parameters:

(a) number of banks,
(b) floors to be served by each bank,
(c) number of cars in each bank,
(d) speed and capacity of cars in each bank.

An example of a feasible banking arrangement for a 30-storey building would be to have three banks of cars arranged as shown in Table 2.3.

Figure 2.5 shows a schematic representation of a building with 3 banks of elevators. The solid lines represent express elevator service, and the broken lines represent floors to which local service is rendered. An alternative banking arrangement might be to use 4 banks instead of 3, with different floor splits, numbers of cars per bank, and speeds.

This section describes a computerized optimization procedure based on a dynamic programming algorithm for finding banking arrangements for multistorey buildings that will (i) equalize service among all banks, (ii) keep the waiting time (as measured by the average time between car departures from the main floor) less than a predetermined maximum value, and (iii) use as few cars as possible subject to constraints developed later. The speed of cars in a given bank of elevators normally must meet or exceed the minimum speed that meets the industry's 'speed versus rise' guidelines. The optimization procedure can be used during the elevator contract negotiation process for proposed new buildings. For the planner, this procedure can provide several good banking arrangements that would meet building requirements.

As a general objective, we would like to find the banking

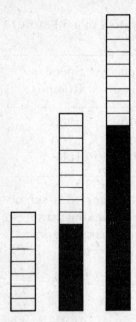

Fig. 2.5 Banking configuration where each vertical bar represents a group of elevators (usually four to eight cars).

arrangement that has the smallest number of cars that can still give 'adequate' service. The following facts were considered in determining an objective function:

1. Elevator service to a group of floors is easily measured by the total amount of time required by the cars to fill the floors during the morning up-peak period. (This is what we were calling FILLT.)
2. The waiting time at the main floor should not be 'too long'.
3. Service should be equalized among all banks.

The actual cost of each banking configuration is considered indirectly under the following guidelines:

1. A banking configuration with fewer cars that still satisfies the waiting time restriction is less costly than one requiring more cars.
2. the cost of a slower car is always less than the cost of a faster car.
3. The cost of a bank of n cars at a faster speed is always less than $(n+1)$ cars at a slower speed.

As commonly done, elevator service is equalized on the basis of filling time. The equal filling time objective is accomplished by the 'min–max' criterion which will be explained with an example. Say that you had a 20-storey building and you want to use 3 banks of elevators. Let x_1, x_2, and x_3 denote the *lowest* upper floor of each bank. Now, $x_1 = 2$ because bank 1 is the lowest. Let $F_k(i, j) =$ FILLT for the kth bank of elevators serving floors $i, i+1, \ldots, j$. Then the filling times for the 3 banks are

$$F_1(2, x_2 - 1), \qquad F_2(x_2, x_3 - 1), \qquad F_3(x_3, 20).$$

The largest of the three times is

$$\max \{F_1(2, x_2 - 1), F_2(x_2, x_3 - 1), F_3(x_3, 20)\}$$

and the min–max criterion says to choose values for x_2 and x_3 to minimize the maximum of the three filling times. Figure 2.6 illustrates the meaning of the variables x_i. The student can see that choice of values of x_2 and x_3 is a combinatorial problem. It is not difficult to see that for a very tall building (say 60 floors) and a large number of banks (say 5 banks), the optimization problem requires an algorithmic solution.

We turn to *dynamic programming* to solve the problem. Consider a building in which m banks of elevators are contemplated. A feasible banking policy is defined by

$$\{x_n, n = 1, 2, \ldots, m\},$$

where bank n serves floors $x_n, x_n + 1, \ldots, x_{n+1} - 1$. The filling time for this bank is

$$F_n(x_n, x_{n+1} - 1)$$

and the time to fill the building completely is the time that the last

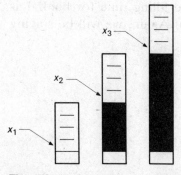

Fig. 2.6   Variables in a three-bank problem.

bank finishes:

$$\max_{n=1,2,\dots,m} \{F_n(x_n, x_{n+1}-1)\}.$$

We want to choose x_n ($n = 1, 2, \dots, m$) to minimize this maximum filling time. Note that implicit in this initial discussion is the fact that the number of cars and speeds are given for each bank. All that we are interested in is determining the values of x_i which correspond to the 'floor-splits'. As an example, we wish to use 3 banks of cars in our hypothetical 20-storey building:

> Bank 1: 3 cars with speeds of 500 ft min^{-1}
> Bank 2: 3 cars with speeds of 500 ft min^{-1}
> Bank 3: 4 cars with speeds of 700 ft min^{-1}

and we want to decide the floor-splits that determine the floors served by each bank.

Now, we launch into the dynamic programming formulation of the problem. If we had only bank 1 available to serve floors $2, 3, \dots, k$, we can calculate the filling time. This is simply $F_1(2, k)$. Equivalently,

$$M_1(k) = \text{Minimum time to fill floors 2 to } k$$
$$= \min \max \{F_1(x_1, k)\}$$
$$= F_1(2, k).$$

We refer to this as Stage 1 of the dynamic programming formulation. The problem is trivial, and the solution is obvious. This is how dynamic programming works. We 'solve' this Stage 1 problem for all values of $k = 2, 3, \dots, 20$.

For Stage 2, assume that only banks 1 and 2 are available to serve the k floors; *see* Figure 2.7. The filling time for bank 1 is $F_1(2, x_2 - 1)$ and for bank 2 is $F_2(x_2, k)$. Again, we will be solving

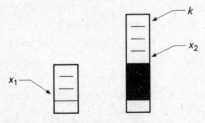

Fig. 2.7 Two-stage problem.

the problem for all values of k. The filling time for the building is

$$\max \{F_1(2, x_2 - 1), F_2(x_2, k)\}$$

and we want to choose x_2 to minimize this maximum quantity. But in Stage 1, we showed that

$$F_1(2, x_2 - 1) = M_1(x_2 - 1).$$

Therefore,

$$M_2(k) = \min_{x_2} \max \{F_2(x_2, k), M_1(x_2 - 1)\};$$

that is, bank 2 serves floors x_2 through k, and bank 1 serves floors 2 through $(x_2 - 1)$ optimally.

Define $M_n(k) = $ min–max filling time associated with the first n banks serving floors $2, 3, \ldots, k$. Then, by Bellman's 'principle of optimality', we have the following recursive equations:

$$M_n(k) = \min_{x_n} \max \{F_n(x_n, k), M_{n-1}(x_n - 1)\}.$$

When the preceding equations are solved for $n = 3$ and $k = 20$, an optimum banking policy can be obtained.

2.7 Generalized optimum elevator banking

The previous section assumed that only floor-split calculations were needed. In banking a real building, the elevator engineer has to choose not only floor splits but also the number and speeds of the cars. This section will present the dynamic programming formulation of this general problem.

To simplify the mathematical statement of the problem, we must assume the following notation: L is the lowest floor above the main lobby that is served by elevators; H is the highest floor of the building; V is the set of feasible car speeds (e.g. 500, 700, 800, 1000 ft min^{-1}); v is any particular car speed from the set V; MXWAIT is the maximum allowable waiting time; RDTRIP (x, k, v) is the average round-trip time for a car with speed v to serve floors $x, x + 1, \ldots, k$; c is the number of cars in a bank; $F(x, k, v, c)$ is the filling time for c cars of speed v serving floors x through k; CAP is the car capacity (number of passengers); POP(x, k) is the total population of floors x through k.

The filling time of floors x through k is easily determined to be the product of the number of round-trips necessary to fill the floors ($= \text{POP}(x, k)/\text{CAP}$) and the interval ($= \text{RDTRIP}(x, k, v)/c$); that is, the filling time for floors x through k served by c cars with speed v is given by

$$F(x, k, v, c) = \frac{\text{POP}(x, k)}{\text{CAP}} \times \frac{\text{RDTRIP}(x, k, v)}{c}. \qquad (2.4)$$

The details on the calculation of round-trip time are given in Gaver and Powell [1] and will not be discussed here.

The general idea of the algorithm is to use dynamic programming to perform the optimization. Briefly, we first find the best banking arrangement for 1 bank when floors $L, L + 1, \ldots, k$ are served. Possible values of k range from L to H, the highest floor in the building. Then, the best 2-bank arrangement is found by choosing x so that the second bank serves floors $x, x + 1, \ldots, k$ and bank 1 serves floors $L, L + 1, \ldots, x - 1$. Values of k again range from $L + 1$ to H. Then, the best 3-bank arrangement is found by requiring the third bank to serve floors $x, x + 1, \ldots, k$ and the first two banks to serve floors $L, L + 1, \ldots, x - 1$ as best they can. Values of k range from $L + 2$ to H. Since we have already determined the best way for 2 banks to serve floors $L, L + 1, \ldots, x - 1$, our computational problem is greatly reduced. The method continues in an analogous fashion until the number of banks equals a predetermined maximum number of banks (usually 5 or 6).

In addition to the waiting time constraint and equalized service, elevator experience dictated that four additional constraints be placed on banking algorithm. These constraints, labeled C1–C4, are given below:

C1. All banks must contain an even number of cars.
C2. Car speeds in any bank must be no slower than the speed of the cars in the next lowest bank.
C3. Car speeds are subject to a minimum speed restriction that is a function of the lowest floor in the bank.
C4. Passenger handling capacity must meet or exceed a predetermined value (e.g. 12 percent of the bank's population in a 5-min period).

These constraints arise out of tradition and years of experience. However, in order to identify the effects of such constraints, we have made the constraints optional in our computer program. An example of banking both with and without C1–C4 will be given later.

Constraint C3 has made it necessary to have a dynamic programming problem with two state variables. Assume the following notation: v_x is the minimum car speed that could be used when floor x is lowest in the bank; HC is the minimum acceptable handling capacity for all banks, expressed as a percentage of population carried away from main floor per 5-min period (this notation will be used to implement constraint C4); $M_n(v, k)$ is the filling time associated with the optimum policy when banks $1, 2, \ldots, n$ serve floors $L, L+1, \ldots, k$, and the speed for bank n must be less than or equal to v.

The optimum policy will satisfy the four new restrictions discussed above and the following conditions:

1. The filling times of all banks are as nearly equal as possible.
2. The number of cars used is as small as possible, subject to the 'even number of cars' constraint and the handling capacity constraint.
3. The waiting times are usually less than MXWAIT.

The term 'usually' is used in property 3 above because of the manner in which the number of cars in a bank is computed. As explained below, the exact number (including the fraction) of cars needed to keep a waiting time of exactly MXWAIT seconds is changed to the nearest even integer. In the expressions that follow, the square bracket notation $[\,\cdot\,]$ is used to denote the 'greatest integer less than or equal to'.

For the case of a single bank serving floors $L, L+1, \ldots, k$, we can see that

$$M_1(v, k) = F(L, k, v^*, c(v^*)), \tag{2.5}$$

where v^* is the smallest value of the speed u that satisfies the following when $x = L$:

(a) $u \in V$,
(b) $v_x \leqslant u \leqslant v$,
(c) the expression

$$c(u) = 2\left[\frac{1}{2}\frac{\text{RDTRIP}(x, k, u)}{\text{MXWAIT}} + \frac{1}{2}\right], \tag{2.6}$$

is minimized,

subject to the 5-min (or 300-s) handling capacity constraint

$$\frac{\text{CAP}}{\text{POP}(x, k)} \times \frac{300 \times c(u)}{\text{RDTRIP}(x, k, u)} \times 100 \geqslant \text{HC}.$$

The v^* and $c(v^*)$ pair is chosen simultaneously so that $c(u)$ is at a minimum. If several speeds u tie, the lowest u is chosen for v^*. Expression (2.6) is a way to denote that a number is changed to the nearest even integer. This calculation implements the requirement that there be an even number of cars in each bank.

For n banks $(n \geqslant 2)$, we have developed a set of recursive equations, the solutions to which represent the optimum banking arrangements:

$$M_n(v, k) = \min_{L+n-1 \leqslant x \leqslant k} \max \{M_{n-1}(v^*, x-1), F(x, k, v^*, c(v^*))\},$$

$$(2.7)$$

where v^* satisfies (a), (b), and (c) above. Constraint (a) requires that the value of car speed be one of those specified (e.g. 500, 700, ...). Constraint (b) guarantees a car speed of at least v_x when x is the lowest floor of bank n. Constraint (c) is used to determine the number of cars in the bank. Finally, the formulation of the problem with two state variables – speed and highest floor – guarantees that car speeds will increase as the express zone lengthens. The value of $M_n(v, H)$ is the maximum filling time associated with the optimum banking arrangement when n banks serve the entire building and the highest speed allowed in the nth bank is v. When the $\bar{v}$ is the maximum speed in the set of speeds V and m is the number of banks, then the optimum arrangement is found when the value of $M_m(\bar{v}, H)$ is obtained.

2.8 Numerical example of generalized banking

Consider the problem of determining good banking arrangements for a 30-storey building. The following information is needed in order to apply the optimization algorithm:

1. Floors served: M, 2–30.
2. Main floor height: 25 ft.
3. Floor-to-floor height: 12 ft 10 in.
4. Population by floor (upper floors only): 208, 177, 222, 130, 181, 191, 236, 236, 139, 272, 272, 272, 270, 300, 264, 200,

200, 200, 200, 207, 207, 207, 207, 205, 205, 132, 132, 136, 140.

5. Maximum allowable interval: 30 s.

6. Maximum number of banks that would be practical: 5 banks.

7. Car speeds that can be used: 500, 700, 800, 1000, 1200 ft min^{-1}.

8. Capacity of cars: 19 passengers.

9. Minimum handling capacity: 12 percent of population per 5 min period.

In addition to the above building information, we require as input to the algorithm values for the following parameters:

10. Door time.

11. Time required for each passenger to get on the car.

12. Time for each passenger to get off the car.

13. Percentage of full capacity that a car will carry on an average round trip.

Program input cards were prepared and read into the FORTRAN V computer program. The program output consists of the best banking arrangements for 2, 3, 4, and 5 banks. Computer time was approximately 60 s on the Univac 1100 computer.

Table 2.4 shows the optimum banking arrangement for 4 banks of cars, all cars having capacity of 3500 lb. A total of 22 cars are used, and the arrangement is conventional, with even numbers of cars and speeds increasing as the express run lengthens. It must be emphasized that the speeds are somewhat dependent on the values

Table 2.4 Optimum 4-bank arrangement when constraints C1–C4 are used

Bank	Floors	No. cars	Speed	Average round-trip time	Interval	Carrying capability (% population per 5-min period)
1	M, 2–11	6	500	149.9	25.0	13.3
2	M, 11–16	4	700	124.4	31.1	13.2
3	M, 16–23	6	700	157.1	26.2	14.7
4	M, 23–30	6	800	176.1	29.4	14.2

for ν_x that are used. For example, any objection to a 'slow' car (traveling at $800\,\text{ft}\,\text{min}^{-1}$) serving floors 23–30 can be circumvented by inputting a larger value for ν_{23} (e.g. $\nu_{23} = 1000\,\text{ft}\,\text{min}^{-1}$). Then the program can consider only cars which travel at $1000\,\text{ft}\,\text{min}^{-1}$ or faster for banks with the lowest floor at or above no. 23.

An interesting comparison to the optimum solution shown in Table 2.4 is the solution given when constraints C1–C4 are not imposed. As shown in Table 2.5, a saving of one car can be obtained. However, an extremely unconventional banking arrangement results. First, three of the four banks have an odd number of cars. Second, the configuration shows bank 3 with cars which travel at $1000\,\text{ft}\,\text{min}^{-1}$ while the highest bank uses slower cars (which travel at $800\,\text{ft}\,\text{min}^{-1}$). While the configuration of Table 2.5 could be installed in a real building, building owners and architects might be hesitant to install it partly because of the departure from traditional configurations and partly because of additional costs and values not considered in the mathematical model. As an afterthought, an additional computer run was made in which constraint C1 was relaxed (i.e. an even number of cars were not required) but C2–C4 still held. The optimum 4-bank solution gave a total of 21 cars, but of course the number and speeds of cars in each bank and the floor splits differ from those shown in Table 2.5.

2.9 Conclusions about banking optimization

As stated earlier, the dynamic programming algorithm represents a method that has been shown to be useful in generating good

Table 2.5 Optimum 4-bank arrangement when constraints C1–C4 are not required

Bank	Floors	No. cars	Speed	Average round-trip time	Interval	Carrying capacity (% Population per 5 min interval)
1	M, 2–10	5	500	137.6	27.5	13.1
2	M, 10–16	5	500	141.5	28.3	13.2
3	M, 16–23	5	1000	146.3	29.3	13.2
4	M, 23–30	6	800	176.1	29.4	14.2

elevator banking configurations for high-rise buildings. Since traffic is assumed to be in the up-peak mode, no consideration is given to interfloor passengers. A complete elevator system study, however, would not ignore such passengers but would consider them in subsequent simulation studies. The way many systems are designed today is first to generate 'good' banking configurations that are based on up-peak traffic and service defined by average main floor waiting time and system handling capacity. These configurations may be generated via a dynamic programming algorithm or some other means. Then, waiting time statistics are estimated for several other distinct traffic periods: balanced midmorning, lunch hour, and evening down-peak. These other traffic periods differ not only in directions of traffic flow but also in traffic intensity. Also, each building will have its own individual traffic characteristics. Whereas morning up-peak service is not difficult to estimate and will not be significantly different under any elevator system, waiting times during other traffic periods are very much strategy-dependent. As such, elevator service will vary from manufacturer to manufacturer, and therefore it is unrealistic to expect that a single analytical (i.e. nonsimulation) tool can be developed to estimate non-up-peak waiting times. Thus, the dynamic programming algorithm represents only part of the process that should be used in an elevator study.

The computer program is cheap to use. Many runs can be made for a lot less money than it costs in man-hours to do the same job. Use of the program is not restricted to one run per building. Several runs could be made, treating handling capacity, average waiting time, and floor population (if population has been estimated) as parameters. Thus, a wide range of banking configurations would be available for further consideration. Presumably, consultation with the architect and building owner would result in one or more banking configurations to be studied further with respect to non-up-peak traffic.

We have presented a systematic and scientific technique that has proved, through actual applications, to be a useful tool in the study of elevator systems. When combined with a good computer simulation of the system's response to two-way traffic, a comprehensive elevator study can be made. We are not claiming that the dynamic programming algorithm is the only method available to approach the banking problem. Time-consuming and heuristic hand calculations (such as Duty Table methods) can be replaced by a procedure that is easy to use, inexpensive, systematic, and that generates good results. By starting from a principle of equalized service subject to engineering constraints, the computer program will most likely alert the elevator engineer to good banking configurations that he might not have discovered with a back-of-an-envelope procedure.

2.10 Computer simulation of elevator systems

The previous discussion about banking optimization is only one aspect of mathematical modeling in elevator analysis. Recall that the simplifying assumption of up-peak traffic was made. This allowed us to ignore interfloor and down-traveling passengers. Also, it allowed us to ignore complex dispatching strategies.

Take a moment and ask yourself how you might devise a dispatching strategy – which is defined to be a set of rules (i.e. an algorithm) used in dispatching elevators to answer calls registered by passengers. Clearly, there are some good strategies and some that are not as efficient. During the morning up-peak, *all* passengers are assumed to be up-traveling from the main floor. Therefore, the simplest of algorithms is used: load each car in sequence, deliver the passengers, and return to the lobby for the next load. However, when traffic is heavy in both directions, the decision on dispatching each of several cars in the bank is not as obvious. Whereas the average waiting time for up-peak is approximately one-half the interval, such a statement cannot be made for other traffic periods.

Given a sequence of passengers placing demands on an elevator system, we must be able to estimate the average waiting time. First, recognize that waiting times are likely to be short during light traffic and longer during heavy traffic. Second, waiting time is a function of the dispatching strategy used. Westinghouse has several strategies; so does Otis. Third, waiting times will vary as the traffic patterns change. With these basic facts, we emphasize the following point:

> It is meaningless to quote elevator waiting times without reference to traffic conditions and dispatching strategy.

For an identical list of passengers, an Otis strategy and a Westinghouse strategy will more than likely give different waiting times. This section will consider computer simulation of passenger traffic and their service by the elevators.

Before going any farther, let us define some terms:

1. *Corridor call.* When a person wishes to use an elevator, he presses a button (up or down) in the corridor. The person is said to have registered a 'corridor call'.
2. *Car call.* When the passenger steps in the elevator, he presses a button to tell the car of his destination floor. The car is said to have a 'car call' registered for that particular floor.
3. *Waiting time.* The time elapsing between the registering of a corridor call and the canceling of the call is the 'waiting time'. The call is canceled when the car arrives at the passenger's floor of origin. Note that if more than one passenger boards a car at a floor, the waiting time is the time that the first passenger (the person who pushed the corridor button) had to wait.

The key measure of elevator service is waiting time.

If we could be an omniscient observer of an elevator system, we would see records for passengers as they arrive, register corridor calls, and are served by a car. The records would look like those shown in Table 2.6. If, in addition to the records shown in Table 2.6, we knew when each corridor call was cancelled, we would be able to calculate waiting times. Over the years, computer programs have been written to do exactly this.

Elevator simulation involves a three-stage process:

1. passenger traffic generation,

Table 2.6   Records for passengers using an elevator system

Identification of passenger	Time of call registration	Floor of origin	Floor of destination
#1	7:45:03	1	8
#2	7:45:15	1	5
#3	7:45:31	3	1
⋮	⋮	⋮	⋮
#n	12:11:08	12	7
#(n + 1)	12:12:12	1	3

2. simulation of the dispatching strategy responding to the generated passengers,

3. analysis of the simulation output – mainly waiting time data.

The mathematical model used to generate passengers will be discussed in detail later. The actual simulator will not be discussed in depth since this is company proprietary information. Suffice it to say that the simulator for Westinghouse's SMF2 strategy is an event-based simulation program, is written in the SIMULA language and is exceedingly complicated. The analysis of the simulation output consists of sorting waiting times and summarizing them in a useful form.

Before we consider the passenger generator, let us look at a sample output from the output of a simulation run. Table 2.7 shows the distribution of waiting times for a 15-min simulation during rush hour in a 14-storey building. This table illustrates the end result of a simulation.

As we discussed earlier, the waiting times will depend on the traffic characteristics. Consider the traffic periods other than up-peak. One obvious traffic period is the evening rush hour. Virtually all passengers will be traveling from their floor of 'residence' to the lobby. Also, the intensity may be more concentrated about the

Table 2.7 Waiting times from simulation program

Range of waiting times (s)	Number of corridor calls	Percentage of calls	Cumulative percentage of calls
0–5	22	56.4	56.4
5–10	4	10.3	66.7
10–15	3	7.6	74.3
15–20	5	12.9	87.2
20–25	3	7.7	94.9
25–30	1	2.5	97.4
30–40	1	2.6	100
40–50	0	0.0	100
50–60	0	0.0	100
>60	0	0.0	100

Average waiting time = 7.0 s

Maximum waiting time = 37.2 s

quarter hours (e.g. 4:45, 5:00, 5:15, etc.). During mid-day, traffic is likely to be equally balanced, with some passengers traveling up from the lobby and others traveling down to the lobby. There will also be some travel between upper floors – called interfloor traffic. The traffic intensity will be fairly light. Two other periods are of interest – 'noon-in' and 'noon-out'. The noon-out period is the time when people are going to lunch. The noon-in period is their return from lunch. As elevator modelers, we know that each traffic period is different, placing distinctly different demands on the elevator dispatching strategy. Consequently, we must recognize the differences in developing algorithms for dispatching.

2.11   Passenger traffic generator

The mathematical model that underlies the simulation of passenger traffic attempts to reflect the variability that exists in real-life traffic streams. The variability is seen in two general areas:

1. The traffic intensity as measured by the number of passengers using the elevators in a 5-min time period varies throughout the day.
2. The distribution of calls with respect to origins and destinations will vary from morning to evening.

The passenger model will be presented so that appropriate parameters can be entered and the program will generate the proper traffic pattern.

Recall what the omniscient observer saw. It is precisely this information that the passenger generator provides to the simulator. We can describe the random processes underlying the arrivals of passengers to the elevator system using simple probability concepts.

First, consider the number of passengers using the elevators in a given period of time. The Poisson process is a well-known stochastic process which has been well suited for counting the number of occurrences of an event when the occurrences are generated randomly. It has been shown that the generation of such diversified things as radioactive particles, telephone calls, failures in electronic equipment, and automobile traffic can be satisfactorily modeled with the Poisson process. The fact that the same technique could be used to model newly arriving passengers to an elevator system was shown by the author in actual observation in dozens of buildings. The Poisson probability law is easily stated:

$$\Pr\{n \text{ passengers are generated in time } T\} = \frac{(\lambda T)^n e^{-\lambda T}}{n!},$$

where λ is the arrival rate (average number of passengers per unit time) and T is a given period of time. It follows that the distribution of time between passenger arrivals is negative exponential, with mean time between arrivals of $1/\lambda$ time units. The simulator implements the generation of the times of arrivals of successive passengers $1, 2, 3, \ldots$ by the following recursive formula:

$$t_0 = 0,$$

$$t_i = t_{i-1} + \left(\frac{-\ln(r)}{\lambda}\right) \qquad i = 1, 2, 3, \ldots,$$

where t_i is the time of arrival of the ith passenger and r is a random number on the interval $(0, 1)$. Since traffic intensity is typically expressed as a percentage of the population in a 5-min period, the value of λ is given by

$$\lambda = \frac{0.01 \, \text{TI}}{300} \sum_i \text{POP}_i$$

where TI is the given traffic intensity, POP_i is the population of floor i and the unit of λ is in passengers per second.

The preceding formulas have not considered the pattern of origins and destinations. We use information on the expected use of the building to construct an *origin density vector* and an *origin–destination matrix*. The ith element of the origin density vector measures the percentage of new passengers whose floor of origin is floor i. Of all passengers with origin at floor i, the ij-th element of the origin–destination matrix measures the percentage going to floor j. Consider the following example for a four-storey building, where the origin density vector is

$i =$	1	2	3	4
Percentage from floor $i =$	40	24	12	24

and the origin–destination matrix is

To floor $j =$

		1	2	3	4
From floor $i =$	1	0	40	20	40
	2	67	0	11	22
	3	67	16	0	17
	4	67	22	11	0

Once these two items have been calculated, it becomes a simple matter to determine floors of origin and destination for each passenger with Monte Carlo sampling.

To describe how these traffic parameters are constructed in the general case, we must first recognize that traffic to and from a floor is proportional to its population. Second, we recognize that a passenger may be one of three types:

(a) up-traveling passenger with origin at the main floor,
(b) down-traveling passenger with destination of the main floor,
(c) interfloor passenger with both origin and destination other than the main floor.

Assume the following notation: A is the percentage of all passengers that are type (a); B is the percentage of all passengers that are type (b); C is the percentage of all passengers that are type (c); ORIGIN(i) is the percentage of all passengers with origin at floor i; OD(i, j) is the percentage of passengers going to floor j, given origin is floor i; POP(i) is the population of floor i. ORIGIN($\cdot$) is the origin density vector, and OD($\cdot, \cdot$) is the origin–destination matrix. The following formulas are used to compute ORIGIN($\cdot$) and OD($\cdot, \cdot$) as a function of A, B, C, and POP(i). Without loss of generality, the main floor is called floor 1 and the other floors are labelled $2, 3, \ldots, N$. First, compute

$$\rho_i = \text{POP}(i) \bigg/ \sum_{i=2}^{N} \text{POP}(i).$$

Then, the origin density vector is completely specified by

$$\begin{cases} \text{ORIGIN}(1) = A, \\ \text{ORIGIN}(i) = (B + C)\rho_i, \qquad i = 2, 3, \ldots, N. \end{cases}$$

The origin–destination matrix is somewhat more complicated:

$$OD(1, j) = \begin{cases} 0 & \text{if } j = 1, \\ 100\rho_j & \text{otherwise}; \end{cases}$$

$$OD(i, 1) = \begin{cases} 0 & \text{if } i = 1, \\ \dfrac{B}{B+C}\, 100 & \text{otherwise}; \end{cases}$$

$$OD(i, j) = \begin{cases} 0 & \text{it } i = j, \\ \dfrac{C}{B+C}\, 100p_{ij} & \text{otherwise}; \end{cases}$$

where

$$p_{ij} = POP(j) \Big/ \sum_{\substack{k=2 \\ k \ne i}}^{N} POP(k).$$

As an example of the above formulas, consider a balanced traffic pattern with $A = 40$, $B = 40$, $C = 20$, and a four-storey building with floor populations of 50, 200, 100, and 200. The values for ρ_i are $\rho_2 = 0.4$, $\rho_3 = 0.2$, $\rho_4 = 0.4$, and

$$\begin{aligned} \text{ORIGIN}(1) &= A & = 40, \\ \text{ORIGIN}(2) &= (B + C)\rho_2 = 24, \\ \text{ORIGIN}(3) &= (B + C)\rho_3 = 12, \\ \text{ORIGIN}(4) &= (B + C)\rho_4 = 24. \end{aligned}$$

Note that these numbers are shown in the origin density vector given previously. The reader can verify that the formulas for $OD(\cdot, \cdot)$ will give the results shown in the associated origin–destination matrix (*see* p. 47).

It should be noted that, in actual practice, the traffic is not always proportional to actual floor populations. For example, a sparsely populated computer center floor would typically generate much more traffic than a floor of 200 order-entry clerks. In this case, multipliers are used so that traffic is proportional to an 'effective' population.

It is obvious that a single set of values for $\text{ORIGIN}(\cdot)$ and $OD(\cdot, \cdot)$ are good for only one distinct traffic pattern. Other patterns are developed by altering the basic parameters A, B, and C. Table 2.8 lists some typical traffic patterns and parameter values.

Table 2.8 Typical traffic patterns and parameter values

Pattern	A	B	C
Morning up-peak	90	5	5
Mid-morning off peak	45	45	10
Noon – go to lunch	20	60	20
Noon – return from lunch	70	10	20
Evening down-peak	5	90	5

2.12 A simple (but efficient) dispatching strategy

When a corridor call is registered, the available cars in the bank do not stage a race to see which car gets to the call first. There exists a well-defined set of rules that assigns calls to cars. This section will briefly discuss the basic structure of a particular dispatching strategy.

Consider a hypothetical eight-storey building being served by three elevators. Figure 2.8 shows a snapshot of the elevator system at some moment in time. Car 1 (in the box) is oriented in the up-direction at floor 1 and has a car call at floor 8. (Remember that a car-call is registered by a passenger who gets on the car and

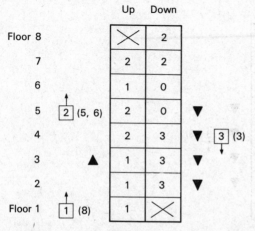

Fig. 2.8 Snapshot of eight-floor elevator system.

pushes the button to go to floor 8.) Car 2 is at floor 5 and has car calls at 5 and 6. Car 3 is at floor 4 in the down-direction with a car-call at floor 3. The symbols ▲ and ▼ represent corridor calls at the various floors.

Indicated by the numbers in the boxes in the 'up' and 'down' columns are cell assignments. A cell is a⟨direction, floor⟩ pair to which a car may be assigned. For example, the down cell at floor 7 is assigned to car 2. If a down corridor call is registered at floor 7, car 2 will (eventually) answer the call – by virtue of the cell assignment. One other term is important – that of *advanced position* of a car. The snapshot of Figure 2.8 might have been taken when car 3 was moving. Since we only track the cars with reference to the integer floor positions, it makes sense to keep track of the car according to the 'nearest floor in the travel direction at which the car can stop'. Floor 4 is the advanced position of car 3. If a car is stopped at a floor, its advanced position is equal to its actual location.

Notice that car 2 has the up cell at floor 4 – and this cell is 'behind' the car. If an up corridor call were to be registered at floor 4, it would not be efficient to assign the call to car 2. Indeed, since the cars are on the move, it does not make sense to have static cell assignments. The key to the simple dispatching strategy is to reassign the cells at regular intervals (say every 2 s).

We must therefore develop the rules by which the cells will be reassigned. The general idea is to try to spread out the cars as

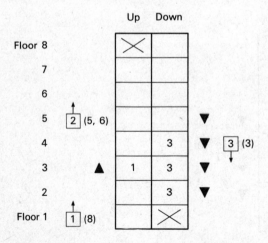

Fig. 2.9

evenly as possible and equalize the number of committed calls. Each car will be responsible for a moving zone of floors in 'front' of the car. The even distribution of cells and calls gives rise to two rules:

> Rule 1. Divide the cells evenly among the cars.
> Rule 2. Establish a maximum number of corridor calls assigned to each car.

There are many algorithmic ways that these rules can be implemented, and the method implemented in real systems is company proprietary. In the discussion to follow, many of the details will be omitted for proprietary reasons. For the system of Figure 2.8, the cell quota is five and the call quota is two.

The first step in reassignment of cells requires another rule:

> Rule 3. Remove all cell assignments except those at which there are unanswered corridor calls.

Figure 2.9 is an implementation of Rule 3.

Since car 3 violates the call quota – it can have at most two corridor calls – the down cell at floor 2 is removed.

The second step is to determine the order in which the cars will be considered for cells. A measure of 'busyness' is again determined by an algorithmic method. The car that is least busy will be given first choice of assignments.

Step 3 is to assign cells to the cars that have car calls. Car 1 has a car call at floor 8; the down-cell is given to car 1. Car 2 is given the

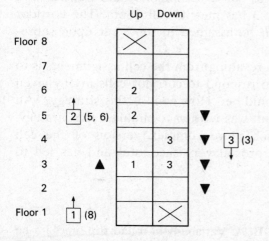

Fig. 2.10

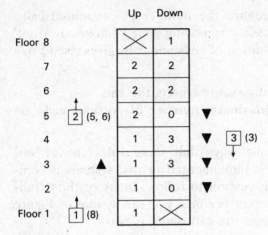

Fig. 2.11 Final cell assignment.

up cells at floors 5 and 6. Figure 2.10 shows the status of the assignments after step 3.

The final step is to assign the other cells. Again, cars are considered in order of busyness. Figure 2.11 shows the final cell assignments. Car 1 is given the up cells at floors 1, 2, and 4 – in addition to the cells previously assigned to car 1. The cell quota is met (at most five cells) for car 1; the algorithm then moves on to car 2. The assignments are made under the quotas established by rules 1 and 2.

The student might notice that two down cells (floors 5 and 2) have not been assigned – and that is acceptable. Cars 1 and 2 have met their cell quotas. Car 3 has met its call quota. The corridor calls at floors 2 and 5 *will* be assigned to some car upon subsequent reassignments.

The dispatching strategy resulting from the cell assignments is to allow only assigned cars to respond to corridor calls in any given cell. A logical question would be: 'How good is this strategy?' An extensive computer program was written to simulate this strategy. In actual practice, a much more complex version of the cell assignment algorithm has proved very successful and has led to several US patents.

Reference

1   Gaver, D. P. and Powell, B. A. Variability in round-trip times for an elevator car during up-peak, *Trans. Sci.*, **5,** 169–179, 1971.

Additional bibliography

Bellman, R. E. and Dreyfus, S. E. *Applied Dynamic Programming*, Princeton University Press, Princeton, N.J., 1962.

Browne, J. J. and Kelly, J. J. Simulation of elevator system for world's tallest buildings, *Trans. Sci.*, **2**, 35–56, 1968.

Hirsch, M. Introduction to dispatching principles, Condensed lecture on modern elevators given to IEEE PES and IAS Division, N.Y. Section, April 11, 1978.

Hummert, G. T., Moser, T. D., and Powell, B. A. Real-time simulation of elevators, in *Proceedings of the 1978 Winter Simulation Conference, Miami Beach, Fla.*, *Dec. 4–6, 1978*, pp. 393–402.

Powell, B. A. Optimal elevator banking under heavy up-traffic, *Trans. Sci.*, **5**, 109–121, 1971.

Powell, B. A. Bounds for simplifying estimation of elevator running times, *Trans. Sci.*, **6**, 453–455, 1972.

Powell, B. A., Savino, H. C., Shaffer, D. H., and Wei, D. P. A new study technique helps improve elevator service, *Westinghouse Engineer*, **31**, 176–179, 1971.

Strakosch, G. R. *Vertical Transportation: Elevators and Escalators*, John Wiley, New York, 1967.

3 Models of traffic flow

DONALD A DREW *Rensselaer Polytechnic Institute*

3.1 Queue length at a traffic light *via* flow theory

Let us consider the following design problem. Suppose we have a road which, under normal operation, has a traffic flow q of 1000 vehicles per hour at a flow concentration k of 20 vehicles per mile. There are two intersections on this road, 0.2 miles apart. We wish to install a stoplight at one of these intersections. Our primary interest is whether the queue which forms at the downstream light backs up to the upstream intersection (*see* Figure 3.1). Clearly, if the downstream queue does interfere with the operation of the upstream intersection, then other considerations must be made, possibly installing a synchronized light at the upstream intersection. (We have already *assumed* that what happens at the upstream intersection is unimportant.)

The modeler's first task is to understand the problem, and to be reasonably sure that enough information is given to get a solution. If the problem statement is not clear, or obvious omissions in information are evident, the modeler is obligated to confront the proposer (a highway engineer, perhaps) for additional information or clarification. When we do this with our traffic problem, we get the important information that the light will be green for 2 min out of a 3-min cycle. (We have already *assumed* that what happens at the upstream intersection is unimportant.)

Let us try to answer the question using a 'simplified' model. (A 'simplified' model is one in which we neglect many things at once, in hope of obtaining a quantitative estimate that will be useful to the proposer and also will help us in checking the estimates obtained from better models.) Let us assume that we add vehicles to the queue at the rate at which they arrive at the downstream intersection. Since that flow rate is 1000 vehicles per hour, there will be $16\frac{2}{3}$ vehicles arriving at the intersection in 1 min.† If the

---

† Since it seems that a vehicle is either in the queue or not, we should now interpret what it means to have $16\frac{2}{3}$ vehicles in the queue. If we go to a stoplight and take data on the problem, we may find that the recorded queue lengths are 16, 17, 17, 16, 18, and 16 vehicles during six randomly selected cycles of the light. The average of these observations is $16\frac{2}{3}$. Thus our predicted queue length of $16\frac{2}{3}$ is an average queue length.

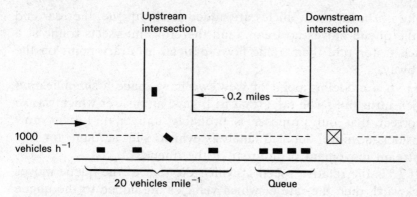

Fig. 3.1 Diagram of traffic intersections.

light is red, for that period of 1 min, then these vehicles must have queued. The resulting queue has $16\frac{2}{3}$ vehicles. The length can be calculated from knowing how much distance is occupied by each vehicle in the queueing mode. Our proposer gives us a slightly different number, the jam concentration $k_j = 257$ vehicles per mile. The above situation is not unusual; often the exact information we want must be extracted from other data. Often the data is not in quite as easy a form to reckon with as this model. For example, in a fluid mechanical problem, we may need to know a value of the pressure. Our proposer may suggest that the data is contained in a book of steam tables.

In our problem, 257 vehicles per mile translates into $\frac{1}{257} \sim$ 0.003 89 miles per vehicle, so that $16\frac{2}{3}$ vehicles occupy 0.065 miles, well short of the 0.2 miles separating the intersections. Based on this information, then, we suggest to the proposer that the lights will probably not interact.

Notice, also, that we have not used one piece of information, the concentration of the flowing stream.

Our proposer returns at a later date, and informs us that he has installed the light, and the queue is much longer than $16\frac{2}{3}$ vehicles at most times when the flow rate is 1000 vehicles per hour. In fact, he has observed that the length of the queue depends on the concentration. When the concentration reaches about 175 vehicles per mile, the queue is very long, and does interfere with the upstream intersection.

One fact which we ignored in our first analysis is that the rear of the queue moves backward as vehicles are added. Essentially, we assumed that the queued vehicles occupy no distance on the highway. In fact, as vehicles are added to the queue, the rear end of the queue moves upstream, and therefore intersects traffic at a much faster rate than traffic flows past an arbitrary point on the highway.

From a modeling point of view, we have made a simplification which turns out to be fatal (that is, it gave an answer which was so incorrect that our proposer is probably unhappy). Let us now consider a more detailed analysis which will account for the upstream movement of the rear of the queue.

If U is the relative speed at which the rear of the queue moves backward, then the rate at which vehicles are added to the queue can be expressed in one of two ways.

First the rate is Uk_j. To see this, look at the number of vehicles added to the queue between the times t and $t+\Delta t$ (Figure 3.2). The length of queue added is $U\Delta t$. The number of vehicles added to the queue, then, is $k_jU\Delta t$. Thus the rate at which vehicles are added is Uk_j.

The rate at which vehicles are added to the queue can also be expressed by

$$q + Uk. \tag{3.1}$$

To see this, consider the *flowing* vehicles at time t and time $t+\Delta t$. In Figure 3.3(b), those vehicles which have flowed through the location of the end of the queue at the instant $t+\Delta t$ during the time interval t to $t+\Delta t$ are added to the queue: this contribution is $q\Delta t$. In addition, those vehicles which lie between the end of the queue at time t and the end of the queue at time $t+\Delta t$ are also added to the queue. This contribution is $kU\Delta t$. Thus the total rate is $q+kU$.

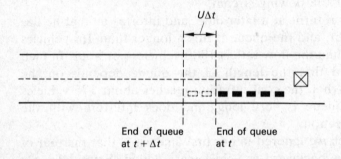

Fig. 3.2 Rate at which vehicles are added to the queue.

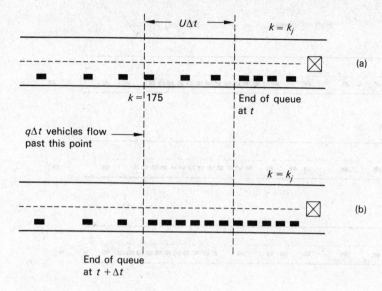

Fig. 3.3 Queues at time t and time $t + \Delta t$.

Equating the two rates of addition gives

$$U = \frac{q}{k_j - k}.$$
(3.2)

(We note that the calculation which we did before essentially used this result with $k = 0$.)

If we assume that the queue grows for 1 min (the length of the red cycle), then its length will be

$$U \times 1 = \frac{q}{k_j - k} \times 1,$$
(3.3)

which, for the heavier operating conditions with $k = 175$ vehicles per mile, is about 0.203 miles. Thus at this heavier concentration we expect the intersections to interact. We might suggest that a light be installed at the upstream intersection and that the light cycles be synchronized so that they complement each other, with the upstream light releasing vehicles so that they arrive at the downstream light as it enters its green cycle.

We have probably satisfied the proposer with our last answer that the intersections will interact. The analysis is still incomplete, however. With a queue of vehicles 0.2 miles long, it is a poor assumption that the queue grows for only the interval of the red

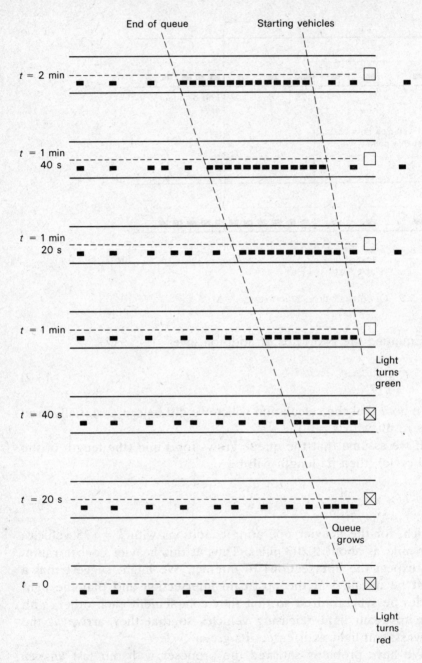

Fig. 3.4 Evolution of queue, with starting wave.

cycle. At the end of the red cycle, the lead car begins to move across the intersection, followed a short time later by the second car, and so on.

Our proposer tells us that the flow rate q_s for this starting process has been observed to be 1500 vehicles per hour, at a concentration k_s of 50 vehicles per mile. If the speed of this starting wave is U_s, then an analysis like the previous one gives

$$U_s = \frac{q_s}{k_j - k_s},\qquad\qquad (3.4)$$

which has a value of about 0.12 miles min^{-1}, as compared with the speed of the rear of the queue of about 0.20 miles min^{-1}. Thus we note that *the queue never really dissipates*; instead, the wave of vehicles starting up travels too slowly to catch up to the rear of the queue (*see* Figure 3.4).

Problems

1. If at 30 miles h^{-1}, cars are at three car lengths behind each other, what is the density of traffic? (One car length is about 16 ft.)

2. For traffic moving at 30 miles h^{-1} at three car lengths behind each other, what is the flow rate?

3. In an experiment the total number of cars to pass a position $x = x_0$ between time $t = 0$ and $t = t_0$ is given as a function of t_0, $M(x_0, t_0)$; *see* Figure 3.5. The histogram represents the actual data points, while the smooth curve represents a 'fit' of the data. What is the flow rate past x_0 at t_0; $q(x_0, t_0)$? (*Answer:* The *slope* of the line.)

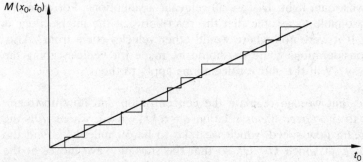

Fig. 3.5

4. Consider a semi-infinite highway $0 \leqslant x < \infty$ with no entrances or exits, except at $x = 0$. Argue that the total number of cars on the highway at time t is

$$N_0 + \int_0^t q(0, \tau) \, d\tau,$$

where N_0 is the number of cars on the highway at $t = 0$.

5. Compute the length of the queue for the light in Section 3.1 at operating conditions given by

   (a) $q = 500$ vehicles per hour, $k = 20$ vehicles per mile;
   (b) $q = 500$ vehicles per hour, $k = 200$ vehicles per mile;
   (c) $q = 1500$ vehicles per hour, $k = 50$ vehicles per mile.

6. In the above analysis, we have ignored the recycling of the light. Describe the growth of the queues obtained when the light is red for 1 min, green for 2 min, red for 1 min, and green for 2 min. Use the values of $q = 1000$ vehicles per hour, $k = 175$ vehicles per mile, $k_j = 257$ vehicles per mile, $q_s = 1500$ vehicles per hour, and $k_s = 150$ vehicles per mile.

7. If a light is installed at the upstream intersection, our assumptions about the arrival of vehicles at the downstream light will no longer be valid. One description which seems somewhat better is to assume that when the upstream light turns green, a platoon (queue) of traffic moves toward the downstream light. Argue that the speed of propagation of these starting vehicles is

   $$U_p = q_s / k_s.$$

   You may assume that the road between the intersections is empty. (*Hint:* Use an argument like that on p. 56–7 leading to equation (3.2).)
   Use your result to compute the time for the first vehicle to arrive at the downstream light. Discuss all relevant assumptions. For example, is it reasonable to assume that the road between the intersections is empty? If it were not, where would other vehicles come from? Also, what considerations could or should be made for vehicles going the other way? Will the above calculations apply to them?

8. Suppose that we can regulate the concentration and flow upstream, subject to the *Greenshields* relation $q = u_f k (1 - k/k_j)$, where u_f is the free stream flow speed, which we take to be 50 miles h^{-1}. Find the value of k at which $U = U_s$, so that the starting wave moves at the same speed as the queue grows. Use $q_s = 1500$, $k_s = 50$.

3.2 Traffic flow theory

3.2.1 Basic equations

Let us derive the basic conservation equation for traffic flow. We consider the flow of vehicles on a long road, where the features of the flow such as bottlenecks, etc., which we wish to calculate are long compared with the average distances between vehicles. Let $n(x, x + \Delta x, t)$ denote the number of vehicles between point x and point $x + \Delta x$ on the road at time t (*see* Figure 3.6). We shall *assume* that there exists $k(x, t)$ such that, for any x, Δx, and t,

$$n(x, x + \Delta x, t) = \int_{x}^{x + \Delta x} k(\hat{x}, t)\, d\hat{x}. \tag{3.5}$$

We note that by the fundamental theorem of calculus,

$$k(x, t) = \lim_{\Delta x \to 0} \frac{n(x, x + \Delta x, t)}{\Delta x}$$

if k is continuous. We shall assume that we can adequately model the situations of interest with the assumption that k is continuous.

In terms of infinitesimals, k is the number of vehicles per unit length in the infinitesimal length between x and $x + \Delta x$ at time t. Empirical values of k can be determined from aerial photographs of roads: we select some 'small' (infinitesimal) length Δx, count the vehicles between x and $x + \Delta x$, and divide by Δx.

Now let us define the flow rate $q(x, t)$. The flow rate q is simply the rate at which vehicles are passing the point x at time t. The total number Q crossing point x between time t and time $t + \Delta t$ is then given by

$$Q(x, t, t + \Delta t) = \int_{t}^{t + \Delta t} q(x, \hat{t})\, d\hat{t}. \tag{3.6}$$

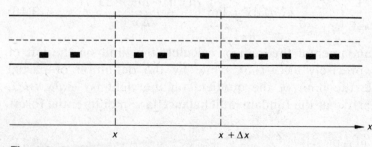

Fig. 3.6 The traffic situation at some time t.

Again, by the fundamental theorem of calculus, we have

$$q(x, t) = \lim_{\Delta t \to 0} \frac{Q(x, t, t + \Delta t)}{\Delta t}. \tag{3.7}$$

Empirical values of q can be obtained by clocked counters which keep a time record of the vehicles crossing point x. We select some 'small' Δt, count the vehicles crossing x between t and $t + \Delta t$, and divide by Δt.

Let us now consider the balance or conservation of vehicles in the road. Let us isolate a segment of the road lying between the point x and the point $x + \Delta x$ and look at the rate of change of the number of vehicles in this segment.

The balance law which applies here is that no vehicles are created or destroyed (neglecting collisions!) in this segment. Thus conservation of vehicles requires that *the rate of increase of the number of vehicles between x and $x + \Delta x$ is equal to the rate at which vehicles flow in minus the rate at which they flow out.* Thus, for any time instant t,

$$\frac{d}{dt} \int_x^{x + \Delta x} k(\hat{x}, t) \, d\hat{x} = q(x, t) - q(x + \Delta x, t). \tag{3.8}$$

This is the fundamental conservation law (balance law) for the segment of road between x and $x + \Delta x$; it is a statement about the balance we would see in a snapshot of the road (*see* Figure 3.6). We note that

$$\frac{d}{dt} \int_x^{x + \Delta x} k(\hat{x}, t) \, d\hat{x} = \int_x^{x + \Delta x} \frac{\partial k}{\partial t}(\hat{x}, t) \, d\hat{x}. \tag{3.9}$$

Let us now divide by Δx and let $\Delta x \to 0$. We have

$$\lim_{\Delta x \to 0} \frac{1}{\Delta x} \int_x^{x + \Delta x} \frac{\partial k}{\partial t}(\hat{x}, t) \, d\hat{x} = \lim_{\Delta x \to 0} \frac{q(x, t) - q(x + \Delta x, t)}{\Delta x}. \tag{3.10}$$

By the fundamental theorem of calculus, the limit on the left of (3.10) is precisely $\partial k(x, t)/\partial t$, while by the definition of partial derivative, the limit of the quotient on the right is $-\partial q(x, t)/\partial x$. Thus we arrive at the fundamental balance law in differential form:

$$\frac{\partial k}{\partial t} + \frac{\partial q}{\partial x} = 0. \tag{3.11}$$

This equation tells us how the concentration k changes in time at each x from the flow q. In order to predict how k changes, then, requires the knowledge of another variable q.

To see that this equation is qualitatively correct, consider the following thought experiment. If $\partial q/\partial x < 0$, then q is decreasing in a neighborhood of the location x, and $q(x + \varepsilon, t)$ is less than $q(x - \varepsilon, t)$ for some small positive number ε. Thus the flow out of this section of road is less than the flow in, and hence k must increase in time near that location. Mathematically, this is expressed by equation (3.11).

We note that we have one equation (3.11) for two unknown functions k and q. Thus our system is *underdetermined*. A little more thought should convince us that this underdetermination is necessary at this stage. After all, we have in no essential way used the fact that we are modeling *vehicular traffic*. The concentration and flow could just as well be concentration and flow of a pollutant in a river, or of heat in a bar, or of electrons in a wire, or almost anything which flows in a one-dimensional situation.

We need more equations which reflect the peculiarities of vehicular traffic. These equations may be balance equations (perhaps an equation for

$$\frac{d}{dt} \int_{x}^{x + \Delta x} q(\hat{x}, t)\, d\hat{x})$$

or may be simply some abstraction of empirical data pertaining to the physical situation at hand. If we use empirical data, then that data contains (we hope!) the essential constitution of the physical situation. Such a relation is called a *constitutive equation*. For the traffic flow problem, we have much data of the form flow rate plotted against concentration (q versus k), as shown in Figure 3.7. (*See* Problem 1 on p. 69.)

Thus we assume that $q = q(k)$. It is noteworthy that the flow of vehicles increases with increasing k for k small, while it decreases to zero as k approaches the jam concentration k_j (here just slightly more than 225 vehicles per mile). The maximum flow rate of 1500 vehicles per hour occurs at about 75 vehicles per mile.

Many different forms of $q(k)$ have been fitted to the data. They range from very simple forms having the above general features, to others which fit the data very accurately. One of the simpler models for $q(k)$ is *Greenshields'* model given by $q = u_f k(1 - k/k_j)$, where u_f is the (empirical) free speed of the road (the speed at

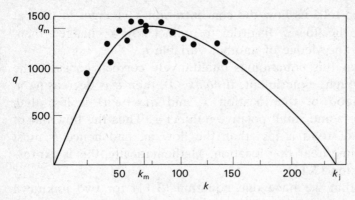

Fig. 3.7 Flow versus concentration.

which a vehicle would travel if it were alone on the highway), and k_j is the jam concentration. (*See* Problem 2 on p. 70.)

3.2.2 Propagation of a disturbance

Let us consider the evolution of the traffic concentration k on a long road. First, let us assume that k as a function of x and t can be described by some intermediary function $\sigma(x, t)$; that is, $k(x, t) = K(\sigma(x, t))$. Then, by the chain rule,

$$\frac{dk}{d\sigma} \equiv \frac{dK}{d\sigma} = \frac{\partial k}{\partial t}\frac{dt}{d\sigma} + \frac{\partial k}{\partial x}\frac{dx}{d\sigma}. \tag{3.12}$$

But the equation of motion is

$$\frac{\partial k}{\partial t} + \frac{dq}{dk}(k)\frac{\partial k}{\partial x} = 0. \tag{3.13}$$

The similarity between the operations on the right-hand side of (3.12) and the left-hand side of (3.13) suggests trying to make the two operators the same. We can do this if σ satisfies

$$\frac{dt}{d\sigma} = 1, \tag{3.14}$$

$$\frac{dx}{d\sigma} = \frac{dq}{dk}(k). \tag{3.15}$$

Then substituting (3.14) and (3.15) into (3.12) and (3.13), we have

$$\frac{dk}{d\sigma} = 0. \tag{3.16}$$

Equations (3.14) and (3.15) give curves $x = x(\sigma)$, $t = t(\sigma)$ called characteristics, on which $dk/d\sigma = 0$ by (3.16). Therefore k does not depend on σ; i.e. k is constant on these curves. But if k is constant on some curve, then $dq(k)/dk$ is constant there, too. If we integrate (3.14) and (3.15) and eliminate the parameter σ, we have

$$x = \frac{dq}{dk}(k)t + x_0$$

as the set of curves on which k is constant. Since k is constant on each of these curves, each curve is a straight line.

If we know the value of k at x_0 at $t = 0$, the value of k at each point on the line

$$x = \frac{dq}{dk}(k)t + x_0$$

is the same as it is at x_0. But in terms of x and t,

$$x_0 = x - \frac{dq}{dk}(k)t.$$

Thus

$$k(x, t) = k(x_0, 0) = k\left(x - \frac{dq}{dk}(k)t, 0\right). \tag{3.17}$$

Thus if we supply the concentration of vehicles k at time $t = 0$, the initial time, the solution is determined by the relation

$$k(x, t) = k\left(x - \frac{dq}{dk}(k)t, 0\right). \tag{3.18}$$

Well, almost. Consider the lines emanating from the neighborhood of $x = 0$ in Figure 3.8. If these lines are extended, they will cross. At a point where they cross, the equation predicts two *different* values of k. Physically, this cannot happen. Thus the partial differential equation cannot be valid everywhere along any two of the characteristic lines which cross at some point (x_1, t_1). A little thought suggests that somewhere on at least one of those characteristic lines; the solution must be discontinuous. We shall discuss the location of the discontinuity shortly. Before that, we note that the set of (x, t) where the discontinuity occurs must be such that each given line must be separated from all others which would intersect it by a discontinuity. Otherwise, two different values

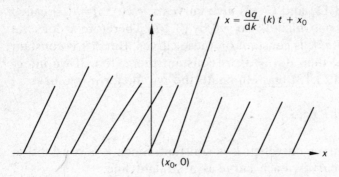

Fig. 3.8 Curves of constant k (characteristics). The slopes of the lines are given by dq/dk for the particular value of k associated with a given line.

of k would be predicted for the point of intersection. This suggests that the discontinuity must be more than a mere point, that it must be a curve in x–t space (*see* Figure 3.9). Such a curve of discontinuities is called a *shock*.

To obtain the condition valid at the shock, we must rederive the balance condition *without* the assumptions of differentiability which we made there. Consider a section of roadway which lies between $x_s - \varepsilon$ and $x_s + \varepsilon$, where x_s is the position of the shock and ε is some small positive distance. Since the shock moves in time, this section of roadway will change in time. We must account for this movement when we compute the inflow and outflow of vehicles from the segment.

First, we note that since the segment of road is small, there will be essentially no vehicles in it, and hence the rate of inflow to this segment must equal the rate of outflow from it.

Let us compute the rate of outflow from the segment of road through the end at $x_s(t) + \varepsilon$. Consider the road at two times t and

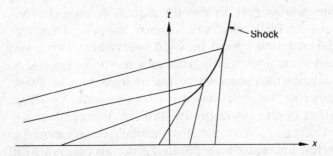

Fig. 3.9 Propagation of a discontinuity.

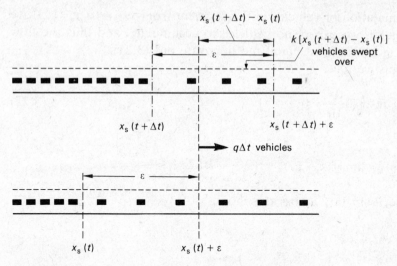

Fig. 3.10 The outflow from the segment at $x_s(t) + \varepsilon$.

$t + \Delta t$, where Δt is small (*see* Figure 3.10). The total number of vehicles which have flowed out of the segment between time t and time $t + \Delta t$ can be computed by considering the flow through the location $x_s(t) + \varepsilon$ during this time, and subtracting those which did not make it out of the segment due to the movement of the end to position $x_s(t + \Delta t) + \varepsilon$.

Thus the number of vehicles flowing out of the segment is given by

$$q(x_s(t) + \varepsilon, t)\Delta t - k(x_s(t) + \varepsilon, t)(x_s(t + \Delta t) - x_s(t)). \qquad (3.19)$$

(Note that we use the flow rate and concentrations evaluated at time t. This approximation is not critical; we could have used other representative values of the time t.)

To compute the rate at which vehicles flow out, we must divide by Δt and let $\Delta t \rightarrow 0$. The rate of outflux of vehicles is then

$$q(x_s + \varepsilon, t) - k(x_s + \varepsilon, t)\frac{\mathrm{d}x_s}{\mathrm{d}t}(t). \qquad (3.20)$$

A similar calculation of the inflow at $x_s - \varepsilon$ gives

$$q(x_s - \varepsilon, t) - k(x_s - \varepsilon, t)\frac{\mathrm{d}x_s}{\mathrm{d}t}(t). \qquad (3.21)$$

Since no vehicles are created or destroyed in this segment, the difference between these two flow rates must equal the rate of accumulation of vehicles in the segment from $x_s - \varepsilon$ to $x_s + \varepsilon$. If we let $\varepsilon \to 0$, we expect no vehicles to accumulate, and thus the flow rate in (3.20) must equal the flow rate out (3.21).

Thus we have

$$[\![q]\!] - [\![k]\!] \frac{\mathrm{d}x_s}{\mathrm{d}t} = 0, \tag{3.22}$$

where

$$[\![f]\!] = \lim_{\varepsilon \to 0} [f(x_s + \varepsilon, t) - f(x_s - \varepsilon, t)]$$

is the *jump* in f across the shock.

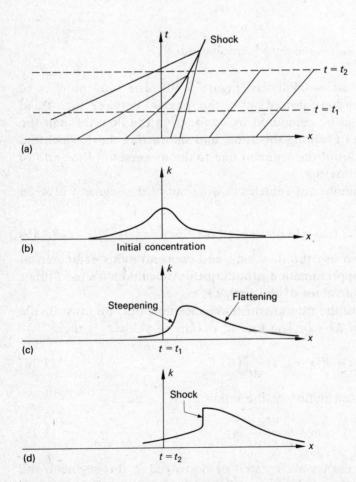

Fig. 3.11 The development of a shock.

Thus the velocity of the shock, dx_s/dt, is given by

$$\frac{q(k_2)-q(k_1)}{k_2-k_1},$$

where k_2 and k_1 are the concentrations ahead of and behind the shockwave. We note that

$$\frac{q(k_2)-q(k_1)}{k_2-k_1}$$

is the slope of the chord connecting the points $(k_1, q(k_1))$ and $(k_2, q(k_2))$ in the flow-concentration diagram (Figure 3.6).

If we use the Greenshields relation for $q(k)$, we find that

$$\frac{q(k_2)-q(k_1)}{k_2-k_1} = \frac{1}{2}\left[\frac{dq}{dk}(k_1)+\frac{dq}{dk}(k_2)\right],$$

so that dx_s/dt, the velocity of the shock, is the *average* of the slopes of the characteristics which meet at the shock.

Using this rule, and practising a bit, it becomes possible to sketch the characteristics and the shocks for relatively complex traffic flows.

For example, let us consider the propagation of a traffic 'hump'. If the 'hump' is as shown in Figure 3.11(b), with characteristics as sketched in Figure 3.11(a), we see that a shock must form somewhere around $x = 0$, and persist, intersecting pairs of characteristics at the average of their slopes.

The situation shown in Figure 3.11 corresponds to low concentration flows, with $k < k_m$, where k_m is the concentration corresponding to maximum flow. If we consider concentrations greater than k_m, the shock will propagate backward. (*See* Problem 7 on p. 72.)

We should also point out that dx_s/dt is the velocity of propagation of the shock, and is not related to the velocities of individual vehicles. The average speed of the traffic, defined by $u = q/k$, is always positive for $0 < k < k_j$. The shock speed, on the other hand, can be positive or negative, depending on the two concentrations on either side.

Problems

1. Given the data in Table 3.1, use least squares to fit

(a) Greenshields' model

$$q = u_f k (1 - k/k_j);$$

(b) Greenberg's model

$$q = u_m k \ln (k_j/k).$$

That is, in (a) choose u_f and k_j to minimize

$$\sum_{i=1}^{N} [q_i - u_f k_i (1 - k_i/k_j)]^2,$$

where (k_i, q_i) is an entry in the Table 3.1.

Table 3.1 Data for Problem 1

k (vehicles per mile)	q/k (miles h^{-1})	q (vehicles h^{-1})
33	31	1023
43	26	1018
43	27	1061
48	23	1104
50	26	1300
92	12	1104
96	12	1112
98	11	1078
103	10	1030
106	10	1060
107	10	1070
110	8	880
110	9	990
114	9	1026
118	9	1062
119	9	1071
119	9	1071
121	9	1089
134	8	1072
135	8	1080
137	8	1096

2. Compute the maximum flow rate using Greenshields' model. At what concentration does the maximum flow occur?

3. (a) Use dimensional arguments to show that q/k has the dimensions of velocity.

(b) Argue that if traffic at concentration k travels uniformly at u miles h^{-1}, the flow rate q will be equal to ku.

(c) An alternative to giving $q(k)$ (as in Figure 3.7) is to give $u(k)$. Argue that $u(k)$ should look as in Figure 3.12. Why is it monotone decreasing? Why is it zero when $k = k_j$?

4. A theoretical expression for $u(k)$ can be derived using the following considerations.

(a) A reasonable rule when following other vehicles is to allow one car length ($l = 16$ ft) for every 10 miles h^{-1} of speed. Show that this implies that the distance from one front bumper to the next, in uniform traffic, is

$$S = l\left(\frac{u}{10} + 1\right). \tag{*}$$

(b) Argue that this *spacing* S is related to the density k by

$$k = \frac{1}{S}.$$

(c) Solve ($*$) for $u = u(k)$.

(d) Sketch a graph of u versus k. Note that $u \to \infty$ as $k \to 0$. Explain why the behavior of u versus k as $k \to 0$ is not physically reasonable.

(e) A good way to 'fix up' this difficulty is to use

$$u(k) = \begin{cases} u_m, & 0 \leqslant k \leqslant k_m, \\ u = 10\,\dfrac{1-kl}{kl}, & k_m \leqslant k \leqslant k_j, \end{cases} \tag{†}$$

where u_m is the speed limit, and

$$k_m = \frac{1}{(l\,u_m/10) + 1}.$$

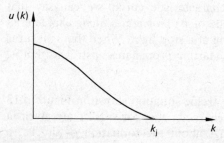

Fig. 3.12

Sketch the graph, and explain this relation.
(f) Sketch the $q(k)$ resulting from (†).

5. Suppose we are interested in the change in the number of cars $N(t)$ between two observers, one moving so his position is given by $x = a(t)$, and the other's position is given by $x = b(t)$, where $a(t) \leqslant b(t)$ for all t.

(a) Argue that

$$N(t) = \int_{a(t)}^{b(t)} k(x, t)\, dx.$$

(b) Show that

$$\frac{dN}{dt} = \frac{db}{dt} k(b, t) - \frac{da}{dt} k(a, t) + \int_a^b \frac{\partial k}{\partial t}\, dx.$$

(The easiest way to show this is to find Leibnitz' rule in an advanced calculus book.)
(c) Without using mathematics, explain why

$$\int_{a(t)}^{b(t)} k(x, t)\, dx$$

is constant if $a(t)$ and $b(t)$ both move with the traffic.
(d) Use this argument to rederive equation (3.11).

6. The characteristic lines

$$x = \frac{dq}{dk}(k)t + x_0$$

are such that (if no shocks occur) k will be constant on these lines.

(a) During an arbitrary time interval Δt, the position x on the characteristic line will change by an amount $\Delta x = V\Delta t$. Show that $V = dq/dk$.
(b) If $q(k)$ is as shown in Figure 3.7, sketch $V = dq/dk$. Note that dq/dk is negative for $k > k_m$. Explain this. What does it mean about the characteristics? Note that $u = q/k$ is still positive.
(c) Since k is constant on a characteristic curve, we can say that *information* (in this case the value of k) *propagates along* characteristics. Consider a line of cars sitting at a stop light. When the light turns green, argue that the process of starting propagates upstream (that is, against the flow).

7. Consider the propagation of the traffic situation shown in Figure 3.13 (a) and (b), where $k > k_m$. The characteristics for small t are given in Figure 5.13(b). Use your feelings about the formation of shocks to predict when a shock will form, and how it will propagate.

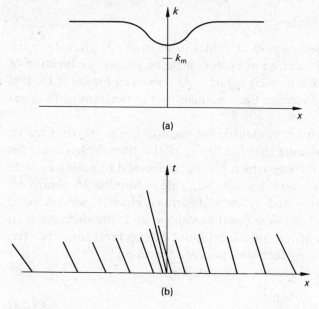

(a)

(b)

Fig. 3.13 (a) Concentration at $t = 0$. (b) Characteristics corresponding to the concentration in (a).

3.3 Car following theory

3.3.1 Introduction

Car following theory is a model for the motion of a number of individual vehicles as they proceed down a long straight road with no passing allowed. Car following theory, then, in a more 'microscopic' model for the movement of vehicular traffic than traffic flow theory. Since it is more microscopic, it allows us to include more of the mechanics of driving and somehow to include certain aspects of individual drivers.

One use which we shall make of car following theory is the prediction of the flow–concentration relation used in traffic flow theory. In addition, many interesting predictions can be made from the model, and the resulting implications and conclusions justify a detailed study of it.

The many mechanical, physiological, and psychological aspects of the driver–vehicle–road system make modeling difficult. However, let us assume that we have a line of n identical vehicles driven by n perfect drivers, in the sense that each driver can follow exactly the law of motion which pertains.

3.3.2 California Code

Let us suppose the position of vehicle j at time t is given by $x_j(t)$. We may mark the location of each vehicle by noting the location of some arbitrary point in each vehicle. As shown in Figure 3.14, it is often convenient to locate each vehicle by the position of its front bumper.

Let us now discuss a model for the motion of the jth vehicle. To do this, we shall assume that the driver of the jth vehicle causes his vehicle to move in a way which has been deemed by safety experts to result in safe freeway driving. The rule is familiar to almost all drivers, and is best stated by the California Vehicle Code: 'A good rule of thumb for following another vehicle at a safe distance is to allow yourself the length of a car [about fifteen feet] for every ten miles per hour [14.67 feet/sec] you are traveling.'

In terms of the functions $x_j(t)$, we have

$$x_{j-1}(t) - x_j(t) = l\frac{dx_j/dt}{14.67} + l, \tag{3.23}$$

where $l \equiv 15$ ft. We note that dx_j/dt is the speed of the jth vehicle. The second term on the right-hand side is the length of a vehicle, and must be added to the separation between vehicles to give the spacing $x_{j-1}(t) - x_j(t)$.

Let us assume that each driver is able to follow equation (3.23) at each time t. We note that following equation (3.23) means that a driver must accelerate (or decelerate) his vehicle according to

$$\frac{d^2x_j}{dt^2} = \lambda\left(\frac{dx_{j-1}}{dt} - \frac{dx_j}{dt}\right), \tag{3.24}$$

where $\lambda = 14.67/l \sim 1\,\text{s}^{-1}$. Thus, to follow the California Code, a driver must observe the relative velocity between his vehicle and the vehicle ahead, and adjust his acceleration or braking accordingly.

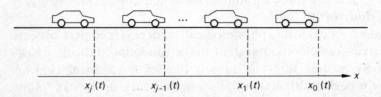

Fig. 3.14

3.3.3 The flow-concentration diagram

Let us now look at the implication of (3.23) on the flow-concentration relationship. Let us consider the section of the road occupied by the ith through $(i+m)$th vehicles, but not including the ith vehicle. The length of this section of the road is

$$(x_i - l) - (x_{i+m} - l) = x_i - x_{i+m}. \tag{3.25}$$

If we sum equation (3.23) for $j = i+1$ through $j = i+m$, we have

$$
x_i - x_{i+m} = \sum_{j=i+1}^{i+m} x_{j-1}(t) - x_j(t)
$$

$$
= \frac{1}{\lambda} \sum_{j=i+1}^{i+m} \frac{\mathrm{d}x_j}{\mathrm{d}t} + ml. \tag{3.26}
$$

The quantity

$$
\sum_{j=i+1}^{i+m} \frac{\mathrm{d}x_j}{\mathrm{d}t} = \bar{u}\,m, \tag{3.27}
$$

where $\bar{u}$ is the average speed of the vehicles in the segment of road under consideration.

The concentration of vehicles for this segment is defined to be

$$
k = \frac{m}{x_i - x_{i+m}}. \tag{3.28}
$$

As it is defined in equation (3.28), concentration is the number of vehicles per unit length.

The flow rate q is defined in terms of the average velocity by

$$q = k\bar{u}. \tag{3.29}$$

The motivation for this definition is as follows. The flow rate q, from a macroscopic point of view, is the rate at which vehicles pass a given point in the road. Since traffic travels at speed $\bar{u}$, and traffic has k vehicles per mile, then on average $k\bar{u}$ vehicles per hour pass a given point.

If we divide equation (3.26) by $x_i - x_{i+m}$, and use definitions (3.27), (3.28), and (3.29) of $\bar{u}$, k, and q, we have

$$
1 = \frac{1}{\lambda} q + lk. \tag{3.30}
$$

Thus the California Code flow-concentration relationship is given by

$$q = \lambda - \lambda lk = \lambda \left(1 - \frac{k}{k_j}\right), \tag{3.31}$$

where $k_j = 1/l$ is the jam concentration of one vehicle per vehicle length (*see* Figure 3.15).

We note that the flow-concentration relationship given by (3.31) gives a flow rate of λ when $k = 0$. This is clearly unrealistic. If $k = 0$, there are no vehicles on the road, and therefore q must be zero. Using (3.31) again, we note that q decreases with k, and $q = 0$ when $k = k_j$. This is quite realistic. We suggest that the California Code model is only valid for concentration of vehicular traffic heavy enough that drivers are essentially all operating in a 'following' mode, as opposed to operating freely on the highway. We shall discuss a car following model later which leads to an expression which seems to be valid for a larger range of concentrations.

3.3.4 A typical solution

Let us now examine the car following model in a typical (although somewhat idealized) road situation. Suppose that all the vehicles are at rest at the jam spacing, and that at $t = 0$, the lead vehicle $(j = 0)$ instantaneously accelerates to achieve a velocity v_0, a constant. The equation of motion for the second vehicle $(j = 1)$ for

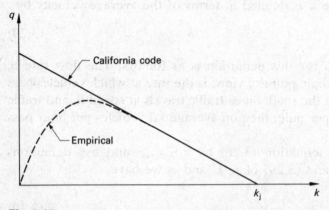

Fig. 3.15

$t > 0$, then, is

$$\frac{dv_1}{dt} + \lambda v_1 = \lambda v_0, \tag{3.32a}$$

$$v_1(0) = 0, \tag{3.32b}$$

with solution

$$v_1(t) = v_0(1 - e^{-\lambda t}). \tag{3.33}$$

The equation of motion for the third vehicle is

$$\frac{dv_2}{dt} + \lambda v_2 = \lambda v_0(1 - e^{-\lambda t}), \tag{3.34a}$$

$$v_2(0) = 0, \tag{3.34b}$$

with solution

$$v_2(t) = v_0(1 - e^{-\lambda t} - \lambda t e^{-\lambda t}). \tag{3.35}$$

The solution for the jth vehicle (Problem 1 on p. 88) can be written as

$$v_j(t) = v_0 \left(1 - e^{-\lambda t} \left[1 + \frac{\lambda t}{1!} + \cdots + \frac{(\lambda t)^{j-1}}{(j-1)!} \right] \right). \tag{3.36}$$

The locations of the vehicles can be obtained by a straightforward (if somewhat tedious) integration. (*See* Problem 2 on p. 88.) We note that for $t > 0$,

$$v_0 > v_1(t) > v_2(t) > \cdots > v_j(t) > \cdots. \tag{3.37}$$

Thus, since $x_0(0) > x_1(0) > x_2(0) > \cdots > x_j(0) > \cdots$, we have

$$x_0(t) > x_1(t) > x_2(t) > \cdots > x_j(t) > \cdots. \tag{3.38}$$

(*See* Problem 3 on p. 88.)

3.3.5 Car following with delay

A shortcoming of the model introduced in Section 3.3.2 is that it assumes that each driver can instantaneously adjust his acceleration (or braking) to account for velocity changes in the vehicle ahead.

In psychological terms, we are giving the jth driver a *stimulus*, namely the relative velocity between his vehicle and the one ahead, and we are asking him to respond by adjusting his acceleration. No real driver (nor any mechanical replacement!) can adjust his acceleration instantly; in general, there is a delay of several tenths of a second before any response occurs at all.

Thus we assume that

$$\frac{dv_i(t+T)}{dt} = \lambda(v_{i-1}(t) - v_i(t)), \tag{3.39}$$

where T is the delay. In this type of model the parameter λ is called the *sensitivity*. In this model, the jth driver observes the relative velocity $v_{j-1}(t) - v_j(t)$, and wishes to accelerate an amount $\lambda(v_{j-1}(t) - v_j(t))$. Since he is 'human', his acceleration does not occur at time t, but is delayed by T seconds.

We note that 'instantaneous' reflex actions occur with a delay of about 0.1 s. In the complex decision-making process involved in driving, certain reactions can be delayed by several tenths of a second. In a vehicle moving at 50 miles h^{-1} a delay of 0.5 s causes the vehicle to travel almost 40 extra feet. This extra distance may be crucial in an accident situation!

Let us examine the delay model in the situation described in Section 3.3.4. We assume that initially a line of vehicles is at rest at the jam density. At $t = -T$, the lead vehicle instantaneously accelerates to v_0. The equation governing the motion of the second vehicle at time t is given by

$$\frac{dv_1(t)}{dt} = \lambda(v_0 - v_1(t-T)) \tag{3.40}$$

for $t>0$.

We can integrate equation (3.40) a little bit at a time. For $0<t<T$, $v_1(t-T) = 0$. For these values of t, then,

$$v_1(t) = \lambda v_0 t. \tag{3.41}$$

For $T<t<2T$, equation (3.40) gives

$$\frac{dv_1(t)}{dt} = \lambda v_0(1 - \lambda t + \lambda T). \tag{3.42}$$

Thus

$$v_1(t) = \lambda v_0\left(t - \frac{\lambda(t-T)^2}{2}\right). \tag{3.43}$$

(*See* Problems 5 and 6 on p. 88)

3.3.6 Stability of car following models

Let us examine the stability characteristics of the car following model. There are two distinct types of stability, local and asymptotic. The concept of local stability is the question of whether a disturbance of the motion of the nth car causes the nth car to execute motions of larger and larger magnitude in time. In physical terms, suppose the driver of the nth car slams on his brakes for an instant at time $t = 0$, and then tries to adjust to 'steady' following again. If he must alternately accelerate and decelerate with bigger and bigger magnitude, his car's motion is erratic, and unstable.

Asymptotic instability is the question of whether a given motion by the zeroth car can cause a larger and larger response as we look down the line to successive cars.

Let us consider the question of asymptotic stability first. Let us assume that the zeroth car moves in some way such that $v_0^0 e^{i\omega t}$ is a component of the motion for some ω. For example, if the motion of the zeroth car is

$$v_0(t) = \sin \omega t = \frac{1}{2i} e^{i\omega t} - \frac{1}{2i} e^{-i\omega t}, \tag{3.44}$$

we shall consider the components $(1/2i)e^{i\omega t}$, $-(1/2i)e^{-i\omega t}$. By superposition, the motion of the nth car can be obtained from the solutions corresponding to these two components.

If we assume

$$v_n(t) = v_n^0 e^{i\omega t}, \qquad v_{n-1}(t) = v_{n-1}^0 e^{i\omega t}, \tag{3.45}$$

we have

$$v_n^0(i\omega e^{i\omega T} + \lambda) = \lambda v_{n-1}^0. \tag{3.46}$$

Thus

$$v_n^0 = \frac{1}{(1 + (i\omega/\lambda)e^{i\omega T})^n} v_0^0. \tag{3.47}$$

The question of asymptotic stability or instability, then, becomes the question of whether $|1 + (i\omega/\lambda)e^{i\omega T}|$ is greater than or less than one. But

$$\left| 1 + \frac{i\omega}{\lambda} e^{i\omega T} \right|^2 = 1 - \frac{2\omega}{\lambda} \sin \omega T + \frac{\omega^2}{\lambda^2}. \tag{3.48}$$

Then

$$\left|1+\frac{i\omega}{\lambda}e^{i\omega T}\right|<1$$

if

$$\frac{\omega^2}{\lambda^2}<\frac{2\omega}{\lambda}\sin\omega T. \tag{3.49}$$

If $\omega/\lambda>0$, then $\omega/\lambda<2\sin\omega T$, or if $\omega/\lambda<0$, $\omega/\lambda>2\sin\omega T$. Plotting both $\omega/\lambda=y_1$ and $2\sin\omega T=y_2$ versus ω gives the graphs shown in Figure 3.16. In Figure 3.16(a), for values of ω between 0 and ω_1, disturbances will grow in n. In Figure 3.16(b), no values of ω lead to growing disturbances in n.

The case separating the unstable and stable cases is when the line $y_1=\omega/\lambda$ is tangent to the curve $y_2=2\sin\omega T$ at the origin.

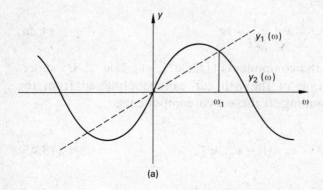

(a)

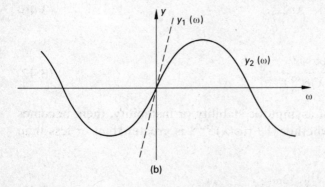

(b)

Fig. 3.16

We compute the slopes at the origin:

$$\frac{dy_1}{d\omega}\bigg|_{\omega=0} = \frac{1}{\lambda} \quad \text{and} \quad \frac{dy_2}{d\omega}\bigg|_{\omega=0} = 2T.$$

Thus the model will be asymptotically stable to disturbances of all frequencies if $1/\lambda > 2T$ or $\lambda T < \frac{1}{2}$. For $\lambda T > \frac{1}{2}$, the model is asymptotically unstable.

Let us now consider the concept of local stability. Essentially, the question is whether a disturbance of the trajectory of any car can have a disastrous effect on the next car behind. The idea, roughly, is that if the nth driver's reaction time is so long that his judgement is based on outdated information he will spend all of his time accelerating to catch up, and then overshooting, and then decelerating to compensate, overcompensating, etc.

The equation of motion for the nth car is

$$\frac{dv_n}{dt}(t+T) = -\lambda(v_n - v_{n-1}), \tag{3.50}$$

where $v_n = dx_n/dt$ is the velocity of the nth car. Let us look for solutions of the *homogeneous* differential-difference equation

$$\frac{dv_n}{dt}(t+T) = -\lambda v_n(t) \tag{3.51}$$

of the form $v_n(t) = e^{\mu t}$. Substitution yields the characteristic equation

$$\mu e^{\mu T} = -\lambda. \tag{3.52}$$

If we let $\mu T = \sigma$, we have

$$\sigma e^{\sigma} + \tau = 0, \tag{3.53}$$

where $\tau = \lambda T$. This transcendental equation is reasonably difficult to analyze.

Let us first look for real σ. We write

$$\sigma = -\tau e^{-\sigma}. \tag{3.54}$$

Sketching both $y_1 = \sigma$ and $y_2 = -\tau e^{-\sigma}$ shows that (i) there are no values of σ satisfying (3.54) if $\tau > \tau_1$, (ii) there is one value of σ satisfying (3.54) if $\tau = \tau_1$ (this is the case pictured), and (iii) there are two values of σ satisfying (3.54) if $\tau < \tau_1$ (*see* Figure 3.17).

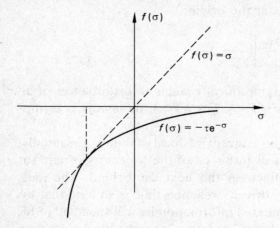

Fig. 3.17

Let us calculate τ_1. The condition that $y_1 = \sigma$ is tangent to $y_2 = -\tau_1 e^{-\sigma}$ is

$$\frac{dy_1}{d\sigma} = \frac{dy_2}{d\sigma} = 1 = \tau_1 e^{-\sigma} \quad \text{and} \quad y_1 = y_2 = \sigma = -\tau_1 e^{-\sigma}.$$

Thus $\sigma = -1$, and $\tau_1 = e^{-1}$.

Thus for $\tau < \tau_1 = e^{-1}$, there are two real values of σ which give solutions. Both solutions have exponentially decaying character.

Now let us consider σ complex. We write $\sigma = \sigma_r + i\sigma_i$, and so

$$(\sigma_r + i\sigma_i)e^{\sigma_r}(\cos \sigma_i + i \sin \sigma_i) + \tau = 0. \tag{3.55}$$

Thus

$$\sigma_r e^{\sigma_r} \cos \sigma_i - \sigma_i e^{\sigma_r} \sin \sigma_i + \tau = 0, \tag{3.56a}$$

$$\sigma_i e^{\sigma_r} \cos \sigma_i + \sigma_r e^{\sigma_r} \sin \sigma_i = 0. \tag{3.56b}$$

Using (3.56b) in (3.56a) results in

$$\frac{\sigma_r}{\cos \sigma_i} + \tau e^{-\sigma_r} = 0. \tag{3.57}$$

Also from (3.56b) we have

$$-\frac{\sigma_r}{\cos \sigma_i} = \frac{\sigma_i}{\sin \sigma_i}. \tag{3.58}$$

A little thought brings us to the conclusion that we should plot

$$y_1(\sigma_i) = -\frac{\sigma_r}{\cos \sigma_i} = \frac{\sigma_i}{\sin \sigma_i} \tag{3.59}$$

and

$$y_2(\sigma_i) = \tau e^{-\sigma_r} = \tau e^{\sigma_i \cos \sigma_i / \sin \sigma_i} \tag{3.60}$$

versus σ_i, and look for intersections of the two graphs (*see* Figure 3.18).

Let us first consider $\tau e < 1$. The picture does not explicitly show the two roots we found before. It does show a sequence of roots (two are shown) near $\sigma_i = \pm 2\pi n$, $n = 1, 2, 3, \ldots$. For the two roots near $\pm 2\pi$, σ_r is negative and large in magnitude (*see* Figure 3.18(b)). The solutions corresponding to these roots die out very

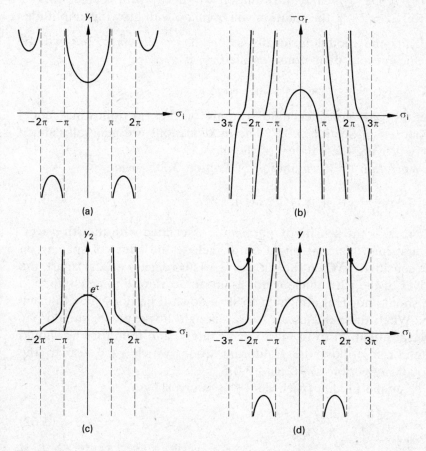

(a)

(b)

(c)

(d)

Fig. 3.18

rapidly. They do oscillate. Superposed on one of the decaying solutions, they are insignificant after a very short time.

Now let us consider $\tau e > 1$. There are no real roots by our previous analysis. There are two new roots between $-\pi < \sigma_i < \pi$. Because $\sigma_i \neq 0$, these roots correspond to oscillating solutions. To see whether these solutions grow in time, we must look at σ_r. If τ is such that $|\sigma_i| < \pi/2$, $\sigma_r < 0$, and the solutions decay. If τ is such that $|\sigma_i| > \pi/2$, the two solutions grow. Let us attempt to find τ_2 such that $\sigma_i = \pi/2$ is a solution of (3.56). From (3.56b), we find $\sigma_r = 0$, as expected. From (3.56a), we find $\pi/2 = \tau_2$.

Let us summarize our results.

(i) If $0 < \tau < 1/e$, the solution will decay, with only some small wiggles.
(ii) If $1/e < \tau < \pi/2$, the solution will decay with oscillation.
(iii) If $\pi/2 < \tau$, the solution will oscillate with growing amplitude.

Thus the model is locally stable if $\tau = \lambda T < \pi/2$, but will be inefficient and dangerous (oscillatory) if $\tau > 1/e$.

3.3.7   Nonlinear car following model

Let us now consider modifications of the car following model proposed in Section 3.3.5. The modifications are generally aimed at improving the validity of the model.

We retain the formulation of Section 3.3.5, using

$$\frac{dv_j(t+T)}{dt} = \lambda_j(v_{j-1}(t) - v_j(t)), \tag{3.61}$$

where λ_j is the sensitivity parameter associated with the jth driver. A first improvement might be to include the effect of spacing on the sensitivity. When the jth and $(j-1)$th vehicles are far apart, the driver of the jth vehicle is not as apt to accelerate to catch up, and he should not feel obligated to slow down if he does start to catch up. When the vehicles are close enough, however, he should pay special attention to trying to drive safely, and therefore he should attempt to follow the California Code, which gave rise to the model in Sections 3.3.2 and 3.3.5.

A simple model which does this is given by

$$\lambda_j = \begin{cases} 0 & \text{if } x_{j-1} - x_j > L, \\ \lambda & \text{if } x_{j-1} - x_j \leq L, \end{cases} \tag{3.62}$$

where λ is the constant sensitivity from Section 3.3.3. We shall refer to L as the interaction distance. This model asserts that if vehicle j is within $L - l$ of the vehicle ahead, then the driver will follow the preceding vehicle according to the California Code. If the following vehicle is farther back than that distance, then the driver maintains his speed, and ignores the vehicles in front of him.

A possible shortcoming of this model is that a driver who finds himself without a vehicle in front cannot change his speed. In particular, imagine a line of vehicles at a stop light. If, at time $t = 0$, we start the lead vehicle at a large speed, the second vehicle may be left 'at the post', and only attain a slow speed before he can no longer accelerate according to the model.

Let us now discuss the flow-concentration relationship using this model. First, consider the situation in which the concentration is so large that it is not possible to have many vehicles which are not following the one in front. In this situation, the non-following vehicles are negligible, and the calculation of Section 3.3.3 is valid.

If the concentration is so small that most of the vehicles are able to be free of interactions, then a different calculation is necessary. The condition that most of the vehicles are not following can be estimated as follows. If there are fewer than one vehicle in each interaction length of road, then (assuming the vehicles are spread out), most of the vehicles will not be interacting. Thus for $k < 1/L$, we expect most of the vehicles to be traveling at a constant velocity. Let us assume that this velocity is of the individual drivers' choosing. Note that the model does not always allow this; attaining it depends on the initial conditions of the problem.

In this low concentration case, the average speed over any section of the road will be a number which does not depend on k. Thus

$$q/k = \bar{u}_0, \qquad (3.63)$$

where $\bar{u}_0$ is the average of the speeds chosen by the drivers. Thus

$$q = \bar{u}_0 k \qquad (3.64)$$

(*see* Figure 3.19).

It is not practical to get a precise form for $q(k)$ for all k using this model.

Another expression for the sensitivity λ_j which has the same qualitative features of the interaction distance model of equation

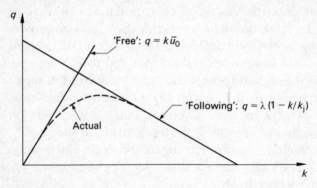

Fig. 3.19

(3.62) is the reciprocal spacing model:

$$\lambda_j = \frac{\alpha}{x_{j-1}(t) - x_j(t)},$$ (3.65)

where α is a constant.

Let us examine the flow concentration relationship using the reciprocal spacing model. The equation of motion for the reciprocal spacing model is

$$\frac{dv_j}{dt}(t + T) = \alpha \frac{\dfrac{dx_{j-1}(t)}{dt} - \dfrac{dx_j(t)}{dt}}{x_{j-1}(t) - x_j(t)}.$$ (3.66)

Integrating both sides with respect to t gives

$$v_j(t + T) = \alpha \ln [x_{j-1}(t) - x_j(t)] + C_j,$$ (3.67)

where C_j is a constant of integration for each j. C_j can be evaluated by assuming that no vehicle moves when there is no space between vehicles, that is, $v_j = 0$ when $x_{j-1} - x_j = l$, the length of a vehicle. Thus

$$C_j = -\alpha \ln l,$$ (3.68)

and so

$$v_j(t + T) = \alpha \ln \frac{x_{j-1}(t) - x_j(t)}{l}.$$ (3.69)

Let us apply equation (3.69) to the steady-state situation where all the vehicles are traveling at a constant velocity for all time. The average velocity, then, is

$$\bar{u} = v_j(t+T) = \alpha \ln \frac{x_{j-1}(t) - x_j(t)}{l}$$

$$= \alpha \ln \left[\frac{k_j}{k} \right], \tag{3.70}$$

where we define $k_j = 1/l$, and $k = 1/(x_{j-1} - x_j)$. Finally, since

$$\bar{u} = q/k, \tag{3.71}$$

we have

$$q = \alpha k \ln \left[\frac{k_j}{k} \right]. \tag{3.72}$$

This is Greenberg's flow-concentration relationship. Green-berg's relation has been fit to flow-concentration data with considerable success. This astonishing fact gives extra credibility to both Greenberg's relation and the reciprocal spacing car following model.

Let us examine other types of car following models. In 1963, Edie suggested that the sensitivity of the jth vehicle would be proportional to the speed of the car at the time when the driver reacts $(t + T)$, and inversely proportional to the square of the spacing. His model gives

$$\lambda_j = \frac{\beta v_j(t+T)}{[x_{j-1}(t) - x_j(t)]^2}. \tag{3.73}$$

Generalizations of (3.73) have been studied. These generalizations are of the form

$$\lambda = \frac{\beta[v_j(t+T)]^m}{[x_{j-1}(t) - x_j(t)]^n}, \tag{3.74}$$

where m and n are positive. The conclusion is that no particular values of m and n give a clearly better fit to the empirical data. The consensus seems to be that the model must be nonlinear, however.

We note that our reasons for studying more complicated models of car following are not as strong as those for studying the simpler models. It is true in general that the earlier, more simple models in any given area of endeavor are easier to solve, and the conclusions and predictions are, if not more important, then at least more general than those of later, more complicated models. In traffic flow, we may study the models which fit the data best in order to have an accurate prediction of some specific feature of the traffic situation, such as the average spacing on a given highway. The understanding of the car following situation generated by these more complicated models is clearly inferior to that generated by the California Code and the delay models, and the effort required to obtain useable information from the more complicated models is greater. Yet each model has its use, and therefore its place in traffic science.

Problems

1. Show that the motion of the jth vehicle subject to the 'California Code' model of equation (3.24) is given by

$$v_j(t) = v_0\left(1 - e^{-\lambda t}\left(1 + \frac{\lambda t}{1!} + \cdots + \frac{(\lambda t)^{j-1}}{(j-1)!}\right)\right).$$

2. Obtain $x_0(t)$, $x_1(t)$, and $x_2(t)$ subject to the initial conditions

$$x_0(0) = 0, \qquad x_1(0) = -l, \qquad x_2(0) = -2l.$$

3. (a) Show that the velocities $v_0, v_1, \ldots$ are such that $v_0 > v_1 > v_2 > \cdots$.
   (b) Assuming that $x_{j-1}(0) - x_j(0) = l$, show that

   $$x_{j-1}(t) - x_j(t) \geq l$$

   for all $t > 0$.

4. Solve the 'sudden stop' problem. Assume that all vehicles are traveling at speed v_0 for $t < 0$, and that at $t = 0$ the lead vehicle ($j = 0$) stops suddenly, so that $v_0(t) = 0$ for $t > 0$. Solve for $v_1(t)$, $v_2(t)$. Do any vehicles collide?

5. Find $v_1(t)$ for $2T < t < 3T$ and for $3T < t < 4T$.

6. Find $v_2(t)$ for $-T < t < 2T$.

7. Solve the 'sudden stop' problem using the car following with delay model. Specifically, find $v_1(t)$ for $-T < t < 2T$, and $v_2(t)$ for $-T < t < 2T$.

8. Compute the q–k relation corresponding to Edie's model, equation (3.73).

The Bosch following system The Bosch radar following system is a device which gives a warning if you are following the vehicle ahead at an unsafe distance. The driver has a line of small lights in his instruments, consisting of a line of green lights, a yellow light, and a line of red lights. If the computer determines that the distance is equal to the safe following distance, all the green lights and the yellow light will be lit; and if the distance is unsafe, some of the red lights will be lit. The number of lights lit depends on the difference between the actual separation and the safe separation. The safe following distance is based on the speed of the vehicle equipped with the device and the speed of the vehicle ahead, according to the formula

$$L_s = \frac{1}{2b_j} v_j^2 - \frac{1}{2b_{j-1}} v_{j-1}^2 + T_r v_j,$$

where L_s is the safe following distance, b_j and b_{j-1} are the braking decelerations of vehicle j and vehicle $j-1$, and T_r is the driver reaction time.

9. Derive a model analogous to the 'California Code' car following model, assuming that the driver of the jth car adjusts his *acceleration* to maintain exactly the safe following distance for all time.

10. If the computer were driving in Problem 9, there would be essentially no time delay. Assume that a human (with a finite delay time) is driving, and attempting to follow the model in Problem 9. What does the model look like now?

11. A more reasonable model which accounts for the device and its effect on a human driver is that the driver accelerates or decelerates based on how many green or red lights are lit on the device. Thus argue that

$$\frac{dv_j}{dt}(t+T) = \mu(x_{j-1} - x_j - l - L_s)$$

provides a car following model based on this idea. Without carrying out the labor involved, suggest some studies to perform with this model.

3.4 Equilibrium speed distributions

One of the fundamental processes in traffic flow, which leads to delays and frustration for individual drivers, is that of overtaking (that is, approaching from behind) a slower vehicle. Trucks, busses, and sightseers ('Sunday drivers') can cause substantial delays to a driver trying to move quickly from one place to another on the standard two-lane, two-way highway encountered in so much of the United States.

We wish to consider the processes of overtaking and passing on a long two-lane, two-way road. In order to study conditions leading to a faster vehicle overtaking a slower vehicle, we must have a mechanism for handling the different speeds of different vehicles. The concept which we use is that of number density function in speed space. (Our speed space is sometimes called phase space.)

We shall approach this concept through some examples. Suppose we count the number of vehicles on the road with speeds between 0 and 10 miles h^{-1}, the number between 10 and 20 miles h^{-1}, and so on. If we plot these data as a bar graph, they will look like Figure 3.20(a). This is the correct type of information; however, it is still too crude.

Let us also take the data on the number of vehicles with speeds between 0 and 5 miles h^{-1}, between 5 and 10 miles h^{-1}, and so on.

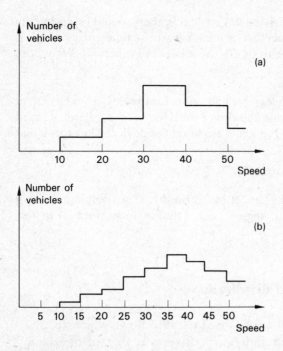

Fig. 3.20 Number versus speed.

These data are shown in Figure 3.20(b). We note that the number of vehicles between 20 and 30 miles h^{-1} in Figure 3.20(b) is the sum of the number with speeds between 20 and 25 miles h^{-1} and the number with speeds between 25 and 30 miles h^{-1}.

It is difficult to see that the data plotted in Figure 3.20(a) and (b) represent the same set of vehicles on the same road. The data look more similar if we plot the *densities,* that is, the number *per unit speed,* versus the speed. To obtain the number density from Figure 3.20(a) and (b), we divide the number in each interval of speed by the length of that interval. The number densities corresponding to Figure 3.20(a) and (b) are plotted in Figure 3.21.

We are not restricted to 5 miles h^{-1} intervals in plotting our number density data, we could use 1 mile h^{-1} intervals, 0.5 mile h^{-1} intervals, 0.1 mile h^{-1} intervals, and so on. Using smaller intervals gives more detail about the speed space structure. Thus, the smaller the interval, the better.

We note that to obtain the number of vehicles n_i in the ith speed interval from the density f_i we need only multiply by the length of that interval, Δu_i:

$$n_i = f_i \Delta u_i. \tag{3.75}$$

If we wish to compute the number of vehicles n with speeds between u_a and u_b, we must sum the number in each subinterval n_i:

$$n = \sum n_i = \sum f_i \Delta u_i, \tag{3.76}$$

where the summation is over subintervals lying between u_a and u_b.

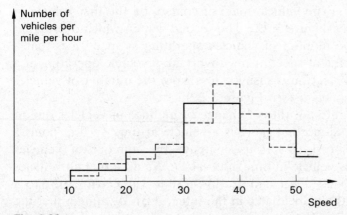

Fig. 3.21

We wish to work with a mathematical abstraction of the discrete number distributions described above. Suppose $f(u)$ is the *continuous* density distribution of vehicles at speed u, obtained by abstracting the number density process above by letting $\Delta u_i \to 0$. Then if u_a and u_b are any two speeds, the number of vehicles on the road with speeds between u_a and u_b is given by

$$n = \int_{u_a}^{u_b} f(u)) \, du. \tag{3.77}$$

In general, the density distribution will change in time. Also, if we look at different subsections of the road, we expect to see different distributions, depending on local disturbances, like the presence of a truck, or a curve in the highway. These time and space dependences could be considered; however, for the sake of simplicity, we shall assume that the density f depends on speed alone, and is independent of space x and time t.

Now let us turn our attention to the processes which shape $f(u)$, specifically, overtaking and passing. When we refer to overtaking, we mean catching up to a slower vehicle ahead. Passing refers to pulling out in the lane of oncoming traffic, getting ahead of the slower vehicle, and then returning to a more desirable speed.

Let us consider the vehicle operating at speed u. Overtaking of vehicles changes the number of vehicles at speed u in two ways. First, a vehicle operating at a higher speed $\bar{u} > u$ may overtake a vehicle operating at speed u, thus causing an addition to the number of vehicles operating at speed u. These vehicles which are slowed down are added to *queues*, or lines of vehicles following other vehicles. (The vehicle may, of course, be the first vehicle in the queue.) (*see* Figure 3.22.) The second way in which overtaking can change the number of vehicles operating at speed u is that a vehicle operating at speed u may overtake a vehicle operating at a lower speed $\bar{u} < u$, thus causing a loss from the number of vehicles operating at speed u (*see* Figure 3.22).

Let us compute the rate of change of number of vehicles due to overtaking. Assume that there is a vehicle at time $t = 0$ at point x traveling at speed u. Let us compute the number of vehicles overtaking this vehicle in time interval Δt. We note that all vehicles which have speed $\bar{u} > u$ and are in the interval $x - (\bar{u} - u)\Delta t$ to x will overtake the vehicle at x in the interval Δt. Assuming that the vehicles are distributed uniformly over a road of length L, the

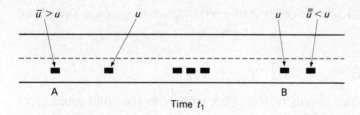

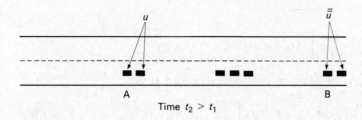

Fig. 3.22 A snapshot of the road at two times t_1 and t_2, showing a vehicle A at speed $\bar{u}$ at time t_1 overtaking a vehicle at speed u, and a vehicle B at speed u overtaking a vehicle at speed $\bar{u}$.

number of vehicles having speed $\bar{u} > u$ in the interval $x - (\bar{u} - u)\Delta t$ to x is

$$\frac{(\bar{u} - u)\Delta t}{L} f(\bar{u}),$$

where L is the length of the road. The total number of such vehicles is

$$\int_u^\infty \frac{(\bar{u} - u)\Delta t}{L} f(\bar{u}) \, d\bar{u}. \tag{3.78}$$

Thus the rate at which vehicles overtake a given vehicle at speed u, location x is the number divided by the time interval Δt, so that the rate is

$$\int_u^\infty \frac{(\bar{u} - u)f(\bar{u})}{L} \, d\bar{u}. \tag{3.79}$$

To obtain the rate of gain of vehicles at speed u to overtaking, we must multiply this quantity by the probability of finding a vehicle at x at speed u. This probability is proportional to the total number of vehicles at speed u, $f(u) \, du$. In fact, the probability of finding a vehicle between x and $x+dx$ between speed u and speed $u+du$ is

$$f(u)\frac{du\ dx}{NL},$$

where L is the length of the road, and N is the total number of vehicles on the road.

Thus the rate of gain of vehicles at speed u between x and $x+dx$ is

$$g(x,u)=\frac{dx}{NL^2}\int_u^\infty (\bar u-u)f(\bar u)\,d\bar u \cdot f(u)\,du.$$

The total rate of gain of vehicles at speed u is

$$G=\int_0^L g(x,u)\,dx = Kf(u)\int_u^\infty (\bar u-u)f(\bar u)\,d\bar u\,du, \qquad (3.80)$$

where $K=1/NL$.

We might comment on the fact that the integration extends to $\bar u=\infty$. We wish to include all vehicles with speed greater than u in the integration. In any reasonable physical situation, we expect $f(\bar u)=0$ for $\bar u>u^*$, where u^* is the mechanical speed limit of a vehicle. By taking the upper limit of integration to be infinite, we bypass the uncertainty of exactly what u^* is.

Let us now compute the rate of loss of vehicles from speed u due to their overtaking a slower vehicle. Let us again consider a vehicle at x traveling at speed u, and consider the number of vehicles having speed $\bar{\bar u}<u$ in the interval x to $x+(u-\bar{\bar u})\Delta t$. That number is

$$\frac{(u-\bar{\bar u})\Delta tf(\bar{\bar u})}{L}. \qquad (3.81)$$

The total number of such vehicles is

$$\int_0^u \frac{(u-\bar{\bar u})\Delta tf(\bar{\bar u})}{L}\,d\bar{\bar u}, \qquad (3.82)$$

and as before, the rate of loss due to overtaking for such vehicles is

$$\mathscr{L}=K\int_0^u (u-\bar{\bar u})f(\bar{\bar u})f(u)\,d\bar{\bar u}\,du. \qquad (3.83)$$

Combining the rate of gain and loss to get a net rate of change of

$f(u)$ due to overtaking gives

$$\Theta = G - \mathcal{L} = K \int_0^\infty (\bar{u} - u) f(\bar{u}) f(u) \, d\bar{u} \, du. \tag{3.84}$$

Now let us turn our attention to an analysis of the passing process. First, we shall assume that a fraction p of those overtaking will pass instantaneously, essentially not interacting with the overtaken vehicle. Thus we have the instantaneous passing rate $P_i = p\Theta$. In addition, a complex passing process will occur, with drivers passing slower drivers depending on the concentration of oncoming traffic, their position in the queue, and their general desire to move faster. This process seems impossible to model in a rational way. However, we shall bypass this difficulty by assuming a *phenomenological* model, essentially a model which does roughly what we expect. We expect that if the drivers were able to remain out of the queues which result from overtaking, they would attain a distribution of desired speeds equal to $f_0(u)$. We assume that if more vehicles are actually traveling at a given speed u than the number of drivers who desire to do so, then drivers will be passing. Therefore, if $f(u) > f_0(u)$, there will be a net loss of vehicles from speed u due to passing. On the other hand, if there are less drivers traveling at speed u than the number of drivers who desire to do so, then some of the drivers who do pass will accelerate to attain this speed. Thus, if $f(u) < f_0(u)$, there will be a net gain of vehicles at speed u due to passing. In fact, we assume that if more drivers are not at their desired speed, then more passing will occur (*see* Figure 3.23).

Thus we assume that the noninstantaneous passing is equal to

$$P_n = -\lambda (f_0(u) - f(u)) \, du. \tag{3.85}$$

We note that λ has dimension (time)$^{-1}$. The quantity $1/\lambda$ is often referred to as a *relaxation* time, and this passing process is called *relaxation*.

Thus our balance becomes

$$\Theta - P_i - P_n = 0 = \left[(1-p) K \int_0^\infty (\bar{u} - u) f(\bar{u}) f(u) \, d\bar{u} \right.$$

$$\left. + \lambda (f_0(u) - f(u)) \right] du. \tag{3.86}$$

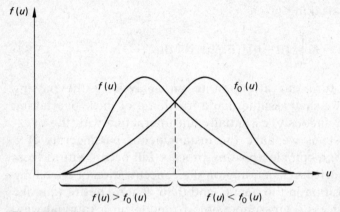

Fig. 3.23 Desired and actual speed distributions. In the range where $f(u) > f_0(u)$, there will be drivers who want to pass. For $f(u) < f_0(u)$, some drivers who have passed will be attaining the speed u.

Equation (3.86) gives a balance between overtaking and passing. Solving for $f(u)$ gives

$$f(u) = \frac{f_0(u)}{1 - \dfrac{(1-p)K}{\lambda} \displaystyle\int_0^\infty (\bar{u} - u)f(\bar{u})\,\mathrm{d}\bar{u}}. \tag{3.87}$$

Let us attempt some qualitative calculations using equation (3.87). We note that for

$$\frac{(1-p)K}{\lambda} \int_0^\infty (\bar{u} - u)f(\bar{u})\,\mathrm{d}u < 0 \tag{3.88}$$

we shall have

$$f(u) < f_0(u). \tag{3.89}$$

Since $p < 1$, $K > 0$, and $\lambda > 0$, equation (3.88) is equivalent to

$$u > \frac{\displaystyle\int_0^\infty \bar{u}f(\bar{u})\,\mathrm{d}\bar{u}}{\displaystyle\int_0^\infty f(\bar{u})\,\mathrm{d}\bar{u}} \equiv u_{\mathrm{a}}, \tag{3.90}$$

where u_{a} is defined to be the average speed of vehicles on the highway.

For $u < u_{\mathrm{a}}$, we have $f(u) > f_0(u)$. Thus one property of our solution (3.87) is that more vehicles are traveling at speeds less than u_{a} than desire to be at that speed, while fewer vehicles are traveling at speeds greater than u_a than so desire. This seems to be an acceptable prediction.

A big problem in attempting to use (3.87) to make predictions is that to do so, we must determine a suitable form for $f_0(u)$, and suitable values for p and λ. Clearly, all of these quantities depend on the density of traffic, which is determined by N, the number of vehicles on the road.

On the other hand, by guessing at reasonable values for λ and p, and taking a somewhat arbitrary form for $f_0(u)$, we can make some predictions for the flow-concentration relationship, which is a fundamental part of traffic flow theory. *See* Problem 2 on p. 98 for a quite simple calculation of this sort.

The ideas involved in this module were first introduced in order to obtain an idea of how the velocity distribution evolved in time as a function of location along the road. The partial differential equation governing the distribution $f(t, x, u)$ is much like the Boltzmann equation studied in statistical mechanics. This analogy stimulates both the traffic theoretician and the statistical mechanician. Interesting predictions have been made about traffic flow from this Boltzmann-like approach; see the monograph by Prigogine and Herman [6]. Some mathematical sophistication is required, however.

Problems

1. Consider a distribution of vehicles where n_1 is the number of vehicles traveling between 40 and 50 miles h^{-1}, and n_2 is the number of vehicles between 50 and 60 miles h^{-1}. Suppose there are no vehicles traveling at speeds lower than 40 miles h^{-1}, or greater than 60 miles h^{-1}. The total number of vehicles on the road is $N = n_1 + n_2$. Let us consider a nonequilibrium model for overtaking and passing in this restricted situation. Let us consider the faster vehicles. The rate of change of faster vehicles is dn_2/dt.

   (a) Argue that the number of vehicles lost from n_2 during an infinitesimal time interval due to overtaking the slower vehicles should be proportional to $n_2 n_1$.
   (b) Argue that the number of vehicles passing n_1 vehicles should be proportional to n_1.
   (c) Hence derive the equation

   $$\frac{dn_2}{dt} = -ln_1 n_2 + kn_1 = (-ln_2 + k)(N - n_2). \qquad (*)$$

(d) Find all equilibrium solutions in terms of N, k_1, and k_2. (Assume $k/l < N$.)

(e) Solve (∗) exactly.

(f) Show that $n_2 \to k/l$ as $t \to \infty$ unless $n_2 = N$.

2. Develop a model similar to that in Problem 1 above, except assume that n_j is the number of vehicles traveling at speeds between $(j-1)\Delta u$ and $j\Delta u$, where Δu is some speed increment.

   Derive a set of equations for n_j of the form

   $$\frac{dn_j}{dt} = -\sum_{i=1}^{j-1} l_{ij} n_i n_j + \sum_{i=1}^{j-1} k_{ij} n_i, \qquad j = 2, \ldots, N.$$

   What properties do you expect l_{ij} and k_{ij} to possess? Will l_{ij} get bigger as $j-1$ gets bigger? Explain.

3. Suppose $f(u) = B e^{-(u-u_1)^2/\sigma^2}$, where B and σ are positive numbers, and u_1 is a reference speed.

   (a) Sketch this distribution.

   (b) Calculate

   $$u_a = \frac{\displaystyle\int_0^\infty u f(u)\, du}{\displaystyle\int_0^\infty f(u)\, du}.$$

   (*Hint:* You will need an integral table or the fact that

   $$\int_0^\infty e^{-x^2}\, dx = \frac{\sqrt{\pi}}{2}.)$$

4. Let

   $$f_0(u) = \begin{cases} C(u-u_1)(u_2-u) & \text{for} \quad u_1 \le u \le u_2, \\ 0 & \text{for} \quad u > u_2 \quad \text{or} \quad u < u_1, \end{cases}$$

   where C is a constant.

   (a) Sketch this desired speed distribution.

   (b) Compute

   $$N = \int_0^\infty f_0(u)\, du.$$

   (c) Assume that $p = 0.5$, $\lambda = 0.01\ \text{s}^{-1}$, $l = 15\ \text{ft}$, $C = 500\,000$ vehicles $(\text{miles h}^{-1})^{-3}$, $u_1 = 20\ \text{miles h}^{-1}$, $u_2 = 40\ \text{miles h}^{-1}$, and $L = 20$ miles.

(i) Compute an approximation to u_a using a power series expansion of $f(u)$ in terms of $(1-p)K/\lambda$.

(ii) Using this approximation to u_a, find $f(u)$.

(d) Again, using $p = 0.5$, $\lambda = 0.01\ \text{s}^{-1}$, $l = 15\ \text{ft}$, $u_1 = 20\ \text{miles h}^{-1}$, $u_2 = 40\ \text{miles h}^{-1}$, and $L = 20\ \text{miles}$, but leaving C as arbitrary, find an approximation to $f(u)$ in terms of C. Using (b), relate C to N, and sketch a graph of q versus N. This is essentially the flow-concentration diagram.

3.5 A Boltzmann-like approach to traffic flow

We wish to consider the nonequilibrium, nonspatially-homogeneous processes which lead to different velocity distributions on long, uniform highways. We shall also derive the flow-concentration relationship obtained through the consideration of the velocity distributions.

The Boltzmann-like description of traffic flow gives a view of the traffic situation which is 'between' the flow theory models and the car following models. Recall that in the flow theory approach, we did not build in any details of individual drivers or vehicles or interaction between these vehicles. On the other hand, in the useable car following models, the vehicles interacted at all times to some degree. Furthermore, in car following theory, we attempted to model the behavior of individual vehicles and drivers. The Boltzmann theory allows us to add some microstructure to the vehicular situation without the consideration of the details of car following.

Let $\psi(u, x, t)$ be the number density of vehicles in velocity–location space (*phase* space); that is, the number of vehicles in the segment from x to $x + \Delta x$ having velocities between u and $u + \Delta u$ is given by

$$ n = \int_{x}^{x+\Delta x} \int_{u}^{u+\Delta u} \psi(\hat{u}, \hat{x}, t)\,\mathrm{d}\hat{u}\,\mathrm{d}\hat{x}. \tag{3.91} $$

We note that in terms of $\psi(u, x, t)$, the concentration $k(x, t)$ is given by

$$ k(x, t) = \int_{0}^{\infty} \psi(u, x, t)\,\mathrm{d}u; \tag{3.92} $$

that is, the number of vehicles per unit length is equal to the 'sum' over all velocities of the number of vehicles per unit length at each velocity. Also, the average velocity $\bar{u}$ is defined by

$$\bar{u} = \frac{1}{k(x, t)} \int_0^\infty u\psi(u, x, t)\, \mathrm{d}u. \tag{3.93}$$

Essentially, we compute the probability of a vehicle having speed u by considering the number density of vehicles at speed u per unit length divided by the total number of vehicles per unit length. To compute the mean value of u, we multiply u by its probability density function and 'sum'. We note from (3.93) that

$$q(x, t) \equiv \bar{u} \int_0^\infty \psi(u, x, t)\, \mathrm{d}u. \tag{3.94}$$

Let us consider what the trajectories of individual vehicles might look like in $x - u$ space. At a given time t, the individual vehicles' locations and velocities might look like that shown in Figure 3.24. Each dot represents one vehicle.

No two vehicles may occupy the same location. Moreover, if there are two vehicles separated by a distance Δx, with the faster vehicle behind, then in some time interval these vehicles will interact (*see* Figure 3.25).

Let us now compute the rate of change of the number of vehicles in a rectangle in $x-u$ space (*see* Figure 3.26).

First, the number of vehicles in the box is given by

$$n = \int_x^{x+\Delta x} \int_u^{u+\Delta u} \psi(\tilde{u}, \tilde{x}, t)\, \mathrm{d}\tilde{u}\, \mathrm{d}\tilde{x}. \tag{3.95}$$

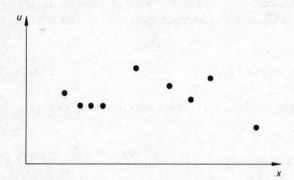

Fig. 3.24

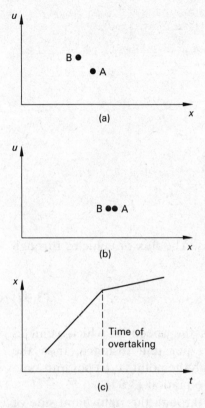

Fig. 3.25 (a) Vehicle B is about to overtake vehicle A. (b) Vehicle B has overtaken vehicle A, and has decelerated to vehicle A's speed. (c) Vehicle B's trajectory.

The rate of change of n, $\mathrm{d}n/\mathrm{d}t$ is given by

$$\frac{\mathrm{d}n}{\mathrm{d}t} = \int_{x}^{x+\Delta x} \int_{u}^{u+\Delta u} \frac{\partial \psi(\tilde{u}, \tilde{x}, t)}{\partial t}\, \mathrm{d}\tilde{u}\, \mathrm{d}\tilde{x}. \tag{3.96}$$

The number of vehicles in the box changes due to the flow of vehicles out of the box due to decelerations such as those shown in Figure 3.25(c), and the corresponding accelerations will be modeled not as a flow, but as an internal 'loss' mechanism. Hence, even though no vehicles are created or destroyed, we shall model the overtaking and passing processes as loss or gain processes. Essentially, we assume that a vehicle which overtakes another slower vehicle decelerates to the lower velocity instantly, exactly at the location of the slower vehicle. The decelerating vehicle is lost from the faster speed, and is gained at the slower speed.

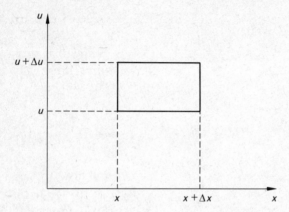

Fig. 3.26

Let us now consider the flux terms. The flux of vehicles through the side of the box at location x is

$$\Phi(x, t) = \int_u^{u+\Delta u} \tilde{u}\psi(\tilde{u}, x, t) \, d\tilde{u}. \tag{3.97}$$

Essentially, (3.97) says that if $\tilde{u}$ is the speed at which vehicles move, and there are $\psi \, d\tilde{u}$ vehicles per unit distance, then the number of vehicles which pass through the point $(x, \tilde{u})$ per unit time is given by $\tilde{u}\psi \, d\tilde{u}$. 'Summing' gives equation (3.97).

Similarly, the flux of vehicles out through the right-hand side of the box is given by

$$\Phi(x + \Delta x, t) = \int_u^{u+\Delta u} \tilde{u}\psi(\tilde{u}, x + \Delta x, t) \, d\tilde{u}. \tag{3.98}$$

By the assumption about the acceleration–deceleration process above, it is evident that no flux of vehicles occurs through the top or bottom of the box.

Thus the balance law for vehicles in the box becomes

$$\frac{dn}{dt} = \Phi(x, t) - \Phi(x + \Delta x, t) + \Gamma - \Lambda, \tag{3.99}$$

where Γ represents the rate of gain of vehicles to the box due to overtaking and passing, and Λ represents the rate of loss from the box due to overtaking and passing.

We break up Γ and Λ into

$$\Gamma = \Gamma_o + \Gamma_p, \tag{3.100}$$

$$\Lambda = \Lambda_o + \Lambda_p, \tag{3.101}$$

where the subscript o represents the process (gain or loss) due to overtaking, and the subscript p represents passing.

Let us now compute the rate of gain of vehicles at speed u due to faster vehicles overtaking vehicles at speed u. Assume there is a vehicle at location x at speed u. The rate at which vehicles at speeds $\bar{u} > u$ interact with the given vehicle is

$$\int_{u}^{\infty} (\bar{u} - u)\psi(\bar{u}, x, t)\, d\bar{u}. \tag{3.102}$$

Equation (3.102) expresses the rate at which vehicles flow to the vehicle at x at speed u in terms of the *relative* velocity $\bar{u} - u$ of approach of vehicles at speed $\bar{u}$ to the vehicle at speed u, times the number of vehicles per unit length $\psi(\bar{u}, x, t)\, d\bar{u}$. Summing over all speeds greater than u gives the rate of overtaking of a given vehicle at speed u.

The rate of overtaking, then, is equal to the rate of overtaking of a given vehicle times the number of times overtaking the point (x, u) results in an actual deceleration. The number of times in which the overtaking results in a deceleration is exactly the probability of finding a vehicle at location x at speed u. This probability is

$$\psi(u, x, t)/k(x, t). \tag{3.103}$$

Thus the rate of overtaking at location x, speed u is given by

$$\Theta(u, x, t) = \frac{\psi(u, x, t)}{k(x, t)} \int_{u}^{\infty} (\bar{u} - u)\psi(\bar{u}, x, t)\, d\bar{u}. \tag{3.104}$$

Hence

$$\Gamma_{o} = \int_{x}^{x+\Delta x} \int_{u}^{u+\Delta u} \Theta(\tilde{u}, \tilde{x}, t)\, d\tilde{u}\, d\tilde{x}. \tag{3.105}$$

Let us now compute Λ_{o}. The rate at which vehicles at speed u interact with slower vehicles is given by

$$\int_{0}^{u} (u - \bar{u})\psi(\bar{u}, x, t)\, d\bar{u}. \tag{3.106}$$

Hence the rate of loss of vehicles from speed u is given by

$$\mathcal{L}(u, x, t) = \frac{\psi(u, x, t)}{k(x, t)} \int_{0}^{u} (\bar{\bar{u}} - u)\psi(\bar{\bar{u}}, x, t)\, d\bar{\bar{u}}. \tag{3.107}$$

Therefore

$$\Lambda_o = \int_x^{x+\Delta x} \int_u^{u+\Delta u} \mathcal{L}(\tilde{u}, \tilde{x}, t) \, d\tilde{u} \, d\tilde{x}. \tag{3.108}$$

Now let us discuss the process of passing. As we have modeled it, overtaking consists of a faster vehicle approaching a slower vehicle from behind, and instantly lowering its speed to follow the slower vehicle. Most drivers who overtake a slower vehicle will try to pass in order to regain some desirable speed. How soon the passing actually occurs depends on many factors, for example, the aggressiveness of the faster driver, the traffic conditions in the passing lane, the difference in the desired speed and the actual speed of travel, the condition of the vehicles, the road, and the drivers themselves. These factors make it nearly impossible to model the passing process accurately.

We shall divide the passing process into two distinct processes, instantaneous passing and noninstantaneous or 'relaxation' passing. A certain fraction of overtaking drivers will pass the slower vehicle with essentially no delay. We shall assume that this fraction p is a constant; that is, we assume that p is independent of speed and traffic density. Thus the instantaneous component of Γ_p, denoted by Γ_{pi}, is given by

$$\Gamma_{pi} = p\Lambda_o, \tag{3.109}$$

and the instantaneous component of Λ_p, denoted by Λ_{pi}, is given by

$$\Lambda_{pi} = p\Gamma_o. \tag{3.110}$$

We shall assume a phenomenological model for the remaining components of Γ_p and Λ_p. We assume that the noninstantaneous passing process can be modeled by

$$\Gamma_{pn} - \Lambda_{pn} = -\lambda \int_u^{u+\Delta u} \int_x^{x+\Delta x} (\psi(u, x, t) - k(x, t)f_0(u)) \, d\tilde{u} \, d\tilde{x}, \tag{3.111}$$

where λ is a constant. We note that λ has dimension $(\text{time})^{-1}$. Hence λ^{-1} is referred to as a relaxation time. In equation (3.111), $f_0(u)$ is a desired speed distribution. This speed distribution represents the way in which drivers would choose their speeds if they were on a road where no interactions (overtakings and passings) occurred.

Let us now derive the partial differential equation for ψ. In equation (3.99), we divide by $\Delta x \Delta u$ and let Δx and Δu approach zero. Using the fundamental theorem of calculus, and assuming sufficient smoothness of ψ, we have

$$\frac{\partial \psi(u, x, t)}{\partial t} + \frac{\partial u\psi(u, x, t)}{\partial x} = -\lambda(\psi(u, x, t) - k(x, t)f_0(u))$$

$$+ \frac{(1 - p)\psi(u, x, t) \int_0^\infty (\bar{u} - u)\psi(\bar{u}, x, t)\,d\bar{u}}{k(x, t)}.$$

$$(3.112)$$

Let us integrate equation (3.112) with respect to u from $u = 0$ to $u = \infty$. We have

$$\frac{\partial}{\partial t} \int_0^\infty \psi(u, x, t)\,du + \frac{\partial}{\partial x} \int_0^\infty u\psi(u, x, t)\,du =$$

$$-\lambda \left(\int_0^\infty \psi(u, x, t)\,du - k(x, t) \right)$$

$$+ \frac{(1 - p)}{k(x, t)} \left\{ \int_0^\infty \psi(u, x, t)\,du \int_0^\infty \bar{u}\psi(\bar{u}, x, t)\,d\bar{u} \right.$$

$$\left. - \int_0^\infty u\psi(u, x, t)\,du \int_0^\infty \psi(\bar{u}, x, t)\,d\bar{u} \right\}$$

$$= 0. \quad (3.113)$$

Recognizing

$$k(x, t) = \int_0^\infty \psi(u, x, t)\,du$$

and

$$q(x, t) = \int_0^\infty u\psi(u, x, t)\,du,$$

we have

$$\frac{\partial k}{\partial t} + \frac{\partial q}{\partial x} = 0. \qquad (3.114)$$

The Boltzmann approach to traffic flow gives us a single partial differential equation for the evolution of velocity distribution on a long road. It is interesting to study the behavior of this model subject to different initial traffic conditions. The information so gained, however, is of limited use to the traffic engineer. The statistical information which is of use in calculation of gaps and delays is usually taken from the equilibrium speed distribution.

3.6 Gap distributions

Suppose we wish to compute the total time spent by drivers at a stop sign controlled intersection. We might want the results of this study in order to determine whether or not it is economically feasible to install a traffic light at the intersection, or whether some kind of control upstream or downstream on the main road might result in a sufficiently more efficient operation of the intersection.

In order to compute the time spent by a single driver at a stop sign, it is necessary to have an estimate of how often a gap of sufficient size avails itself to a driver at the stop sign.

To do this type of calculation, it is necessary to consider the statistics of road traffic flow.

We shall assume that the arrivals of vehicles are random, in the sense that the moment of arrival of any vehicle is independent of the arrival of any other vehicle, and that any two equal time intervals are equally likely to contain equal numbers of arrivals.

Let us assume that the probability of an arrival at the intersection in the time interval between t and $t + \Delta t$ is

$$q\Delta t + o(\Delta t),$$

where $o(\Delta t)$ indicates a quantity for which $o(\Delta t)/\Delta t \to 0$ as $\Delta t \to 0$. We shall further ignore the probability of two arrivals in time Δt. We shall also assume that q is independent of t. Thus the probability of an arrival in a small time interval is proportional to the length Δt of the time interval. If we assume that this time interval is short, we can neglect the probability of two arrivals.

We note that in very dense traffic arrivals at an intersection are not random, and our model is no longer valid.

Let us compute the probability of k arrivals in time t, $P_k(t)$. Let us consider $P_k(t + \Delta t)$. The arrival of k vehicles in time $t + \Delta t$ can occur in two different ways. Either (i) k vehicles arrive in time t, and no vehicles arrive in the interval from t to $t + \Delta t$, or (ii) $k - 1$

vehicles arrive in time t and one vehicle arrives in the interval from t to $t + \Delta t$. Thus

$$P_k(t + \Delta t) = P_k(t)(1 - q\Delta t) + P_{k-1}(t)q\Delta t, \qquad k = 1, 2, 3, \ldots .$$
$$(3.115)$$

Also,

$$P_0(t + \Delta t) = P_0(t)(1 - q\Delta t). \qquad (3.116)$$

If we subtract $P_k(t)$ from both sides of (3.115), divide by Δt, and let $\Delta t \to 0$, we have

$$\frac{dP_k(t)}{dt} = q[P_{k-1}(t) - P_k(t)]$$

and from (3.116)

$$\frac{dP_0(t)}{dt} = -qP_0(t).$$

The initial conditions for the functions $P_k(t)$ are

$$P_0(0) = 1,$$

$$P_k(0) = 0, \qquad k = 1, 2, \ldots .$$

These initial conditions assume that there are no arrivals at time zero. Thus

$$P_0(t) = e^{-qt}$$

and

$$P_k(t) = \frac{e^{-qt}(qt)^k}{k!}, \qquad k = 1, 2, 3, \ldots .$$

If we write $qt = m$, then m is the mean number of arrivals expected in a given time t. The probability of a given number k of arrivals during time t is

$$P(k) = \frac{e^{-m}m^k}{k!}.$$

If we consider a flow of 300 vehicles per hour, and look at time intervals of length 1 min, then $m = 300/60 = 5$, so that

$$P(k) = \frac{e^{-5}5^k}{k!}, \qquad k = 0, 1, 2, \ldots$$

(see Figure 3.27).

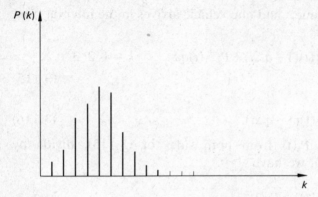

Fig. 3.27

Now let us consider $P_0(t)$. Let us take our time origin ($t = 0$) to coincide with an arrival of a vehicle. The probability of no vehicles arriving in time t, $P_0(t)$, is e^{-qt}, where q is the flow rate on the highway. If we denote the probability that a given gap T is less than or equal to t by $F(t)$ we have

$$P[T \leq t] = F(t).$$

Thus $P[T > t] = 1 - F(t) = \Phi(t)$ is the probability that the gap T is greater than t.

The probability of a gap greater than $t + \Delta t$ is equal to the probability of no arrivals in time t, times the probability of no arrivals in time t to $t + \Delta t$. Thus,

$$\Phi(t + \Delta t) = \Phi(t)[1 - q\Delta t]$$

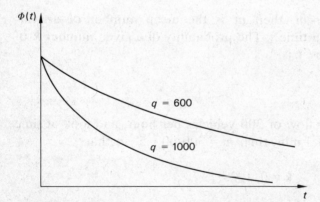

Fig. 3.28

and so

$$\Phi(t) = e^{-qt},$$

so that

$$F(t) = 1 - e^{-qt}.$$

We sketch the distribution $\Phi(t)$ for $q = 600$ vehicles per hour, and for $q = 1000$ vehicles per hour in Figure 3.28.

Problems

1. Derive the solutions $P_k(t) = (qt)^k e^{-qt}/k!$ to the differential equations $dP_0/dt = -qP_0$, $P_0(1) = 1$; and $dP_k/dt = q[P_{k-1} - P_k]$, $P_k(0) = 0$, $k = 1, 2, \ldots$.

2. If $q = 1500$ vehicles per hour, compute the probability of a gap of length greater than 3 s.

Bibliography

1   Ashton, W. D. *The Theory of Road Traffic Flow*, Methuen, London, 1966. This book contains a nice discussion of the connections between flow theory and statistical theory.
2   Drew, D. R. *Traffic Flow Theory and Control*, McGraw-Hill, New York, 1968. No relation. A very general, readable book. It has many simple but important calculations pertaining to different aspects of highway design.
3   Gazis, D. C. (ed.) *Traffic Science*, Wiley Interscience, New York, 1974. *See* Chapter 1, written by L. C. Edie, which deals with flow theories. Quite up to date.
4   Gerlough, D. L. and Huber, M. J. *Traffic Flow Theory, a Monograph*, Special Report 165, Traffic Research Board, National Research Council, Washington, DC, 1975. Everything you always wanted to know about traffic flow theory—and more. This is an expensive paperbound monograph which synthesizes and reports, in a single document, the present state of knowledge in traffic flow theory. Not for children.
5   Haight, F. A. *Mathematical Theories of Traffic Flow*, Academic Press,

New York, 1963. This book is nicely mathematical, quite general, and not too hard to read. It is somewhat dated.

6 Prigogine, I. and Herman, R. *Kinetic Theory of Vehicular Traffic*, Elsevier, New York, 1971. This book is the source for the Boltzman theory. It is highly mathematical, and some advanced knowledge of partial differential equations is suggested before starting to read it.

4 Semiconductor crystal growth

LYNN O WILSON *Bell Telephone Laboratories*

4.1 Introduction

I would like to describe a research problem on which I am currently working. There are two reasons for choosing this topic. First, I think it is pretty interesting. Second, it happens to be ideal for illustrating the process of mathematical modeling. The discussion will be largely chronological, in order to give you a realistic idea of the entire research process: how to formulate a problem, solve it, and communicate the results. I will try to give you an idea of how long it took to complete different segments of the problem. The story will be told in some detail from the time of its beginning (March, 1976) to the time when these notes were written (April, 1977). Then there will be a short postscript which summarizes the rest of the story to date (February, 1979). I hesitate to say that is the end of the tale. Somehow there always seems to be a little more left to do. Occasionally I shall digress to comment on methods or ingredients of mathematical modeling.

There are differences between the research environment in which I find myself at Bell Laboratories and an academic environment. Nothing is clear cut, for example. No one says, 'Consider the following mathematical problem, . . .'. It may be quite a while before a vaguely stated problem turns into, say, a bunch of equations to be solved. Another difference is that collaboration is highly valued in research: several people with quite diverse backgrounds may work together to solve a problem. In academia, students are often encouraged to work independently (so that their grades reflect their own work). As in a university, I learn both from textbooks and from formal lectures. But a great deal of my knowledge also comes from conversations with other scientists and from papers published in technical journals. Another difference between a student's life and mine as a research scientist is that I have no deadlines imposed upon me. While this may seem rather idyllic, it also means that I have a lot of responsibility imposed internally, rather than externally, to get things done. Sometimes I find myself a rather demanding person to have to work for!

The story of this particular research problem begins in late March, 1976. I was finishing up some work concerned with ultrasonic vibrations of crystalline fibers and was interested in switching to a new field. I like to get into a new area of research every couple of years or so.

Method *Find a problem.*

To find a *good* problem is not always easy. The responsibility of doing so is one of the things I feel I am being paid for. Several criteria should be satisfied. Since a lot of time and effort will be invested in solving the problem, it ought to be relevant to something. (The Bell System, perhaps, since I work for Bell Laboratories.) I try to keep in touch with what is going on and to be aware of where some mathematics might come in handy. In my job, another criterion is that the solution to the problem must not be needed *immediately*. It takes time to solve a hard problem. The problem, incidentally, ought to be solvable. How do I know ahead of time whether I shall be able to get a solution? I do not. Sometimes I have failed. But accumulated successes and failures give me some basis for judgment. Also, the problem should not be *too* easy. It is enjoyable to work on something which is challenging and fun.

Sometimes people bring problems to me to solve. In this instance, I went looking for the problem. I talked to an experimental physicist who is currently doing work with glass fibers associated with lightwave communications. He did not have any good problems at the moment, but he introduced me to a materials scientist who, in addition to doing glass research, was involved in crystal chemistry. And *he* had an interesting problem for me to work on.

4.2 Background of the problem

The problem is concerned with the fabrication of crystals which are used in making semiconductor devices. A small amount of impurity or dopant is deliberately introduced into a crystal as it is made. This impurity, which is very important, determines the electrical properties of the crystal. It is highly desirable that the impurity be distributed uniformly. In actuality, striations appear: there are alternating regions of relatively high and low impurity concentration. We need to learn more about how the impurity is incorporated into the crystal, so that we can understand why there are striations. Perhaps this increased knowledge will some day help someone find a way to get rid of the striations.

Method *Learn about the problem, so you can formulate it.*

Do this by reading, to get a greater breadth of knowledge, and by talking to people with diverse backgrounds.

Notice that the statement of the problem is rather vague and is decidedly nonmathematical. The background information is also nonmathematical. It requires a knowledge of chemistry and physics.

4.2.1 Semiconductors

A transistor (and other solid-state devices such as lasers and diodes) is made from a chunk of material called a semiconductor. It is neither a conductor (like copper) or an insulator (like rubber), but is somewhere in between. The basic building block for a transistor is a wafer or chip of a semiconductor material. As a matter of fact, it is possible to construct entire electronic circuits consisting of transistors, diodes, resistors, capacitors, connecting paths, etc., on very tiny semiconductor chips. These are called integrated circuits. They are found in hand calculators, electronic digital watches, telephone tone generators, computers, and in many electronic devices. Integrated circuits are getting smaller and smaller. One about the size of a match head may contain several thousand transistors.

We really ought to discuss how a transistor works and learn how an integrated circuit is constructed, but we will not do so here. For our purposes, it will suffice to know that you start out with a thin wafer consisting of a semiconductor crystal. It is called the substrate. Layers of other things are deposited on top of it.

4.2.2 The impurity

In a semiconductor, current is provided by ionization of impurity ions. You start with a crystal of an element of valence +4, such as Si or Ge. The atoms are arranged in a regular lattice structure.

Each has four nearest neighbors. The four valence electrons of an atom form four covalent bonds. Next, substitute in the lattice a Group III impurity such as Ga, Al, or B, or a Group V impurity such as As, P, or Sb. These fit in the lattice structure pretty nicely. The Group III impurities have only three valence electrons. This leaves a deficiency of one electron in the tetrahedral covalent bonds to the four nearest Si (say) atoms. A Group V impurity has five valence electrons and can complete the normal covalent bonds with one valence electron left over. Each atom is electrically neutral. So is the crystal. But the neutral atoms can be easily ionized. An Al impurity, for example, can bind another electron to it. It has a negative charge, and there is a hole which moves off into the bulk of the crystal. This is known as conduction by holes. It happens in a p-type semiconductor. Similarly a Sb atom, say, can lose one electron. Then there is conduction by electrons in an n-type semiconductor.

Only a certain number of impurity atoms can be substituted, because they are a different size than the regular atoms in the lattice. There is a solubility limit. If this is exceeded, a second phase may be precipitated. This will have different electrical properties and is undesirable. The concentration levels in semiconductors are well below the solubility limit. Silicon, for example, has approximately 5×10^{22} atoms cm^{-3}. The dopants may range from 10^{12} to 10^{17} atoms cm^{-3}. So the concentration levels are at most a few parts per million. Solubility limits vary, but are approximately 10^{18} atoms cm^{-3}.

4.2.3 Getting the impurity into the crystal

There are a number of ways to incorporate the dopant in the crystal. We will consider a method which involves a phase transformation from a liquid to a solid. The method is fast, and it is possible to grow large single crystals easily. Solidification will be concerned with things which freeze at *one* temperature, not over a freezing range. An example of the latter is sea water. Dendrites (feathery crystals) extend every which way. The sea water freezes into a mush because it is composed of different substances with different freezing temperatures.

A semiconductor, on the other hand, can be considered as a *pure* substance, since the impurity is so dilute. It has an isothermal freezing interface. This is important, because when you solidify something, you need a temperature gradient. This gives a planar, controlled interface. The temperature profile constrains the position of the interface. The atoms line up in precisely the same way with the same orientation to produce a single crystal.

In a cast structure, there is no control of the solid/liquid interface. A polycrystalline material results. A single crystal is needed for a semiconductor: grain boundaries between crystals are sources of imperfection. They donate electrons, too, and we do not know what is going on, the way we do with a single crystal.

4.2.4 Czochralski growth

The first transistor was built on a single grain of a polycrystalline material. Later, single crystals were laboriously cut out of polycrystalline substances. There was a need to grow single crystals. In 1949, Teal implemented Czochralski growth at Bell Laboratories. The first single crystal of germanium was grown there.

In the Czochralski process (Figure 4.1), the material to be grown is first melted in a crucible. A seed crystal is then lowered to the surface of the melt. As the crystal grows, it is withdrawn from the melt.

The resulting single crystals may be several feet in length and several inches or more in diameter. One such silicon boule can yield more than a thousand integrated circuit wafers containing a total of billions of transistors. Approximately 85 percent of the silicon crystals produced are grown by the Czochralski process.

4.2.5 Segregation

In order to understand how the dopant gets into the crystal, we need to learn about a mechanism called segregation. Since the

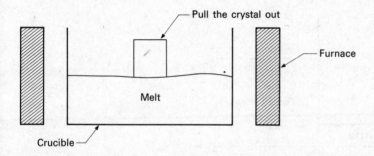

Fig. 4.1

structure of a liquid is different from that of a solid, it is reasonable to expect the dopant to behave differently in the two phases.

Gibbs showed that when the liquid and the solid are at equilibrium, the impurity concentrations in the two phases are unequal. There is an abrupt change at the interface (Figure 4.2).

During crystal growth, the system is not in chemical equilibrium. But the impurity distributions in the two phases are still not the same. As the crystal grows, segregation takes place; the impurity is rejected at the growth interface and starts to pile up at the liquid side of the interface. It has to go somewhere.

4.2.6 Diffusion

The impurity diffuses away from the interface, where it is highly concentrated. Diffusion is a slow process. We want to grow the crystal rapidly by comparison. How much impurity actually gets into the crystal is going to depend on the growth rate. The faster the crystal grows, the more impurity that will pile up at the interface. It is fairly reasonable to assume that the impurity concentration in the solid is proportional to that at the interface:

$$C_S = k_0 C_0, \tag{4.1}$$

where k_0 is known as the *equilibrium distribution coefficient*. So the faster the crystal grows, the more impurity that will go into it.

There is a constant D, the *diffusion coefficient*, which characterizes the ability of the impurity to diffuse. With $D \sim 10^{-4}\,\mathrm{cm^2\,s^{-1}}$ and a crystal growth rate $f \sim 10^{-3}\,\mathrm{cm\,s^{-1}}$, a very rough approximation of the distance over which diffusion takes place is $\delta = D/f \sim 10^{-1}\,\mathrm{cm}$ (Figure 4.3). The impurity concentration in the melt changes rapidly in the diffusion boundary layer and then stays fairly constant in the rest of the melt.

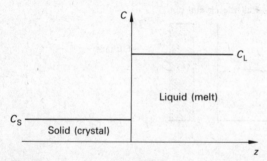

Fig. 4.2

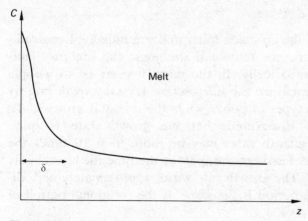

Fig. 4.3

4.2.7   Convection

Temperature gradients within the melt cause convection currents. If fluid velocities (other than that due to the crystal's growing) are important within the diffusion boundary layer, they will also affect the diffusion process, and hence the dopant incorporation process. Thermal convection messes things up!

4.2.8   Control

We need to control the growth process. The electrical conductivity must be constant over the region of the device to within a few percent. We also need reproducibility. If the device is small, the conductivity may be constant across it. But a number of such devices may be fabricated on a single chip and then cut apart. The conductivity should be the same for each device. This means that the donor or acceptor concentration cannot vary by more than a few percent throughout the crystal. So we must control the incorporation process at the interface.

Somebody had a bright idea: why not rotate the crystal while it is growing and average things out? It worked. If the crystal was rotated, the radial composition flattened out. *But* as a point on the interface moved in different parts of the melt, it saw different temperatures. As the material scientists put it, 'the thermal center of symmetry doesn't correspond to the rotational center of symmetry.'

4.2.9 Experimental results

The composition of the crystal is fairly uniform radially. Longitudinally, however, there are *rotational striations*: the impurity concentration varies periodically. In the past 10 years or so, people have been able to measure the microscopic crystal growth rate by introducing various types of pulses while the crystal is growing. To their horror, they discovered that the growth rate is quite nonuniform. Peak growth rates may be more than 10 times the average growth rate. Furthermore, part of the time the crystal may actually be melting! The growth rate varies approximately periodically with time; the period is the same as the rotational period of the crystal (Figure 4.4).

4.2.10 Conjecture

All of the preceding background information leads us to make the following conjecture: the microscopic growth rate fluctuations cause the rotational striations in the crystal. Our mathematical model will be concerned with investigating this conjecture quantitatively.

4.3 Formulating a mathematical model

Method   *Start thinking about formulating a mathematical model.*

It will be quite a while yet before we actually get the full equations written down. Nevertheless, all the time we are learning about the problem, we should be aware that eventually we want to model it mathematically. Two criteria have to be met. Physically,

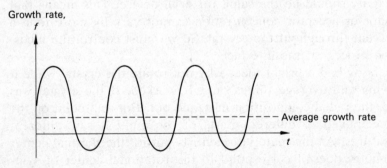

Fig. 4.4

the model should be (somewhat) realistic. And mathematically, it should be solvable, somehow.

These criteria may be conflicting. It may take a lot of interaction – refinement of physical assumptions, development of new mathematical techniques – to come up with an acceptable model. We may not even succeed.

As a start, let us organize our thoughts and make a list of things which ought to be considered in making the model:

1. heat flow,
2. fluid flow,
3. impurity flow,
4. shape of the crucible, the crystal, the meniscus,
5. values of the physical parameters.

Heat flows from the furnace into the crucible, within the melt, into and out of the crystal, etc. This is very complicated. The fluid within the crucible moves as the crystal is being rotated. It also flows *into* the crystal during crystal growth. The impurity diffuses within the melt and also gets incorporated in the growing crystal. The shape of the crucible will play a role. So will that of the crystal interface. And the shape of the free surface of the melt will have to be determined. And, of course, the actual values of the physical parameters are important.

The first item on the list basically involves conservation of energy. The second and third both involve conservation of mass and momentum. The fourth is concerned with dimensional factors.

If we take everything into account, the problem is going to be too difficult! How do I know? From experience, I guess.

Method *Start thinking about making some simplifying assumptions.*

Ultimately, the results of the model must be tested against physical reality. We will return to this point later. When making simplifications, we must realize that certain things (such as the fact that the crystal growth rate varies with time) are absolutely essential to the problem and cannot be neglected. On the other hand, it may be reasonable to ignore some other factors in order to obtain a tractable model. Compromises have to be made. Nothing is exact.

Method   *See what other people have done.*

After all, the problem may be solved already. Or it may be analogous to a problem in some other field. Chances are, the specific problem has not been solved, but *some* work related to it has been done. This often provides valuable input toward the solution of the full problem. Besides, it is satisfying to get feedback from this other work that your own work is on the right track! Of course, there may be discrepancies, and the published earlier work is not necessarily correct. In the long run, either there should be reasonable agreement or else you should have some idea about the cause of the differences.

Fortunately, an excellent paper treating the crystal growth problem was available. The next section will be devoted to a discussion of the model proposed by Burton, Prim, and Slichter [3].

4.4   The Burton–Prim–Slichter model

We shall often refer to this as the BPS model. In its formulation, a number of drastic assumptions are made, not all of which are stated explicitly. Yet in spite of these assumptions, the model seems to capture the essence of the basic problem.

The model is a steady-state one. Since time does not appear in the equations, we know right away that the model does not solve the time-varying crystal growth problem. Nevertheless, the steady-state assumption was quite reasonable to make back in 1953 when the paper was published. That the crystal growth rate varies with time is a relatively recent discovery.

Heat flow is ignored. This simplifies the problem considerably. It is probably a reasonable assumption. Knowledge of the temperature distribution is not *essential* to learning about the incorporation of impurity in the crystal. Neglecting the heat flow, however, means that we must *postulate* the crystal growth rate *f* rather than determine it as part of the solution.

Most dimensional considerations are ignored. The crucible walls and bottom are thrown out: the melt is taken to be infinite in depth and in lateral extent. The crystal/melt interface is assumed to be flat and infinite in extent. Assuming that dimensions are infinite is not reasonable. It does make the resulting analysis a lot simpler, though. Since the diffusion boundary layer is believed to be thin compared with the width of the crystal, one can hope that the results of the analysis are not too bad provided we limit ourselves to regions close to the interface and away from the edges of the crystal and crucible. The assumption that the interface is flat is probably not too bad.

These assumptions provide a good example of how compromises are made in modeling physical reality in order to achieve mathematical simplicity. Something like this has to be done if there is to be any hope of solving the problem.

4.4.1 Conservation of impurity atoms

The basic equation has essentially already appeared earlier in this book! In the discussion on traffic flow theory [5], an equation for the conservation of vehicles (one-dimensional theory) was obtained:

$$\frac{\partial k}{\partial t} + \frac{\partial q}{\partial x} = 0, \tag{4.2}$$

where k represents the concentration of vehicles on the road and q denotes the flux of vehicles, i.e. the rate at which vehicles pass a point x at time t. There was also a constitutive equation for q. This equation, when generalized to three dimensions, becomes

$$\frac{\partial k}{\partial t} + \nabla \cdot \mathbf{q} = 0. \tag{4.3}$$

Let us replace k by C, the concentration of impurity in the melt. The appropriate constitutive relation for the flux $\mathbf{q}$ is

$$\mathbf{q} = C\mathbf{u} - D\nabla C, \tag{4.4}$$

where $\mathbf{u}$ is the fluid velocity of the melt as a whole (not just of the impurity atoms) and D is the diffusion coefficient of the impurity. The first term on the right-hand side expresses the fact that the impurity atoms are transported convectively by the motion of the fluid. The second term indicates that mass transport occurs because of a gradient in mass concentration. This is known as Fick's law of diffusion.

Substitution of (4.4) into (4.3) results in the diffusion equation

$$\frac{\partial C}{\partial t} + \nabla \cdot (C\mathbf{u} - D\nabla C) = 0. \tag{4.5}$$

4.4.2 Conservation of mass

Let us use (4.2) again. This time, replace k by ρ, the density of the melt. The mass flux is

$$\mathbf{q} = \rho\mathbf{u}. \tag{4.6}$$

So the equation for conservation of mass is

$$\frac{\partial\rho}{\partial t} + \mathbf{\nabla}\cdot(\rho\mathbf{u}) = 0. \tag{4.7}$$

It is quite reasonable to assume that the density ρ is constant throughout the melt. Then (4.7) reduces to

$$\mathbf{\nabla}\cdot\mathbf{u} = 0, \tag{4.8}$$

which is known as the incompressibility condition.

Equations (4.5) and (4.8), combined, give

$$\frac{\partial C}{\partial t} + \mathbf{u}\cdot\mathbf{\nabla}C - D\nabla^2 C = 0. \tag{4.9}$$

The equations we use, incidentally, are really quite basic. They express conservation of mass or momentum.

It is natural to choose a cylindrical coordinate system. We let the fluid velocity $\mathbf{u} = (u, v, w)$. The z axis will have its origin at the original position of the interface and will be taken to be positive going into the melt.

Next assume that

$$C(r, \theta, z, t) = C(z). \tag{4.10}$$

That the concentration is independent of time is the steady-state assumption. The lack of dependence of the concentration on r and θ seems to be fairly well borne out experimentally. Equation (4.9) reduces to

$$w\frac{dC}{dz} - D\frac{d^2C}{dz^2} = 0. \tag{4.11}$$

In order to solve this equation, we need to know the axial fluid velocity w and two boundary conditions.

4.4.3 The axial velocity

Burton, Prim, and Slichter [3] assumed that the axial velocity was the sum of two velocities,

$$w = W - f, \tag{4.12}$$

where W is the axial velocity due to an infinite disk rotating on a semi-infinite liquid and $-f$ is the flow *through* the interface as a result of the crystal's growing at a rate $f > 0$. The assumption that velocities are additive in this manner is incorrect. (The governing fluid dynamical equations of motion are nonlinear. The axial velocity should actually be that obtained by solving the appropriate equations for the flow due to a porous rotating disk through which fluid is flowing.) Nevertheless, (4.12) turns out to be a fairly reasonable approximation to the axial flow very close to the interface.

The flow pattern due to a rotating disk had been calculated earlier by Cochran [4]. The disk acts like a centrifugal fan, spinning fluid out radially and tangentially. It also draws material toward it from the body of the fluid. Cochran's solution involves the angular velocity ω of the disk and the kinematic viscosity ν of the fluid. The axial velocity is independent of r and θ, and is a function only of z. Since Burton, Prim, and Slichter were interested in the concentration near the interface, they used an approximation for W which holds only near the interface:

$$W \doteq -0.51\omega^{3/2}\nu^{-1/2}z^2, \qquad z \ll \nu^{1/2}\omega^{-1/2}. \tag{4.13}$$

Hence

$$w = -f - 0.51\omega^{3/2}\nu^{-1/2}z^2. \tag{4.14}$$

Notice that a number of fluid dynamical approximations are made in the BPS model.

4.4.4 Boundary conditions

Far away from the growth interface, the concentration is constant:

$$C(z) \to C_L \quad \text{as} \quad z \to \infty. \tag{4.15}$$

At the interface, the flux coming out of the melt is the same as that going into the crystal:

$$C'(z)[-f + W(z)] - D\frac{dC}{dz} = C_s[-f] \quad \text{at} \quad z = 0, \tag{4.16}$$

or

$$(C_0 - C_s)f + D\frac{dC}{dz} = 0 \quad \text{at} \quad z = 0, \tag{4.17}$$

where C_0 is the impurity concentration in the melt at the interface and C_S is the impurity concentration in the solid. At this stage, we do not know the value of C_S.

4.4.5 Solution of the differential equation

Let

$$B = 0.17\omega^{3/2}\nu^{-1/2}f^{-3}D^2, \tag{4.18}$$

$$\zeta = fD^{-1}z. \tag{4.19}$$

Then (4.11), (4.14), (4.15), and (4.17) reduce to the following:

$$(1+3B\zeta^2)\frac{dC}{d\zeta} + \frac{d^2C}{d\zeta^2} = 0, \tag{4.20}$$

$$C \to C_L \quad \text{as} \quad \zeta \to \infty, \tag{4.21}$$

$$(C_0 - C_S) + \frac{dC}{d\zeta} = 0 \quad \text{at} \quad \zeta = 0. \tag{4.22}$$

This system has the solution

$$C(\zeta) = C_L + (C_0 - C_S)\int_{\zeta}^{\infty} \exp\left[-(X+BX^3)\right]dX. \tag{4.23}$$

So once we know C_S we know the impurity concentration anywhere in the melt. The BPS paper does not include equation (4.23). Instead, it gives the result at the interface:

$$\frac{C_0 - C_L}{C_0 - C_S} = \int_0^{\infty} \exp\left[-(X+BX^3)\right]dX. \tag{4.24}$$

Incidentally, this integral goes from zero to infinity even though assumptions were made about the velocity which are valid only for small z (or X). The integrand decays rapidly with X, though.

We have not said anything about the segregation process, yet. The impurity concentration in the solid is assumed to be proportional to that in the melt at the interface:

$$C_S = k_0 C_0, \tag{4.25}$$

where $k_0 < 1$ is the equilibrium distribution coefficient.

It is difficult to measure C_0 experimentally. However, C_L, k_0, and the material parameters which appear in the constant B are known. Equations (4.24) and (4.25) can be combined to give an expression for C_S in terms of known quantities:

$$C_S = \frac{k_0}{1 - (1 - k_0) \displaystyle\int_0^\infty \exp\left[-(X + BX^3)\right] dX} = kC_L. \tag{4.26}$$

The constant k is called the *effective distribution coefficient*. Materials scientists and crystal growers are very interested in learning about this quantity.

4.4.6 A cruder model

Actually, Burton, Prim, and Slichter did not write down equation (4.26) in their paper. They gave numerical results for k only indirectly. They began by doing a second, rather crude, analysis for the concentration distribution. The basic model is the same. But different approximations are made for the fluid flow and for the concentration. They assume that all the change in the concentration occurs within a distance δ from the interface. They also ignore the fluid dynamical effects of rotating the crystal and assume that within δ, the axial flow is merely that due to crystallization. The appropriate equations are

$$f\frac{dC}{dz} + D\frac{d^2C}{dz^2} = 0, \tag{4.27}$$

$$C_S = C_L \quad \text{at} \quad z = \delta, \tag{4.28}$$

$$(C_0 - C_S)f + D\frac{dC}{dz} \quad \text{at} \quad z = 0. \tag{4.29}$$

These give the solution at the interface:

$$\frac{C_0 - C_S}{C_1 - C_S} = e^\Delta, \qquad \Delta = f\delta/D. \tag{4.30}$$

If we again take $C_S = k_0 C_0$, we find the effective distribution coefficient is

$$k = \frac{k_0}{k_0 + (1 - k_0)e^{-\Delta}}. \tag{4.31}$$

But what is δ? It was taken to be some arbitrary distance. Compare (4.26) and (4.31). If

$$e^{-\Delta} = 1 - \int_0^\infty \exp\left[-(X + BX^3)\right] dX, \tag{4.32}$$

then the two formulas for k agree. Burton, Prim, and Slichter *define* Δ, and hence δ, in this manner.

The quantity δ is called the diffusion boundary layer thickness. It is rather arbitrary. It is defined in such a way as to make two models give the same result for k. Does it really have anything to do with the *physical* diffusion boundary layer thickness, the distance over which the concentration is changing rapidly? Much later, we shall think about this some more.

Actually, the important thing to determine is the effective distribution coefficient k. It can be found from the main BPS analysis. The cruder model is then employed to get δ. Determining δ is really a secondary issue, though, since you do not need to know anything about it in order to find k. Unfortunately, crystal growers are accustomed to thinking in terms of δ.

4.5 The crystal growth model

I first heard about the crystal growth problem in late March 1976. In April, May, and June, I gathered background information, studied the BPS analysis, and thought about various ways to formulate a model. I did not come up with a formulation which I found satisfactory until early July.

Method *Formulate a mathematical model.*

We must keep in mind all the physical processes we have learned about and decide which elements absolutely *must* go into the model. We also should take into consideration any work which has already been done (such as the BPS analysis). Finally, we have to be aware of what we are capable of doing mathematically. These mathematical capabilities increase with time, incidentally. For example, it is now possible to use a computer to solve equations which would have been entirely too formidable at the time Burton, Prim, and Slichter wrote their paper.

4.5.1 Preliminary thoughts

The BPS model has been used extensively over the years and it is probably basically correct. It would not be a bad idea to do something similar. Since we are interested in what happens when the crystal growth rate fluctuates, the governing equations simply have to depend on time. We can probably still get away with ignoring the heat flow portion of the problem. What *causes* the fluctuating growth rate is another important question. But here, we are interested in the *effect* of the fluctuations. We shall just postulate a time-varying crystal growth rate.

The BPS analysis involved a number of fluid dynamical approximations. It would be nice to eliminate them. It also would be nice to put the crucible walls and bottom into the model. But that is definitely going to make the problem a lot more difficult. We may have to compromise.

4.5.2 The model

The model will extend that developed by Burton, Prim, and Slichter. Essentially, there are three changes. First, we assume that the crucible has a bottom. It is modeled by an infinite plane or disk. The melt is then infinite in lateral extent, but is bounded above by the growth interface and below by the crucible bottom. The two disks are initially a distance d apart. Adding walls to the crucible in the model makes the problem considerably more complicated, so we will not do it. The addition of the crucible bottom makes the problem slightly more realistic. This assumption will turn out to have interesting ramifications.

Second, we eliminate the approximations to the fluid flow which Burton, Prim, and Slichter made. We will consider the flow everywhere within the melt, not just near the growth interface. No assumptions about additivity of flow velocities will be made. The fluid dynamical part of the problem consists of determining the flow between a stationary disk and a porous rotating disk through which suction is being applied.

Third, we allow the crystal growth rate f (and hence all the dependent variables in the problem) to be a function of time. The function $f(t)$ can assume negative values (remelt) as well as positive values (growth). If the crystal is pulled out of the melt at a constant rate, say at the average growth rate, then the position of the growth interface will oscillate with time.

This model has the advantage of being closely related to the BPS model. It is probably fairly reasonable. And people who have used the BPS model will probably accept this one. The new model seems to include the basic phenomena which are essential to the problem.

On the other hand, a lot is still being ignored. In particular, it is entirely unreasonable to assume that the fluid is infinite in lateral extent.

Other extensions of the model can be visualized. In Czochralski growth, it turns out that often the crucible, as well as the crystal, is rotated. The crucible may either rotate in the same direction as the crystal or in the opposite direction. By changing one boundary condition, we can extend our model to treat such cases. But it seems wise to consider the simplest possible case (a stationary crucible) first and understand the implications of that model before adding any more complications.

4.5.3 Basic conservation principles

In Section 4.4 we wrote down the diffusion equation

$$\frac{\partial C}{\partial t} + \mathbf{u} \cdot \nabla C = D \nabla^2 C, \tag{4.33}$$

which describes the conservation of impurity atoms in the melt, and the incompressibility condition

$$\nabla \cdot \mathbf{u} = 0, \tag{4.34}$$

which describes the conservation of mass of the entire fluid.

We will also need equations for the conservation of momentum in the fluid. They could be derived in a manner similar to that used for the derivation of the equation for the conservation of traffic [5]. Here, we will just write the equations in vector form:

$$\frac{\partial \mathbf{u}}{\partial t} + \mathbf{u} \cdot \nabla \mathbf{u} = -\frac{1}{\rho} \nabla p + \nu \nabla^2 \mathbf{u}. \tag{4.35}$$

These are the Navier–Stokes equations. Here ρ is the density of the fluid, p is the pressure, and ν is the kinematic viscosity. The equations represent Newton's law: the rate of change of momentum of a fluid element is equal to the force applied to it. In this instance, there are forces due to a pressure gradient and to viscous stresses. In general, there could be other forces as well, such as gravitational and electromagnetic forces.

4.5.4 Boundary and initial conditions

The conservation equations say nothing about segregation, the crystal growth rate, rotating the crystal, pulling the crystal out of the melt, or the positions of the crucible bottom and the crystal/melt interface. Information about all of these items goes into the boundary conditions, which we write down later.

The viscous fluid satisfies a no-slip condition: at a boundary it moves along with the boundary. Thus at the crucible bottom (the stationary disk), the fluid is stationary. At the crystal/melt interface, it rotates along with the interface. Growth and remelt will be described by the flow of fluid *through* the interface.

We shall assume that the dopant concentration is constant at the crucible bottom. At the crystal/melt interface, impurity is rejected during crystal growth. During remelt, part of the solid crystal turns into liquid again, contributing whatever impurity it has accumulated.

The position of the growth interface depends upon the rate of crystal growth and the rate at which the crystal is pulled from the melt.

We assume that the fluid and disks are initially at rest and that the concentration is initially uniform. Crystal rotation and growth will then be introduced by means of the boundary conditions.

Method   *Make everything dimensionless.*

The solution depends upon many parameters: ρ, ν, D, ω, d, f, c_L, and k_0. Do we have to consider the dependence of the solution on each of these parameters separately, or are only certain combinations important? A natural first step for an applied mathematician is to recast the equations in a dimensionless form. Certain dimensionless combinations of the parameters will appear. Making things dimensionless, then, is a procedure to identify precisely what parameter combinations are important. This procedure is commonly used by applied mathematicians, but is less familiar to other scientists. The BPS analysis, for example, was not done in a dimensionless form. When we eventually communicate our results to people in other fields, we must remember that they may not be accustomed to thinking in dimensionless terms. So we must be prepared to explain this method to them.

4.5.5   Dimensionless conservation equations

Put asterisks on all the variables to indicate they are dimensional.

Then normalize with respect to characteristic dimensions. Let

$$\mathbf{x} = \mathbf{x}^*/d,$$
$$t = t^*\omega,$$
$$\mathbf{u} = \mathbf{u}^*/\omega d, \tag{4.36}$$
$$p/\rho = (p/\rho)^*/(\omega d)^2,$$
$$C = C^*/C_L.$$

Then, in dimensionless form, (4.33)–(4.35) become

$$\boldsymbol{\nabla} \cdot \mathbf{u} = 0, \tag{4.37}$$

$$\frac{\partial \mathbf{u}}{\partial t} + \mathbf{u} \cdot \boldsymbol{\nabla} \mathbf{u} = -\frac{1}{\rho} \boldsymbol{\nabla} p + R^{-1}\nabla^2\mathbf{u}, \tag{4.38}$$

$$\frac{\partial C}{\partial t} + \mathbf{u} \cdot \boldsymbol{\nabla} C = (RSc)^{-1}\nabla^2 C, \tag{4.39}$$

where

$$R = \omega d^2/\nu \tag{4.40}$$

is the Reynolds number and

$$Sc = \nu/D \tag{4.41}$$

is the Schmidt number. From now on, everything we use will be in a dimensionless form. The boundary conditions and initial conditions will be dimensionless, too, but we will not consider them quite yet.

Equations (4.37)–(4.39) form a coupled system of five nonlinear partial differential equations for $\mathbf{u} = (u, v, w)$, p, and C. They involve three space variables and one time variable. The Navier–Stokcs equations are notoriously difficult to solve. The problem is even more difficult here, since the diffusion equation is thrown in as well. The model really cannot be simplified very much more. Some essential physics would be lost. But the prospect of a mathematical solution does not look very encouraging at this stage.

4.5.6 A major breakthrough

Fortunately, thanks to a discovery von Kármán [8] made in 1921, the situation is not as dismal as it looks. It turns out to be possible to reduce the partial differential equations to a system involving *one* space variable and one time variable. We first assume that the flow is axisymmetric so that everything is independent of θ. This is probably quite reasonable. Next, we suppose that

$$w(r, \theta, z, t) = R^{-1/2} H(z, t), \tag{4.42}$$

i.e. that the axial fluid velocity is a function only of z and t. This is really what von Kármán assumed, except that he happened to be concerned with equations which were time independent. The axial fluid velocity used in the BPS analysis was also independent of r and θ. The scaling with R in (4.42) is not necessary, but turns out to be convenient.

We also assume, as in the BPS analysis, that

$$C(r, \theta, z, t) = C(z, t). \tag{4.43}$$

Using subscripts to denote partial derivatives, we write (4.37) as

$$\frac{1}{r}(ru)_r + v_\theta/r + w_z = 0. \tag{4.44}$$

Since $v_\theta = 0$ and w_z is a function only of z and t, it follows that

$$u = rF(z, t). \tag{4.45}$$

(An integration constant can be shown to vanish because, for example, $u = 0$ at the crucible bottom $z = 1$.) The three components of (4.38), with the θ-derivatives no longer included explicitly, are

$$u_t + uu_r - v^2/r + u_z w = -p_r/\rho + R^{-1}(u_{rr} + u_r/r + u_{zz} - u/r^2), \tag{4.46}$$

$$v_t + uv_r + uv/r + wv_z = R^{-1}(v_{rr} + v_r/r + v_{zz} - v/r^2), \tag{4.47}$$

$$w_t + uw_r + ww_z = -p_z/\rho + R^{-1}(w_{rr} + w_r/r + w_{zz}). \tag{4.48}$$

The terms with slashes through them either cancel or vanish because of (4.42) and (4.45). Equation (4.42) implies that $p_{zr} = 0$ and hence that

$$p_r = \psi(z, t). \tag{4.49}$$

Then (4.46) implies that

$$v^2/r^2 - \psi(r, t)/r\rho = G_1(z, t). \tag{4.50}$$

Now at the crucible bottom ($z = 1$), $v = 0$. Hence $\psi(r, t)/r$ is independent of r and

$$v = rG(z, t). \tag{4.51}$$

This also means that $p_r = r\rho\phi(t)$, so that

$$p/\rho = \tfrac{1}{2}r^2\phi(t) + R^{-1}\Phi(z, t), \tag{4.52}$$

where the scaling with R is just chosen for convenience. Upon collecting these results, we have

$$u = rF(z, t), \tag{4.53}$$

$$v = rG(z, t), \tag{4.54}$$

$$w = R^{-1/2}H(z, t), \tag{4.55}$$

$$p/\rho = \tfrac{1}{2}r^2\phi(t) + R^{-1}\Phi(z, t), \tag{4.56}$$

$$C = C(z, t). \tag{4.57}$$

The basic equations (4.44), (4.46)–(4.48), and (4.39) are then replaced by

$$\phi_z = 0, \tag{4.58}$$

$$2F + R^{-1/2}H_z = 0, \tag{4.59}$$

$$F_t = G^2 - F^2 - R^{-1/2}F_zH - \phi + R^{-1}F_{zz}, \tag{4.60}$$

$$G_t = -2FG - R^{-1/2}G_zH + R^{-1}G_{zz}, \tag{4.61}$$

$$H_t = -R^{-1/2}H_zH - R^{-1/2}\Phi_z + R^{-1}H_{zz}, \tag{4.62}$$

$$C_t = -R^{-1/2}HC_z + (RSc)^{-1}C_{zz}. \tag{4.63}$$

(The scaling with R was chosen so that R and d/dz appear in the combination $R^{-1/2}\,d/dz$.) These equations form a coupled system of second-order nonlinear partial differential equations in one space variable and one time variable. They still look pretty horrendous, but at least we got rid of two space variables.

The function $\Phi(z, t)$ appears only in (4.62) and can be determined. Since we are not particularly interested in learning about the pressure function anyway, we will not use this equation any more.

4.5.7 The boundary conditions

We will consider the boundary conditions at the crucible bottom first, because they are easier. The crucible bottom (stationary disk) is at $z = 1$, since the coordinate system is normalized with respect to the initial distance between the two disks and the growth interface (rotating disk) is initially at $z = 0$. In accordance with the no-slip condition, there is no fluid motion at the stationary disk, so

$$F(1, t) = 0, \tag{4.64}$$

$$G(1, t) = 0, \tag{4.65}$$

$$H(1, t) = 0. \tag{4.66}$$

The impurity concentration was normalized with respect to its initial value C_L throughout the liquid. We assume that it retains this value at the stationary disk:

$$C(1, t) = 1. \tag{4.67}$$

(Actually, a flux condition should be used. However, such a condition causes difficulties which we will not discuss here. The above assumption turns out to be reasonable enough.)

The situation is a little more complicated at the crystal/melt interface (rotating disk). In order to determine the position $I(t)$ of the interface, we need to know the (dimensionless) rates at which the crystal is growing and is being pulled from the melt. If the dimensional growth rate is $f(t)$, we can define a dimensionless growth rate by

$$f(t)/(\omega d) = R^{-1/2} a(t). \tag{4.68}$$

Notice that by (4.40)

$$a(t) = f(t) \omega^{-1/2} \nu^{-1/2}. \tag{4.69}$$

(We chose the seemingly illogical notation $a(t)$ in order to be consistent with some notation which appears in the fluid dynamics literature.)

If the dimensionless pulling rate is $R^{-1/2} P(t)$, then the position of the interface is

$$I(t) = \int_0^t R^{-1/2} [a(s) - P(s)] \, ds. \tag{4.70}$$

At the rotating disk, the tangential motion of the fluid is the same as that of the disk:

$$F(I(t), t) = 0, \tag{4.71}$$

$$G(I(t), t) = \omega_I(t). \tag{4.72}$$

The angular velocity function $\omega_I(t)$, which describes the interface as a function of time, must be specified. We will start with the disk at rest and gradually rotate it up to speed. The normalization is such that the final value of $\omega_I(t)$ is unity.

As the crystal grows or melts, fluid flows through the interface. The crystal growth is described by the boundary condition

$$H(I(t), t) = -a(t). \tag{4.73}$$

When $a(t)$ is positive, the crystal is growing; when it is negative, the crystal is melting. Fluid dynamically, these correspond to suction or blowing through a porous disk.

The boundary condition concerning the concentration at the interface takes two forms, depending on whether the crystal is growing or remelting. During growth, impurity is being rejected at the interface. When we were discussing the BPS model, we came up with the boundary condition

$$(C^* - C_s^*)f^* + D\frac{dC^*}{dz^*} = 0 \qquad \text{at the interface.} \tag{4.74}$$

We have put asterisks on the variables to indicate that they are dimensional. In nondimensional terms, this boundary condition now becomes

$$a(t)[C(I(t),t) - C_s(0, t)] + C_z(I(t), t)/(ScR^{1/2}) = 0 \quad \text{at} \quad z = I(t). \tag{4.75}$$

Here $C_s(0, t)$ is the dimensionless (normalized with respect to C_L) concentration in the solid at the interface. But what *is* $C_s(0, t)$? We have to figure out what the concentration in the solid is, both at the interface and everywhere else. After all, that is what we are really doing this whole problem for!

When the crystal is growing, we assume, as in the BPS model, that

$$C_s(0, t) = k_0 C(I(t), t) \qquad a(t) \geqslant 0. \tag{4.76}$$

When the crystal is melting, the situation is a little more complicated. Let $C_s(\zeta, t)$ denote the impurity concentration in the crystal at time t, where $\zeta \geqslant 0$ measures distance from the growth interface. (This coordinate system in the solid is fixed with respect to the crystal interface. The z coordinate system in the melt, on the other hand, is fixed with respect to the original position of the interface.) Notice that

$$L(t) = \int_0^t R^{-1/2} a(s)\, ds \tag{4.77}$$

is the length of the crystal at time t. Now any point within the crystal was at the growth interface at some time or other. During crystal growth, equation (4.76) holds. During remelt, layers of the crystal return to the melt. The interface will be the same as one which was there previously during the growth process:

$$C_S(0, t) = C_S(0, \sigma), \qquad a(t) < 0 \tag{4.78}$$

where σ is the largest number less than t for which

$$\int_\sigma^t a(s)\, ds = 0.$$

If we know the concentration at the interface as a function of time and if we know the growth rate of the crystal, we can determine the concentration anywhere within the crystal. For $0 < \zeta \leqslant L(t)$,

$$C_S(\zeta, t) = C_S(0, \mu), \tag{4.79}$$

where μ is the largest number less than t for which

$$\zeta - \int_\mu^t R^{-1/2} a(s)\, ds = 0.$$

4.5.8 Initial conditions

If we now write down the initial conditions, we have the entire system of partial differential equations, boundary conditions, and initial conditions in mind. We start out with the fluid at rest and the concentration uniform:

$$\left.\begin{aligned}
\phi(0) &= 0, \\
F(z, 0) &= 0, \\
G(z, 0) &= 0, \\
H(z, 0) &= 0, \\
C(z, 0) &= 1.
\end{aligned}\right\} \tag{4.80}$$

4.6 A hierarchy of problems

The problem, as we have formulated it, consists of solving the system of partial differential equations (4.58)–(4.61) and (4.63), subject to the boundary conditions (4.64)–(4.67), (4.71)–(4.73), and (4.75) and the initial conditions (4.80). There are also the auxiliary equations (4.76) and (4.78) which describe the impurity concentration in the crystal.

It is a formidable problem. It took approximately 3 months for me to learn enough just to formulate it. There is little hope of my being able to do much with it analytically. At this point, I would ordinarily give up and call it quits: the problem is just too difficult. To do so, though, would fail to take advantage of an extremely important ingredient in the research process.

Ingredient   *Serendipity (dumb luck).*

Norm Schryer is an exuberant numerical analyst whose office is two doors down the hall from mine. While I was busy formulating this problem, he was busy writing a general purpose numerical routine designed to solve a coupled system of nonlinear second-order partial differential equations in one space variable and one time variable. He had just finished checking the program out on some sample problems and was looking around for some users who had some real-life problems to throw at it.

Very often, it seems, someone is in the right place at the right time in this manner. The trick is to be *aware* of the possibility of such fortunate circumstances – to be ready to take advantage of them when they happen.

So it looks as if we will be able to tackle the problem. Let us take another look at the governing equations. Notice that $C(z, t)$ appears in only one of the partial differential equations, plus in two boundary conditions and an initial condition. If $H(z, t)$ were known, the equations for $C(z, t)$ would decouple from the rest of the system. The remaining equations for the fluid flow variables do not decouple from one another. It appears that we can learn about the fluid flow part of the problem first and then learn about crystal growth. Also, it would be nice to learn about steady-state solutions to the system of equations before considering the full time-dependent crystal growth problem.

Method   *Isolate segments of the problem.*

Sometimes a large problem can be broken down into several smaller and more manageable problems. While working on the segments, though, we should keep in mind the basic structure of the entire problem.

It turns out that the crystal growth problem can be considered as a hierarchy of three problems:

1. *Fluid flow.* This in itself can be broken down into two problems. The first is to learn about the flow of a viscous fluid between two infinite parallel disks, one of which is stationary and the other of which is rotating. The second is to learn about the flow when a uniform suction is applied through the rotating disk.

2. *Steady-state crystal growth.* Solve the diffusion equation as well as the fluid dynamic equations. Start with the fluid and disks at rest and the concentration uniform within the melt. Then set the disk (crystal) rotating and apply suction (crystal growth). Find out what the solution settles down to when the rotation rate and growth rate are held constant. Compare the results with those of Burton, Prim, and Slichter.

3. *Time-varying crystal growth.* Now let the growth rate vary with time, preferably periodically. Allow the possibility of re-melt. Learn about the incorporation of impurity in the solid under these conditions.

Each of these problems builds upon the one preceding it.

Method   *Search the literature again.*

The entire problem is now much more clearly defined. It is time again to read articles and talk to people to find out if work has been done on any aspect of the problem. Since we will be attacking the problems in sequence, we will start thinking about the problem concerning the viscous flow between two disks. Notice that the field of study has shifted. We started out in materials science and chemistry. Now we are talking about fluid dynamics. So we have to search through a different type of literature now.

I had thought that the first problem in the hierarchy would be pretty much solved. I hoped to look up the solution in the literature, use it, and get on to the second problem in the hierarchy. I was mistaken. I soon discovered that Problem 1 was a full-fledged research problem in itself and that I was deep in the midst of it.

An extensive literature was available concerning this problem. Some of it I discovered by browsing in the library. The rest I learned about by talking to a number of people. Especially helpful were a couple of discussions I had with people I met at a meeting of the Society for Industrial and Applied Mathematics.

This often happens: the problem grows! Also, a number of interesting side avenues for research may develop. It is sometimes fun to take trips down these avenues. Nevertheless, a bit of perspective is required. After all, the people who grow semiconductor crystals still want to know more about the rotational striations they observe. If we are ever to get any insight into that problem, we probably will not have enough time to explore every interesting side avenue along the way. But maybe some day we will return to do further exploration!

4.7 The partial differential equation solving routine

Method   *Collaboration.*

Fortunately, you do not have to be an expert about everything! I do not understand the details of Norm Schryer's program to solve partial differential equations (and, accordingly, my description of it will be brief). On the other hand, Norm does not know most of the chemistry, physics, and fluid dynamics which goes into the formulation of the problem. But we both have broad enough backgrounds (i.e. we both know about partial differential equations) that we can communicate with each other.

Collaboration can be very valuable. People with quite varied backgrounds, work styles, and methods of solving problems can often work together fruitfully. Scientists do not spend all of their time working alone in their laboratories or writing at their desks with the office door closed.

4.7.1 POST (partial and ordinary differential equation solver in space and time)

By using a procedure called Galerkin's method, the routine approximates the solution at a given instant of time by piecewise polynomials. It projects the solution onto the space of piecewise polynomials given by B-splines; this space can be used to approximate any reasonable function very accurately. Also, a computationally convenient basis for this space exists.

Let $\pi = \{z_1, \ldots, z_N\}$ be a mesh on $[0, 1]$, where $0 = z_1 \leqslant z_2 \leqslant$

$\cdots \leqslant z_N = 1$. Let the multiplicity m_i of z_i be the number of times z_i appears in the list π. The space of B-splines of order k defined on the mesh π is defined to be the collection of all functions f

(i) which are polynomials of degree $<k$ on each interval $[z_i, z_{i+1}]$
   in the mesh $(i = 1, \ldots, N-1)$,
(ii) for which $d^{k-1-m_i}f(z_i)/dz^{k-1-m_i}$ exists and is continuous at each
   z_i $(i = 1, \ldots, N)$, and
(iii) for which $f \equiv 0$ outside $[0, 1]$.

We shall use B-splines of order $k = 4$, so the functions are approximated by piecewise cubic polynomials. We choose a spatial mesh for the problem. This then defines the B-spline space and the basis functions $B_j(z)$, $j = 1, \ldots, N-k$.

If $u_i(z, t)$ is some component of the solution vector, then it is approximated by

$$u_i(z, t) = \sum_{j=1}^{N-k} U_{ji}(t)B_j(z), \qquad (4.81)$$

where the $U_{ji}(t)$ have to be determined. This leads to ordinary differential equations in time, which must be solved for the $U_{ji}(t)$. Solution of ordinary differential equations is much easier than solution of partial differential equations. Many numerical methods exist.

4.7.2 Special features

The spatial mesh can be non-uniform. Some popular numerical methods use a uniform mesh. In our problem, we know that the concentration changes rapidly near the growth interface and is fairly uniform elsewhere. We shall see that the flow functions change rapidly near the disks and slowly elsewhere. If these functions were to be approximated accurately by functions defined on a uniform mesh, the mesh would have to be quite fine. This means that the computations would be relatively expensive. If a non-uniform mesh is used, it can be made finer where the solution varies rapidly and coarser where it changes slowly.

Incidentally, many of the published numerical results concerning the fluid flow problem were obtained through computations using uniform meshes. Authors of such papers should take care to demonstrate how they have determined the accuracy of their results. If the mesh is not fine enough, the results can be quite misleading. It would be wise to view such papers initially with skepticism.

Another special feature of the POST numerical routine is its ability to perform computations automatically to a specified accuracy, both in time and in space.

If the solution changes rapidly in time, a small time step is required. On the other hand, if the solution is slowly varying, a large time step can be used. The routine automatically adjusts the time step to be as large as possible, consistent with maintaining the desired error tolerance in the solution. When it is near an equilibrium solution, it really gallops along.

In space, the accuracy of the solution depends upon the fineness of the spatial mesh. For the fluid flow and steady-state crystal growth problems, we choose a spatial mesh and eventually compute equilibrium solutions. The routine then automatically refines the mesh until the equilibrium solution is within a specified error tolerance of the exact solution.

Another rather unusual feature of the program is that it will ultimately be available for others to use.† The POST package [13] is built upon the PORT library of FORTRAN subprograms for numerical mathematics [6].

The program, incidentally, is based upon a lot of solid theory: convergence theorems and error analysis. Writing it required a large knowledge of numerical analysis.

So we coded our system of equations into the program and put it on the machine. It did not work. Norm Schryer and I spent the entire next week arguing with each other. We argued physics. We argued mathematics. We argued numerical analysis. He claimed I was wrong. I claimed he was wrong. We finally found the error. It turned out to be a subtle combination of a bug in the compiler and a bug in POST.

Ingredient *Perseverance.*

Research does not always proceed smoothly. In fact, frustration seems to be an inherent part of research. One must proceed with self-confidence (when justified) and keep plugging away at a problem. Eventually, some day, there will be a moment of exhilaration

---

† Inquiries should be directed to Bell Laboratories Computing Information Service, Murray Hill, NJ 07974, USA.

when something becomes crystal clear or a segment of the problem is solved or some pieces of the puzzle finally fit together. But this exhilaration will quickly be replaced by more frustration and internal tension as you begin to tackle another aspect of the whole problem.

In late July 1976 we got the computer program to work. Things moved very quickly for several months after that, as we learned about the fluid flow.

4.8 Values of physical parameters

So far, we have hardly said anything about the actual values of the relevant physical parameters. We need to know about them in order to do numerical computation. I returned to the materials scientist who had given me the crystal growth problem in the first place and asked him to give me an idea of what the ranges of various parameter values were. These were the values he came up with:

$$\nu = 2 \times 10^{-3} \, \mathrm{cm^2 \, s^{-1}},$$

$$D = 5 \times 10^{-5} \, \mathrm{cm^2 \, s^{-1}},$$

$$k_0 = 0.01 \text{ to } 0.3,$$

$$\omega = 1 \text{ to } 100 \, \mathrm{rev/min^{-1}} = 0.1 - 10 \, \mathrm{rad \, s^{-1}},$$

$$d = 2 \text{ to } 8 \, \mathrm{in.} = 5 \text{ to } 20 \, \mathrm{cm},$$

Crystal pulling rate $= 0.1$ to $20 \, \mathrm{cm \, h^{-1}} = 3 \times 10^{-7}$ to $5 \times 10^{-3} \, \mathrm{cm \, s^{-1}}$
Maximum crystal growth rate $=$ approximately ten times the pulling rate.

The dimensionless parameters in our problem are $R = d^2 \omega / \nu$, $Sc = \nu / D$, $a(t)$, and k_0. Upon combining the values of d, ω, and ν to give the smallest and largest Reynolds number R, we find that R lies between 10^3 and 10^6. The latter limit is probably unrealistic, but at any rate R is large. It turns out that this is all we really need to know.

The Schmidt number is $Sc = 40$. The values for the pulling rate or average growth rate yield values for the suction parameter $a = f/(\omega\nu)^{1/2}$ which lie between 10^{-5} and 10^{-1}. The maximum growth rate, and hence the instantaneous value of $a(t)$, may be ten times as large.

4.9 The fluid flow in the melt

The first problem to consider in the hierarchy is that of the viscous flow between a stationary and a rotating disk through which a uniform suction is applied. The pertinent equations, which we derived in Section 4.5, are

$$\phi_z = 0, \tag{4.82}$$

$$2F + R^{-1/2}H_z = 0, \tag{4.83}$$

$$F_t = G^2 - F^2 - R^{-1/2}F_zH - \phi + R^{-1}F_{zz}, \tag{4.84}$$

$$G_t = -2FG - R^{-1/2}G_zH + R^{-1}G_{zz}, \tag{4.85}$$

where

$$\left.\begin{aligned} u &= rF(z, t), \\ v &= rG(z, t), \\ w &= R^{-1/2}H(z, t), \\ p/\rho &= \tfrac{1}{2}r^2\phi(t) + R^{-1/2}\Phi(z, t), \end{aligned}\right\} \tag{4.86}$$

and the function $\Phi(z, t)$ is determined from another equation. The boundary conditions are

$$\left.\begin{aligned} F(0, t) &= 0, & F(1, t) &= 0, \\ G(0, t) &= \omega_I(t), & G(1, t) &= 0, \\ H(0, t) &= -a(t), & H(1, t) &= 0, \end{aligned}\right\} \tag{4.87}$$

and the initial conditions are

$$F(z, 0) = G(z, 0) = H(z, 0) = \phi(0) = 0. \tag{4.88}$$

The angular velocity function $\omega_I(t)$ will ultimately tend to unity; the suction function $a(t)$ will tend to a value a, called the suction parameter.

Method *Isolate a simpler problem.*

We have done this before. Here we have to learn how the solution depends upon two parameters, R and a. We begin by setting $a(t) \equiv 0$, so there is no suction through the disk. After we have thoroughly understood the flow without suction, and how it depends upon R, we will study the effects of suction.

Method *Guess.*

Who knows? You might be lucky! We know that R is large. We will be interested in a solution which holds after the disk has been rotating at a constant velocity for a long time. So try neglecting terms multiplied by inverse powers of R; set terms with time derivatives to zero. We see from (4.82)–(4.85) that this would mean that

$$F = 0, \qquad G^2 = \phi = \text{const.} = ?, \qquad H = \text{const.} = ? \qquad (4.89)$$

The resulting motion is that of a spiraling rigid body. The boundary conditions cannot all be satisfied. Nevertheless, it turns out that a solution of this form, known as the inviscid solution, is okay *except* near the boundaries. Thin momentum boundary layers exist near the boundaries. The velocity functions change rapidly across these layers. Although we cannot guess the full solution, we can at least learn something.

4.9.1 History

Before discussing our numerical results, let us get some perspective by learning more about the background of the problem. During the actual research process, this type of learning takes place before, during, and after the time numerical results are obtained. Things never seem to get completely into perspective until the time comes to consolidate all the new results into a technical paper.

The problem's origins lie in the investigation of flow due to a single rotating disk. Von Kármán [8] made the basic assumption that the axial velocity is independent of radius. He reduced the Navier–Stokes equations for the steady (time-independent) flow due to a rotating disk to a set of ordinary differential equations. He obtained an approximate solution to the equations, but made a mistake in his analysis. Cochran [4], doing painstaking calculations by hand, corrected the error and obtained a numerical solution. Today, such a solution can easily be obtained with the use of a computer. Cochran's approximation for the axial velocity close to the disk was used by Burton, Prim, and Slichter [3].

Bödewadt [2] considered a related problem. He obtained a numerical description of the flow over a stationary plane when the fluid infinitely far from it is in a state of solid rotation. Batchelor [1] extended the discussion to a family of rotationally symmetric flows the members of which are distinguished by the ratio of the angular velocity of the fluid at infinity to that of the disk. There was also some work done on the effect of suction through the rotating disk.

Batchelor also noticed that an extension of von Kármán's analysis will also reduce to ordinary differential equations the Navier–Stokes equations for steady rotationally symmetric flows between two infinite coaxial disks, either or both of which may have a uniform suction through its surface. Pearson [12] seems to have been the first to consider the time-varying flow problem. Very little else has been done about this.

In our crystal growth problem, we are interested in the special case for which one disk rotates and the other is stationary. But we might as well keep aware of what is being done on the more general case, since Czochralski growth may involve rotation of the crucible as well as the crystal.

The nature of the steady flow when the disks are counterrotating, especially when they are rotating with the same speed but in the opposite sense, has provoked a number of investigations, not all of which are in agreement. Less attention has been paid to the case of disks corotating with nonzero angular velocities, possibly because early conjectures about the character of the flow were in agreement.

The remaining case, in which one disk is at rest and the other rotates, has received much attention in the literature. Batchelor [1] predicted that at large Reynolds number the fluid, except for that in thin layers near each disk, would rotate at a uniform angular velocity intermediate between those of the two disks. Stewartson [14], on the other hand, predicted that the main body of the fluid would have no angular velocity and that, in the limit of large Reynolds number, the solution would approach the single disk solution. Herein lies the beginning of a controversy which, even today, is not completely resolved.

Lance and Rogers [9] solved the steady-state equations for Reynolds numbers up to $R = 441$. Pearson [12], for Reynolds numbers as large as $R = 10^3$, studied the time evolution of the flow from an impulsive start and zero initial conditions. Both of these investigations indicated that Batchelor's qualitative picture is correct. Then Mellor, Chapple, and Stokes [11] presented numerical evidence that many steady-state solutions are possible, including both of the above type. Other numerical solutions have been obtained as well. In recent years, analytical proofs have demonstrated that a number of these solutions are incorrect.

From a theoretical standpoint, the question of existence of solutions to two disk flow problems has not yet been settled, let alone that of uniqueness. There is some rigorous discussion, however, about the behavior of solutions.

As far as I know, no work at all has been done on the case of the viscous flow between two rotating disks when there is suction through one or both disks.

Unfortunately, none of the work discussed above quite answers the questions we are asking. For one thing, the problem we eventually have to solve is dependent on time. Almost all of the earlier work concerning the fluid flow behavior is for a steady-state situation. We could content ourselves with studying that case, too, for the first of our hierarchy of problems. But we know that we have to incorporate time variation into the system sooner or later, so we might as well get some experience in doing so from the start.

For another thing, we need to know how the flow depends upon the suction parameter a. And it would be nice to know how it depends upon the Reynolds number R as well.

So let us get started! Equations (4.82)–(4.85) form a sixth-order coupled system of partial differential equations for the four unknowns F, G, H, and ϕ. There are four initial conditions (4.89). There are six boundary conditions (4.88) which match up with the differential equations in a somewhat unusual way: there are two conditions each on F, G, and H, and none on ϕ.

To begin with, we set $a(t) \equiv 0$. There are several other decisions which have to be made before computation can proceed.

What is R? Realistic values are large: greater than $R = 10^3$ at least. Yet this seems to represent the upper range of values for which computations are presented in the technical literature. This gives us a hint that the larger the value of R is, the harder the computation is going to be. We had better start small. We will try $R = 10^2$. (Later, we did computations for $R = 10^3$ and $R = 10^4$ as well and learned how the solution scales with R.)

How should we define the angular velocity $\omega_I(t)$ of the disk (crystal interface)? It should start at zero and end up at unity, preferably getting there monotonically. Other than that, the exact form of $\omega_I(t)$ probably does not matter too much. Numerical computation is likely to proceed more smoothly if the disk spins up gradually rather than too abruptly. With these considerations in mind, we rather arbitrarily decided to use a linear ramp for $\omega_I(t)$ such that $\omega_I(0) = 0$ and $\omega_I(R^4) = 1$. For $t \geqslant R^4$, we set $\omega_I(t) = 1$.

What sort of mesh spacing should be used? Here, prior information comes in handy. We used some published results of Pearson [12] to get an idea of the boundary layer thicknesses. We had reason to believe the thickness would scale with $R^{-1/2}$, so we included that in our specification of the mesh spacing. In the interior, away from the disks, the solution was pretty nearly constant, so we used a coarser mesh. Some results from numerical analysis indicate that if the ratio of the largest to the smallest mesh spacing is too large, there may be difficulty with numerical stability. Norm Schryer and I found this out the hard way, and hence included a provision to add more mesh points in the interior when necessary.

How do you know when you have reached an equilibrium solution? How long do you compute? Since the numerical routine chooses very large time steps when the solution is near equilibrium, there is no harm in choosing a rather large stopping time. We decided to compute out to $t = 100R^4$, then refine the spatial mesh as necessary to achieve the desired accuracy, and then compute to $t = 200R^4$.

4.9.2 Equilibrium results: no suction ($a = 0$)

We will not present *all* our results, but just enough to give an idea of what is going on. Figures 4.5, 4.6, and 4.7 show the equilibrium profiles for F, G, and H with $R = 10^4$ for several values of the suction parameter a. Let us just look at the results for $a = 0$ for the moment. Notice that well defined boundary layers exist near both disks and that they are separated by a core region in which the motion is very nearly that of a rigid body. Near the rotating disk, the fluid is drawn toward the disk (Figure 4.7) and is thrown centrifugally outward (Figure 4.5). In the core region, the fluid swirls toward the rotating disk (Figures 4.6, 4.7). The interior rotation rate is approximately one-third that of the disk (Figure 4.6). So we get a solution of the type Batchelor [1] predicted. The flow exhibits an oscillatory nature in the boundary layer near the stationary disk. Regions of inward and outward swirling flow are present; the predominant flow, which is closest to the stationary disk, is one of inward swirling. Some of the fluid rotates faster than that in the core region. Axially (Figure 4.7), the fluid moves rapidly

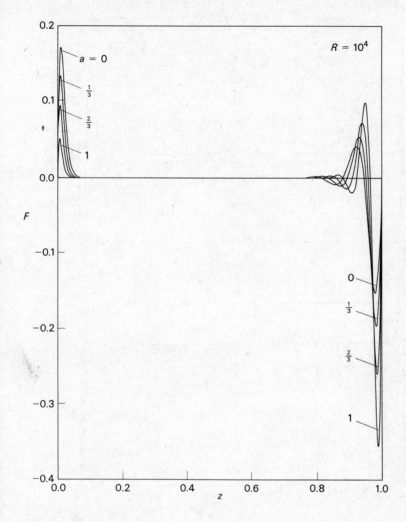

Fig. 4.5

away from the stationary disk, then slows down somewhat as it enters the core region.

We also did computations for $R = 10^2$ and 10^3. These, combined with those for $R = 10^4$, clearly indicated the asymptotic nature of the solution for large Reynolds number. Both boundary layers have a thickness of order $R^{-1/2}$. Within the boundary layers, the magnitudes of F, G, and H are nearly independent of R; the solutions scale with $zR^{-1/2}$. In the interior, F, G, and H become increasingly independent of z and of R as R increases. Figure 4.8,

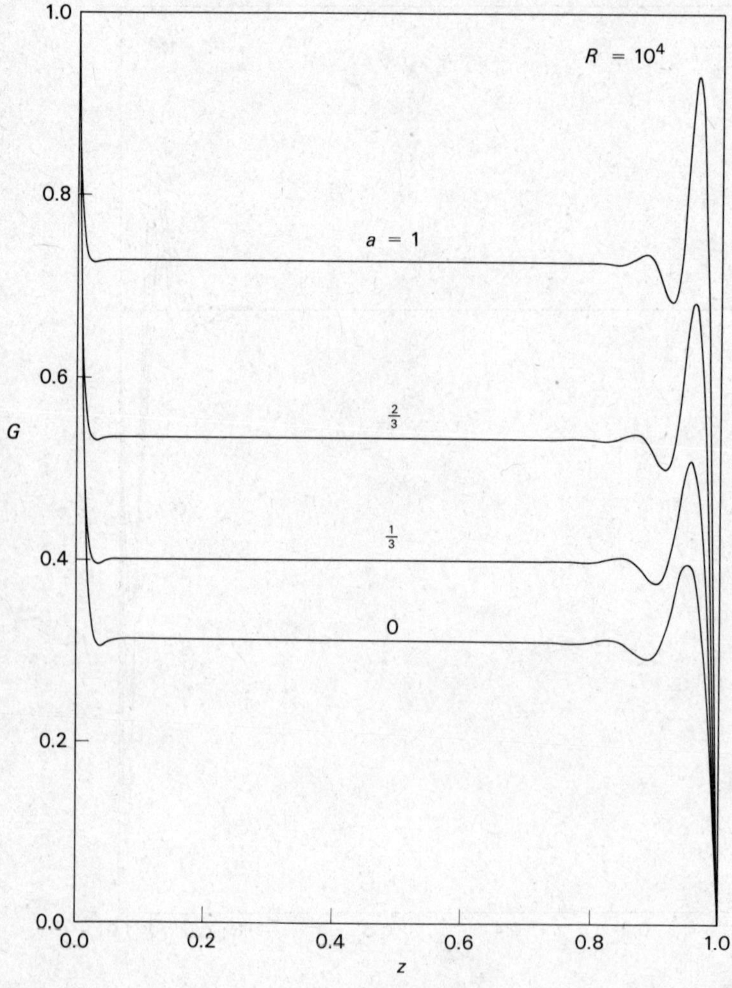

Fig. 4.6

which shows the equilibrium profile for G with $R = 10^3$, when compared with Figure 4.6, should illustrate these results.

4.9.3 Equilibrium results: suction ($a > 0$)

Figures 4.5 through 4.8 also show the equilibrium profiles when there is a uniform suction ($a = \frac{1}{3}, \frac{2}{3}, 1$) through the porous rotating disk. Increasing the suction causes the fluid in the interior to rotate more rapidly and to flow more rapidly toward the rotating disk. As a matter of fact, we found that if the suction is large enough, the

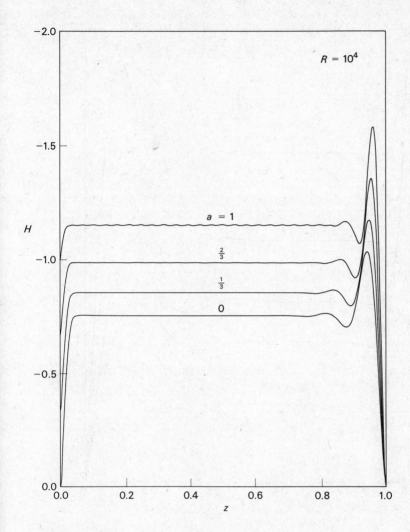

Fig. 4.7

interior rotation rate is actually larger than that of the rotating disk!

The flow description in the boundary layer near the rotating disk differs according to whether the interior rotation rate is smaller or larger than that of the disk. If it is smaller, then near the disk the fluid is thrown centrifugally *outward*. As the amount of suction increases, the radial outflow decreases. As the suction increases further (and the interior rotation rate exceeds that of the disk: $a \geqslant 1.34$), the radial flow is an *inward* flow.

Near the stationary disk, the qualitative description of the flow is

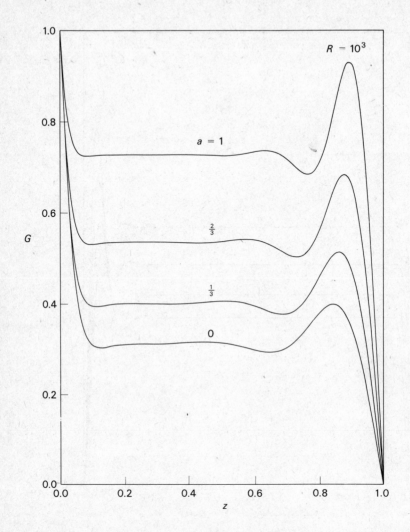

Fig. 4.8

much like that for the case of no suction ($a = 0$), but the velocity amplitudes are larger.

Method   *Interpret the results.*

It is not enough to get graphs for F, G, and H. You have to know what the solution means physically. Think about it and be sure you believe it.

Also, consider the results in the context of the crystal growth problem. We know, for example, that the suction parameter is not going to be terribly large. The interior rotation rate is not likely to approach that of the crystal.

Method *Compare results with what others have done.*

How do you know your answers are correct? One should be quite concerned about this, especially with numerical results. Compare with other numerical work, with analytical work, with experiment – with whatever is available.

(*Note added much later*: For example, that wiggle in Figure 4.7 in the $a = 1$ curve is pretty disconcerting, is it not? That is not a physical phenomenon. It is a numerical artifact. That wiggle was to cause me much grief before I understood it and got rid of it.)

4.9.4 Comparisons

By way of example, here are a few comparisons. All are for results with no suction. Pearson [12] published results for equilibrium solutions after the disk had been started impulsively from rest, with $R = 10^2$ and 10^3. Our computations agree. Our results agree with those of Greenspan [7] for $R = 10^2$, but disagree for $R = 10^3$. However, he used a uniform mesh spacing, independent of R. When $R = 10^3$, there was only one mesh point within the boundary layer. One cannot hope to get reasonable results with such a coarse mesh.

Analytically, McLeod and Parter [10] show that for large R, the angular velocity cannot vary monotonely. Our results are in agreement. The scaling with Reynolds number is also in agreement with various results.

I do not know too much about what has been done experimentally, but the results seem to be in qualitative agreement with what I have found on the subject.

Another check which can be made is against physical intuition. Do the results seem reasonable? I discussed them with several of my colleagues in order to get their opinions as well.

All of these comparisons seem to indicate that we are basically on the right track. BUT some questions remain. Mellor *et al.* [11] and others found additional solutions to the steady-state equations. Are their solutions correct? If they are (or if some of them are), are they solutions only to the steady-state equations? Or does some rotational start-up scheme exist which will enable us to get them as solutions to the time-varying equations of motion as well?

Principle *Keep the basic problem in mind.*

Here are all sorts of interesting questions. But how closely are they related to the crystal growth problem? We have a goal to reach eventually.

Well, let us do a *little* bit of investigating, anyway! We were curious as to whether it was possible to get a Stewartson-type solution to the time-dependent problem (with no suction), i.e. one in which the interior fluid does not rotate. The only possible way there seems to be to try to obtain it is to vary the way the disk is set in motion. Actually, one can vary the rotation rates of *both* disks.

We never were able to obtain a Stewartson-type solution. But we did get another rather interesting solution. We first gradually *counterrotated* the disk at $z = 1$ (which is ultimately to be at rest) up to some designated speed and held it there until the flow reached equilibrium. Then we simultaneously gradually returned that disk to rest and brought the disk at $z = 0$ up to its normalized speed of 1. We tried counterrotation rates one-tenth and one-twentieth of the rotation rate finally achieved by the disk at $z = 0$. The final equilibrium computations were the same in both instances and were rather startling. All of the fluid except that in a boundary layer near the rotating disk ($z = 0$) had an angular velocity *opposite* in direction to that of the disk, with an interior rotation rate approximately 0.11 that of the disk!

This result has a number of interesting implications. It tells us that there is not a unique equilibrium solution to the time-dependent equations of motion. So we have to decide *which* solution to use in the crystal growth problem. The one obtained by merely rotating the disk representing the growth interface up to speed surely seems the most reasonable.

The counterrotating solution, on the other hand, seems quite unrealistic physically. This is most disturbing. It means that the model we are using is capable of giving physically unrealistic results. So the model is, at least in part, unrealistic. Are we even sure that the other solution is reasonable? Not really.

We can speculate on the source of the difficulty. It is quite likely to arise from the assumption that the fluid is infinite in lateral extent. We were unhappy about this assumption in the first place.

So now what do we do about this dilemma? How do we proceed with the crystal growth problem? Several things come to mind.

First, we are aware that the present model has deficiencies. So we should try to revise it. This will require modeling the crucible walls. The resulting partial differential equations will involve at least *two* space variables. They are going to be very difficult to solve. This does not seem too feasible right now, but maybe it will be possible later. (A colleague of mine is just starting to write a numerical routine which may be useful.)

So we are probably stuck with the present model for now. Let us at least remain aware that it is not perfect and that it is capable of giving unreasonable results.

A multitude of mathematically interesting questions remain, especially about counterrotating fluids. Their answers, while mathematically correct, may be physically unacceptable. It is probably not worthwhile, from our (somewhat practical) point of view, to spend a lot of time worrying about these questions.

Method *Communicate the results.*

This is very important! Communication takes many forms. It happens during the problem-solving process, as well as at the end of it.

I obtained my first numerical results in August 1976. In September, I began writing a preliminary draft of a paper. Computations on the rotating disk problem continued through October, though. I talked with quite a few people about the results, got ideas from them about more computations to do, and was simultaneously communicating old results and obtaining new ones for a couple of months. The written version of the paper, of course, changed its form considerably during this process.

Writing a technical paper can be a slow agonizing procedure. It is first necessary to decide who the audience is. There could be several audiences, and it may be necessary to write different papers for them. In this instance, I decided the readership would be composed of fluid dynamicists. In the paper, I did not even mention semiconductor crystals. But I also wanted the paper to be read by a group of people at Bell Laboratories with backgrounds outside of fluid dynamics. So I circulated the paper as an internal memorandum and included a few introductory paragraphs which placed the fluid dynamics problem in its crystal growth context. Later on, when I describe the crystal growth problem to an audience of materials scientists, I will have to present the information about the fluid flow in the melt in an entirely different manner.

The material has to be presented concisely and at the proper level. It is fair to assume that the readership has a lot of technical knowledge in the area. But the main object is to *communicate* the results to the audience, not to obscure things. Too often, an author seems to be on an ego trip, using statements like, 'It is obvious that . . . ', which can do nothing but frustrate the poor reader if it is *not* obvious to *him*!

I finished polishing up the first version of the paper in mid-December 1976. Four months later, I was still working on yet another revision of the paper.

4.10   Steady-state crystal growth

We now turn to the second problem in the hierarchy of three. This is to learn about the incorporation of the dopant in the semiconductor crystal during growth at a constant rate. It also involves learning about the impurity concentration profile in the melt. We will want to compare our results with those obtained in the analysis by Burton, Prim, and Slichter.

We derived the basic equations in Section 4.5. They are

$$\phi_z = 0, \tag{4.90}$$

$$2F + R^{-1/2}H_z = 0, \tag{4.91}$$

$$F_t = G^2 - F^2 - R^{-1/2}F_zH + R^{-1}F_{zz}, \tag{4.92}$$

$$G_t = -2FG - R^{-1/2}G_zH + R^{-1}G_{zz}, \tag{4.93}$$

$$C_t = -R^{-1/2}HC_z + (RSc)^{-1}C_{zz}. \tag{4.94}$$

The boundary conditions are

$$\left. \begin{array}{ll} F(0, t) = 0, & F(1, t) = 0, \\ G(0, t) = \omega_I(t), & G(1, t) = 0, \\ H(0, t) = -a(t), & H(1, t) = 0, \\ (1 - k_0)a(t)C(0, t) + C_z(0, t)/(ScR^{1/2}) = 0 & C(1, t) = 1. \end{array} \right\}$$

$$\tag{4.95}$$

The angular velocity $\omega_I(t)$ of the crystal/melt interface and the crystal growth rate $R^{-1/2}a(t)$ must be specified. We will start with everything at rest:

$$F(z, 0) = G(z, 0) = H(z, 0) = \phi(0) = 0, \qquad C(z, 0) = 1, \tag{4.96}$$

and then gradually set the crystal rotating. After it is rotating at a constant speed, we will gradually increase the growth rate to a specified value and hold it constant. Implicit in the formulation is the assumption that the crystal is being pulled out of the melt at precisely its rate of growth, so that the interface position remains at $z = 0$.

Notice that the solution depends upon four parameters: R, k_0, Sc, and a. Do we have to do extensive numerical computations to determine the complicated dependence of the solution on all four parameters? The answer (which is not obvious) is, 'No'. Several tricks will come in handy. They did not come to me immediately, but rather evolved during the course of work on this problem from October 1976 through January 1977. Things (as always) did not proceed smoothly. There were difficulties along the way. I became motivated to get the solution more cheaply and more accurately, and to do as much analytically as possible.

4.10.1   Dependence on R

Notice that R and d/dz appear only in the combination $R^{-1/2} \, d/dz$. In the preceding section, we discovered that the solution scales with R. The momentum boundary layers have thicknesses of order $R^{-1/2}$. The fluid functions F, G, and H are independent of R in magnitude within the boundary layers and scale with $R^{-1/2}$. In the interior region, F, G, and H tend to constants as R increases.

We can expect C to scale similarly with R. (Here we expect only one boundary layer, a diffusion boundary layer, near the rotating disk.) This means we only need to do numerical computations at one value of the Reynolds number, provided R is large enough. Solutions at other values can be determined by appropriate scaling. We shall use $R = 10^3$. This is reasonably large, and yet not so large that it makes the computations excessively difficult.

4.10.2   Dependence on k_0

Let us first introduce the convention that the equilibrium solution (obtained after the disk rotation and suction have been held constant for a long time) is denoted by the functions $F(z)$, $G(z)$, etc., in which the parameter t no longer appears explicitly.

Notice that k_0 appears in only one place, in one of the boundary conditions for the concentration C. Also, in the diffusion equation, only derivatives of C appear. These two facts allow us to use a trick which is not entirely legal, but which seems to work. Define a normalized concentration function

$$D(z, t) = \frac{C(z, t) - 1}{C(0) - 1}. \tag{4.97}$$

Then the diffusion equation and its associated boundary conditions and initial condition are replaced by

$$\left. \begin{array}{l} D_t = -R^{-1/2}HD_z + (RSc)^{-1}D_{zz}, \\[2mm] D(0, t) = \dfrac{C(0, t) - 1}{C(0) - 1}, \qquad D(1, t) = 0, \\[3mm] D(z, 0) = 0. \end{array} \right\} \tag{4.98}$$

Notice that $D(0, t) = 0$ at $t = 0$, tends to 1 as t gets large, and is presumably a monotone increasing function of t. At this stage of the game, we are only interested in looking at the equilibrium solution. Let us replace the function $D(0, t)$ by another which tends to 1 even faster! Let

$$D(0, t) = 1, \qquad t > 0. \tag{4.99}$$

Observe that the partial differential equation has the same form as before. $D(z, t)$ will scale with $R^{-1/2}$ in the same manner that $C(z, t)$ does. Also notice that $D(z, t)$ has fixed values at both boundaries and that k_0 does not appear at all in the entire system of equations! How does the equilibrium solution depend upon k_0? Well, $C(0)$, which appears in the definition of $D(z, t)$, is unknown. It turns out that we have not used one of the boundary conditions for $C(z, t)$, yet. In the equilibrium limit, that remaining boundary condition implies that

$$C(0) = [1 + (1 - k_0)aScR^{1/2}/D_z(0)]^{-1}. \tag{4.100}$$

So once we have solved for $D(z)$, we know $C(0)$. Incidentally, it is very simple to calculate the derivative $D_z(0)$ numerically, for the numerical routine approximates $D(z)$ by piecewise polynomials. Then, since by (4.97),

$$C(z) = 1 + [C(0) - 1]D(z), \tag{4.101}$$

we know $C(z)$. If we then *define*

$$\tilde{\Delta} = -\ln\,[1 + aScR^{1/2}/D_z(0)], \tag{4.102}$$

then the effective distribution coefficient $k = C_s = k_0 C(0)$ is given by

$$k = \frac{k_0}{k_0 + (1 - k_0)e^{-\tilde{\Delta}}}. \tag{4.103}$$

This has the same form as equation (4.31), obtained by Burton, Prim, and Slichter! But we determine $\tilde{\Delta}$ in a different manner.

Incidentally, the ability to cast our results in a form already familiar to crystal growers will simplify considerably the task of communicating our findings to them.

Actually, we have pulled a bit of a swindle. We cannot arbitrarily replace the boundary condition (4.98) for $D(0, t)$ by (4.99) and be sure we will get the same equilibrium solution. But comparison of computations with and without the swindle indicate that we do!

4.10.3 Dependence on *Sc* and *a*

In the BPS analysis, the effective distribution coefficient k depends upon a *single* other parameter

$$B = 0.17 f^{-3} \omega^{3/2} D^2 \nu^{1/2} = 0.17 a^{-3} Sc^{-2}, \tag{4.104}$$

which often appears in the form $B^{-1/3}$, proportional to the growth rate f. This led us to wonder whether the numerical solution of the full equations would yield a dependence of the effective distribution coefficient upon Sc and a in a similar manner. Typically, $Sc = 40$ or 50. We were not interested in varying it over a wide range. We performed computations with $Sc = 40$ and 60 for a variety of values of a and found that to a good degree of approximation, the solution depends only on the combination $aSc^{2/3}$. This empirical result should *not* be expected to hold if Sc is varied over a considerably wider range.

So, by means of a combination of analysis, prior computational results, and empirical results based on a guess motived by the BPS analysis, we now find that we only have to compute the solution as a function of *one* parameter, $aSc^{2/3}$, rather than the *four* parameters R, k_0, a, and Sc.

4.10.4 Getting things started

We begin by gradually raising the angular velocity of the disk at $z = 0$ to its final normalized value of unity and then letting the flow settle down to its steady-state configuration. During this process,

$D(z, t) \equiv 0$. In a similar fashion, we then simulate crystal growth by applying suction through the rotating disk, gradually raising it to a specified value a, and letting the solution settle down to its new steady-state configuration. Notice that for a given value of R, the steady-state solution to the spin-up part of this process is always the same, no matter what values are subsequently chosen for the parameters Sc and a. We computed that solution once and then used it as an initial condition for various crystal growth problems involving different values of Sc and a.

4.10.5 A computational difficulty

At first, we computed the steady-state functions F, G, H, and D to an accuracy of 1 percent relative to their maximum absolute values. We discovered numerically that as a increases (or $aScR^{1/2}$ increases), $D_z(0)$ approaches $-aScR^{1/2}$. This led to complications in determining

$$\tilde{\Delta} = -\ln\left[1 + aScR^{1/2}/D_z(0)\right]$$

of equation (4.102). A small error in the computation of $D_z(0)$ leads to a much larger error in the computation of $\tilde{\Delta}$. This led us to introduce the difference function

$$E(z, t) = D(z, t) - \hat{D}(z), \tag{4.105}$$

where

$$\hat{D}(z) = \frac{e^{-\zeta z} - e^{-\zeta}}{1 - e^{-\zeta}}, \qquad \zeta = aScR^{1/2} \tag{4.106}$$

satisfies (4.98) and (4.99) with $H(z, t)$ replaced by $-a$. Notice that $\hat{D}_z(0)$ tends to $-\zeta$ with large ζ. In actuality, then, we computed the functions F, G, H, and E, obtaining the steady-state results to an accuracy of 1 percent.

Ingredients *Computing and analysis*

Every so often, these interact in a delightful manner. For example, the numerical results may lead us to conjecture about the behavior of the solution. Then we may be able to do some more analysis and prove that conjecture correct. This may lead to some new ideas about how to do the next series of computations.

To participate in such interaction is most satisfying. One takes pride in skillfully combining analytical and numerical techniques.

4.10.6 Results: the effective distribution coefficient

Recall that the effective distribution coefficient k is given by (4.103) in terms of k_0 and $\tilde{\Delta} = -\ln\left[1 + aScR^{1/2}/D_z(0)\right]$. Now $D_z(0)$ is a function of R, Sc, and a. It follows from our earlier discussion about the scaling of the solution with R that $R^{-1/2}D_z(0)$ is independent of R, for large R. So $\tilde{\Delta}$ is independent of R. We also found that $\tilde{\Delta}$ depends upon Sc and a in the combination $aSc^{2/3}$. (Hence $R^{-1/2}D_z(0)$ is $Sc^{1/3}$ times a function of $aSc^{2/3}$.) In Figure 4.9, we show our computational results for $\tilde{\Delta}$ as a function of

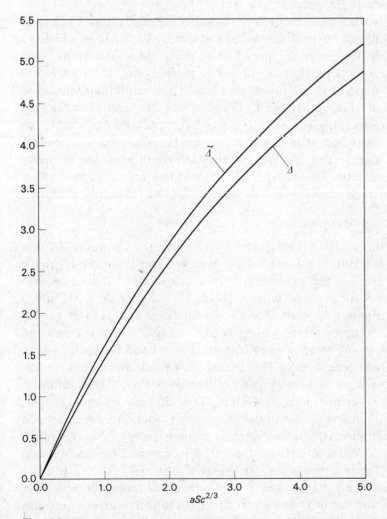

Fig. 4.9

$aSc^{2/3}$. We also plot Burton, Prim, and Slichter's quantity Δ, defined in (4.31).

Our values for $\tilde{\Delta}$ and those of the BPS theory for Δ are in reasonably good agreement for small values of $aSc^{2/3}$, i.e. at small crystal growth rates. At larger rates, our values are consistently larger than those of the BPS model. The discrepancy is approximately 6 percent when $aSc^{2/3} = 5.0$. While this may not seem appreciable, we must remember that the physically relevant quantity is not $\tilde{\Delta}$ (or Δ), but rather k, which involves the exponent of $\tilde{\Delta}$ (or Δ). The corresponding discrepancy in k (for small k_0) is approximately 25 percent.

Actually, this agreement is remarkably good. Burton, Prim, and Slichter did not have available the computing technology which we have today. Of necessity, they had to make approximations (such as the fluid dynamical ones implicit in their model) if they were to have any hope of solving their problem. Their model has withstood the test of time fairly well. When today we use sophisticated computing techniques to solve a more complicated version of the problem, we find that the results for the quantity of primary interest, namely the effective distribution coefficient, are in pretty good agreement. This is especially true at low crystal growth rates. Higher growth rates have only been achieved relatively recently.

4.10.7 Results: concentration in the melt

Recall from (4.101) that $C(z) = 1 + D(z)[C(0) - 1]$, where $C(0)$ is given by (4.100). In Figure 4.10, we plot the function $D(z)$ for several values of the parameter combination $aSc^{2/3}$. These computations were performed with a Reynolds number $R = 10^3$ and a Schmidt number $Sc = 40$. The curves for large values of R can be obtained by appropriate scaling of the z axis. Notice that, except very close to the interface between the crystal and the melt ($z = 0$), $D(z)$ is very nearly zero. This means that the impurity concentration in the melt is nearly uniform except within a thin diffusion boundary layer next to the interface. This diffusion boundary layer, incidentally, lies well within the momentum boundary layer defined by the fluid flow (when the Schmidt number Sc is within our range of interest). With $R = 10^3$ and $a = 0$, for example, the momentum boundary layer extends to approximately $z = 0.1$.

We have seen that as $aSc^{2/3}$ (and hence the crystal growth rate) increases, the impurity concentration $C(0)$ at the interface becomes significantly larger. This, in conjunction with Figure 4.10, tells us

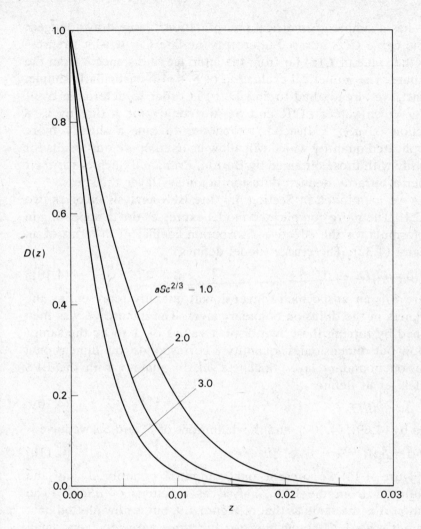

Fig. 4.10

that the concentration profile $C(z)$ becomes both steeper and thinner with increasing crystal growth rate.

4.10.8 Results: thickness of the diffusion boundary layer

A natural definition for the (dimensionless, normalized by d) thickness $\bar{\delta}$ of the diffusion boundary layer is

$$\bar{\delta} = \frac{C(0) - 1}{-C_z(0)} = -\frac{1}{D_z(0)}. \qquad (4.107)$$

This has a simple geometrical interpretation: a line drawn tangent to the curve $C(z)$ at $z = 0$ intercepts the line $C = 1$ (which represents the value of $C(z)$ far from the interface) a distance $\bar{\delta}$ from the ordinate. The numerical evaluation of $\bar{\delta}$ is also particularly simple. In fact, we already had to find $D_z(0)$ in order to determine $\bar{\Delta}$.

For given values of R and Sc, we could plot $\bar{\delta}$ directly as a function of $aSc^{2/3}$. Instead, we choose to plot a slightly more complicated quantity which will allow us to compare our results for $\bar{\delta}$ easily with those obtained by Burton, Prim, and Slichter for their rather arbitrarily defined diffusion boundary layer thickness.

As we mentioned in Section 4.4, the BPS analysis involves two models. The more complicated model expresses the Δ appearing in the formula for the effective distribution coefficient in terms of an integral (4.32). The cruder model defines

$$\Delta = \delta f/D, \tag{4.108}$$

where δ is an unspecified (dimensional) quantity representing the thickness of the diffusion boundary layer. The quantity δ was then defined by forcing these two distinct values of Δ to be the same.

Now our dimensionless quantity $\bar{\delta}$ corresponds to a dimensional diffusion boundary layer thickness $\bar{\delta}d$. In analogy with the BPS model, let us define

$$\bar{\Delta} = \bar{\delta}df/D. \tag{4.109}$$

Then by (4.69), (4.107), and the definitions of R and Sc, we have

$$\bar{\Delta} = \bar{\delta}aR^{1/2}Sc = 1 - e^{-\bar{\Delta}}. \tag{4.110}$$

In Figure 4.11 we present our computed quantity $\bar{\Delta}$ and the quantity Δ from the BPS analysis as functions of $aSc^{2/3}$. (The function Δ is the same as that of Figure 4.9, but is now plotted on a different scale.) Although the two functions agree for very small values of $aSc^{2/3}$ (i.e. at small crystal growth rates), they differ *considerably* at larger values of the parameter.

Notice that at small values of $aSc^{2/3}$, $\bar{\delta}$ is nearly independent of a, and hence of the crystal growth rate f. As the growth rate increases further, though, the thickness of the diffusion boundary layer decreases. For large enough crystal growth rates, the thickness is almost proportional to f^{-1}.

So now we have a serious discrepancy between the results of our model and the BPS model. The BPS analysis defined δ by forcing two different models to agree. The definition was not based on physical reasoning and it seems to have failed.

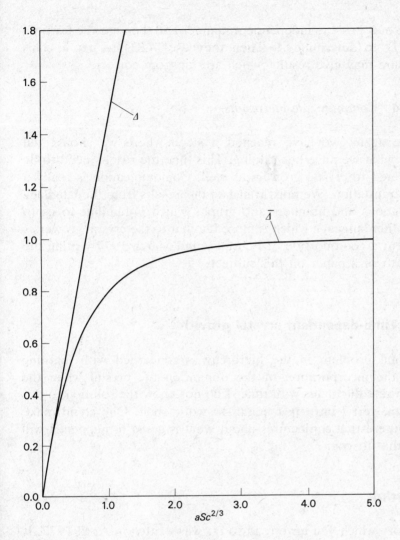

Δ

$\bar{\Delta}$

$aSc^{2/3}$

Fig. 4.11

In the implementation of the BPS model, it is not really necessary to know δ in order to find the effective distribution coefficient k. One can use a graph in the paper by Burton, Prim, and Slichter to determine Δ as a function of the physical parameters. Then k is found from (4.31). If this procedure is followed, then the value of k obtained is not too bad.

Sometimes, however, people may implement the model in ways other than Burton, Prim, and Slichter intended. They may arrive at a value of δ in some independent manner and then use the formula $\Delta = \delta f/D$ to determine Δ. Then they use (4.31) to get k. This procedure may give results which are far from correct.

Method *Communicate the results.*

Once again, we have reached a stage where we should tell people what we have been doing. This time the results need to be interpreted to crystal growers as well. Communication is really a job of translation. We must translate our results from the language of equations and numbers and graphs which is familiar to us to some other language which is more familiar to the crystal growers.

I spent a good portion of February and March 1977 writing the first draft of a paper on this subject.

4.11 Time-dependent crystal growth

The final problem in the hierarchy is concerned with learning about the incorporation of the dopant in the crystal when the growth rate fluctuates with time. I do not know the solution to this problem, yet! I have just begun to work on it. One could make some interesting conjectures about what is going to happen. I will leave that to you.

Postscript

The story which you have read so far was written in April 1977. It represents a snapshot of research *in progress*, complete with lots of questions, some partial answers, a few mistakes, and the germ of a research idea which was to take another two years, nearly, to reach fruition. Now, in February 1979, I would like to give you a quick glance at that research *completed* (almost). Also, it might be interesting to sketch very briefly what happened in the past two years.

With the aid of the mathematical model which I have been discussing, I have been able to obtain a quantitative relationship between periodic variations in growth rate and compositional inhomogeneities (striations) in crystals grown by the Czochralski technique. The flow of the fluid in the model melt is understood. I also have a good deal of insight into the time-dependent behavior of the diffusion layer in the melt and the resulting incorporation of dopant in the crystal. Many of the results are in very nice qualitative agreement with experimental data. I have not yet attempted a detailed quantitative comparison. The results of the research have been written up and either have been published or, hopefully, will be published in the near future [15]–[20].

So that is where we are now. We pretty much seem to understand what is going on, in a way which did not seem to be possible before this mathematical theory arrived on the scene.

Let us pick up the threads of the tale where we left off a couple of years ago, though, and see what some of the things were which happened in the course of getting those results. In this brief discussion, I will pay little attention to the technical details of the research, and even less to a description of the results. Instead, I will concentrate on certain events which occurred. Similar things could happen during any research project.

Well, the first thing that happened was that I submitted a paper about the flow between the two disks to the *Journal of Fluid Mechanics*. It was rejected. Or at least it was not accepted. The referee felt that the paper was worth publishing, but that the emphasis should be a little different. Certain material should be deleted. Further computations should be performed and other material added. The referee's comments were well thought out. Surprising as it may sound, I was happy to take several months to make the suggested revisions. I felt that the referee's suggestions had resulted in my having a much better paper. The revised paper was accepted. It appeared in print [20] in January 1978, nearly two years after the initial work leading to it had been started.

At the time that I was writing up the original lecture notes included here, I was perplexed about the discrepancy between the way I defined the diffusion boundary layer thickness and the way Burton, Prim, and Slichter did. I was not terribly concerned about the issue, though, because you do not really need to know anything about the diffusion boundary layer thickness in order to learn about the quantity of immediate physical interest, the effective distribution coefficient.

In July 1977, the Fifth International Conference on Crystal Growth was held in Boston, Massachusetts. I gave a short talk about my numerical results for steady-state crystal growth and about the discrepancy between the two definitions of the diffusion boundary layer thickness. The response to the talk really startled me. Perhaps a couple hundred people attended the talk. This is a surprisingly large attendance for a 'contributed paper'. The discussion period following the talk was extremely lively. One person, in essence, said 'You're wrong'. I replied 'I don't think so'. Others were less outspoken, but had their doubts. And others backed up what I had said. For days, people came up to me commenting on my talk. Later, others wrote letters. A year and a half later, I still occasionally run across someone who mentions that twelve minute talk to me.

What a shock! I had never expected such repercussions. It turns out that the concept of a diffusion boundary layer thickness is extremely important to crystal growers. I had to reevaluate my approach completely. The feedback from my talk prompted me to isolate my thoughts about the diffusion boundary layer thickness and to write a separate paper about the subject [15].

I learned something else from this experience, too. At one point, several very upset people came to me and said, 'If we can't use the formula we have for the diffusion layer thickness, what *can* we use?' I came to realize that if something is truly to be used, it must be available in an easily usable form. A partial differential equation will not do. A graph may, but it really is not good enough. A simple formula is excellent. I approximated my numerical results for the diffusion boundary layer thickness and came up with a simple formula.

At the same time that I was involved with this side issue, I was continuing computations on the basic time-varying problem. It became evident that the problem was big enough to be split into two subproblems: the case in which the crystal never melts back and the case in which it experiences melting during a portion of its growth cycle.

I will not bore you with all the computational details and difficulties. Some inspired further research. For example, if the growth rate fluctuates, then the momentum and diffusion boundary layers change with time. It would be nice if the spatial mesh specifications in the numerical routine did so, too, automatically. My numerical analysis colleague, Norm Schryer, got working on this problem and has now developed a procedure for doing a time-dependent automatic mesh specification. However, it took him a while to develop this procedure and I needed to proceed with my problem quickly. So I used a stationary mesh and did the best I could. Such things happen often: you make do with the mathematical and numerical tools you have. However, your work may motivate the development of better tools which will then become available for use on later problems.

At any rate, after doing computations for the unsteady crystal growth problem (no melting back), I ended up with an enormous pile of numerical output. I had numbers for the flow, numbers for the concentration in the melt, numbers for the growth function. Each time I changed some input parameter, these numbers changed. Now what? What did it all *mean*?

I sat down and stared at those numbers for weeks. Could I understand what they were telling me? Could I convey that understanding to other people? I drew graphs. I tried plotting all sorts of things. How *do* you present information about an unsteady phenomenon without making a movie? Eventually, I came to understand what was happening in the diffusion layer and found a way to plot it. It was sort of complicated, but it seemed to get the idea across.

Then I started looking at the concentration profile in the crystal itself to see how it was related to the growth profile associated with it. It was pretty exciting to observe that the profiles were in nice qualitative agreement with some experimental data which had been published in the literature. I finally decided to characterize the concentration profiles by three quantities. These I believed would contain most of the information the crystal growers really wanted. These quantities depended upon the various dimensionless parameters used as input to the computer program. But how? Having learned my lesson earlier, I knew that I ought to come up with some empirical formulas describing the dependence. So I did. To my astonishment, they were extremely simple – far simpler than I had imagined they would be. I was thrilled. I had managed to boil down a considerable amount of work into a few very elegant empirical formulas. There was even hope that people might use them!

But this also raised a perplexing question. If I could get such a simple result, why did I have to go through such a complicated process to obtain it? Was there an easier way? Using the increased knowledge I now had, I tried making some additional assumptions in order to reduce the model to something simpler. Although I could cut the model down somewhat, I was not able to reduce it to something yielding any sort of simple solution, like a 'back of the envelope' calculation.

Finally, I set out to do computations for the case in which the crystal melts back during part of its growth cycle. I had not had to look at the remelt boundary condition since the time when I formulated the original problem. I found that it was wrong. (It has been corrected in the present text.) It is sort of scary to have errors lying around undetected for so long, but it can happen.

The actual computations turned out to be rather uneventful. I decided that getting a qualitative picture of what is happening during the remelt process was more important than getting a detailed quantitative picture. There are just too many things which are unknown about the growth history of an actual crystal for us to expect to be able to make a detailed comparison of theory and experiment. And yet we need more insight about the basic phenomena which are occurring. Hence, I did calculations in order to understand what was going on; however, I made no attempt to condense a wealth of results into a few simple formulas.

With all these numerical results in hand, I again was faced with the big job of communicating. I wrote several papers. People in the crystal growth community had certain ways of looking at things. Consequently, I sometimes had to emphasize points differently than I would have if I were not building upon the crystal growers' prior knowledge and beliefs. One example of this is the discussion of the diffusion boundary layer thickness. I did not feel that it was an important issue, but the crystal growers did. Another example arises from prior attempts to use the steady-state Burton, Prim, and Slichter theory to analyze unsteady phenomena. These were originally done out of desperation: no unsteady theory was available. Eventually, though, people came to believe that the steady-state theory could properly be applied in this fashion, at least part of the time. I found it necessary to write down convincing arguments as to why this procedure was incorrect. A point which seemed almost obvious to me as a mathematician was not so evident to those whose expertise lay in other areas.

This point, incidentally, produced another paper [19]. People were analyzing their experimental data by using the steady-state theory. Sometimes it even seemed to work. But it should not. One day I got an idea: why not pretend that my numerical results were 'experimental data' and then analyze them by the steady-state method? By doing this, I was able to show (1) that the method was incorrect and (2) that even when it seemed to work, it produced erroneous results.

In addition to writing everything up, I hoped to have a chance to give a formal talk about my completed work to the crystal growth community. I was very pleased to be given an invitation to do so. I spoke about my work at a Gordon Research Conference on Crystal Growth in Santa Barbara, California, in January 1979. There was a considerable amount of interest in the work. Also, several possibilities for collaborative research emerged, including one for a direct comparison of my theory with some experimental results.

It is perhaps too early to have a clear perspective about the value of this entire research project. At this time, I feel that its worth lies (1) in obtaining a far better understanding of the phenomena which occur during Czochralski growth when the crystal growth rate is nonconstant and (2) in dispelling some incorrect beliefs. Whether this understanding will ultimately help lead to practical methods for eliminating or reducing growth striations remains to be seen.

References

1 Batchelor, G. K., Note on a class of solutions of the Navier–Stokes equations representing steady rotationally-symmetric flow, *Quart. J. Mech. Appl. Math.*, **4,** 29–41, 1951.

2 Bödewadt, U. T. Die Drehströmung über feste Grunde, *Z. Angew. Math. Mech.*, **20,** 241–253, 1940.

3 Burton, J. A., Prim, R. C., and Slichter, W. P. The distribution of solute in crystals grown from the melt, Part I. Theoretical, *J. Chem. Phys.*, **21,** 1987–1991, 1953.

4 Cochran, W. G. The flow due to a rotating disc, *Proc. Camb. Phil. Soc.*, **30,** 365–375, 1934.

5 Drew, D. A., Models of traffic flow, Chapter 3 of this book.

6 Fox, P. A., Hall, A. D., and Schryer, N. L. The PORT mathematical subroutine library, *Bell Laboratories Computing Science Technical Report #47*, 1976.

7 Greenspan, D. Numerical studies of flow between rotating coaxial disks, *J. Inst. Maths. Applic.*, **9,** 370–377, 1972.

8 Kármán, T. von. Über Laminare und Turbulente Reibung, *Z. Angew. Math. Mech.*, **1,** 233–252, 1921.

9 Lance, G. N. and Rogers, M. H. The axially symmetric flow of a viscous fluid between two infinite rotating disks, *Proc. Roy. Soc. A,* **266,** 109–121, 1962.

10 McLeod, J. B. and Parter, S. V. The nonmonotonicity of solutions in swirling flow, *Proc. Roy. Soc. Edinb. A*, **76,** 161, 1977.
11 Mellor, G. L., Chapple, P. J., and Stokes, V. K. On the flow between a rotating and a stationary disk, *J. Fluid Mech.*, **31,** 95–112, 1968.
12 Pearson, C. E. Numerical solutions for the time-dependent viscous flow between two rotating coaxial disks, *J. Fluid Mech.*, **21,** 623–633, 1965.
13 Schryer, N. L. Numerical solution of time-varying partial differential equations in one space variable, *Bell Laboratories Computing Science Technical Report #53*, 1976.
14 Stewartson, K. On the flow between two rotating coaxial disks, *Proc. Camb. Phil. Soc.*, **3,** 333–341, 1953.
15 Wilson, L. O. On interpreting a quantity in the Burton, Prim, and Slichter equation as a diffusion boundary layer thickness, *J. Cryst. Growth*, **44,** 247–250, 1978.
16 Wilson, L. O. A new look at the Burton, Prim, and Slichter model of segregation during crystal growth from the melt, *J. Cryst. Growth*, **44,** 371–376, 1978.
17 Wilson, L. O. The effect of fluctuating growth rates on segregation in crystals grown from the melt. Part I. No backmelting, *J. Cryst. Growth*, **48,** 435–450, 1980.
18 Wilson, L. O. The effect of fluctating growth rates on segregation in crystals grown from the melt. Part II. Backmelting, *J. Cryst. Growth*, **48,** 451–458, 1980.
19 Wilson, L. O. Analysis of microsegregation in crystals, *J. Cryst. Growth*, **48,** 363–366, 1980.
20 Wilson, L. O. and Schryer, N. L. Flow between a stationary and a rotating disk with suction, *J. Fluid Mech.*, **85,** 479–496, 1978.

5 Shortest paths in networks

CHRISTOPH WITZGALL, JUDITH F GILSINN AND
DOUGLAS R SHIER *National Bureau of Standards*

Introduction

The purpose of this chapter is to illustrate the application and
adaptation of techniques for finding shortest paths in networks. It
has three parts:

Part I   Basic Methodology of Shortest Paths, by Christoph
           Witzgall;

Part II   Two Case Studies, by Judith Gilsinn;

Part III   Extensions of Shortest Path Methods, by Douglas
           Shier.

The first part deals with the definitions and some basic properties of networks. The second part presents two case studies, both
involving very large networks and requiring adaptations of common shortest path techniques. This theme is stressed even more in
the third part, which lists a variety of tractable extensions of the
shortest path problem and discusses some unifying theoretical
concepts.

Part I: BASIC METHODOLOGY OF SHORTEST PATHS

5.1 Networks

We will use the term 'network' synonymously with 'directed
graph'. A *network* (N, A) in this sense is determined by its *node set*
N, its *arc set* A, and two maps $I \,|\, A \to N$ and $J \,|\, A \to N$, which
assign to each arc $a \in A$ an *origin* $I(a) \in N$ and a *destination*
$J(a) \in N$. The term 'vertex' is sometimes used instead of 'node', as
are the terms 'edge' and 'link' instead of 'arc'. Also there are
various obvious synonyms for 'origin' and 'destination'. $(N, \bar{A})$ is a
subnetwork of (N, A) if $\bar{N} \subseteq N$, $\bar{A} \subseteq A$, and $\bar{I}(a) = I(a)$, $\bar{J}(a) = J(a)$
for $a \in \bar{A}$; that is, each arc in the subnetwork $(\bar{N}, \bar{A})$ has the same
ends as in (N, A).

Examples of networks abound. One large group of networks is concerned with *transportation* in the widest sense of the word: streets, highways, railroads, pipelines, power lines, communications, ... Here nodes are cities, intersections, stations, etc., whereas arcs are roads, street segments, ... Other examples are job assignments, organization charts, the 'PERT' (= Program Evaluation and Review Technique) networks of program planning, and many more.

The analyst should realize that, as a rule, there are different networks in terms of which a given problem can be represented, and that it is important to find the 'right network'. The second case study in Part II will illustrate this point. Also networks which appear at first glance to be geographical in nature will actually have to be appended to include operational aspects. This is illustrated in Figure 5.1, which represents a portion of a city street-network. In this example, nodes and arcs are not just intersections and street segments, respectively, but represent lane positions from which turns may or may not be permitted. Networks are abstractions: Figure 5.2 represents the same network as Figure 5.1.

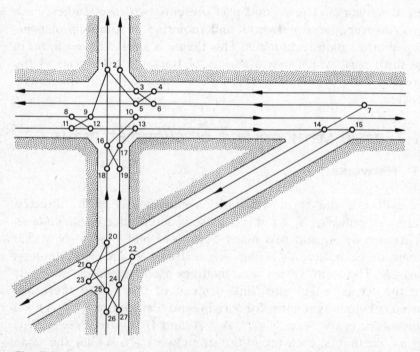

Fig. 5.1

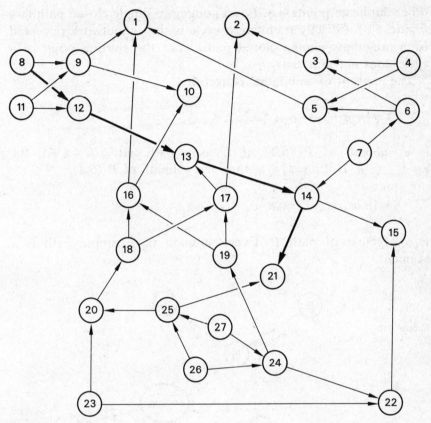

Fig. 5.2

5.2 Paths in networks

The key concept in networks is that of 'paths'. As a *path* in
network (N, A), we denote any alternating sequence of nodes and
arcs

$$P = \{n_0 a_1 n_1 a_2 \cdots n_{k-1} a_k n_k\} \tag{5.1}$$

with $n_{i-1} = I(a_i)$ and $n_i = J(a_i)$ for $i = 1, \ldots, k$. Path P is *from* n_0 *to*
n_k. We call n_0 the origin of path P, and n_k its destination, using also
the notation $n_0 = I(P)$ and $n_k = J(P)$.

Path P is *empty* if $k = 0$, i.e. $P = \{n_0\}$; it is *simple* if $n_i \neq n_j$ for
$i \neq j$ and $i, j = 1, \ldots, k$, i.e. if there are no 'duplicate nodes'; it is
closed if $I(P) = J(P)$, i.e. if the origin equals the destination; and
finally it describes a *cycle* if $k > 0$, $I(P) = J(P)$, and there are no

other duplicate points, i.e. P is a nonempty simple closed path (*see* Figure 5.3). (Strictly speaking a cycle is the subnetwork occupied by a nonempty simple closed path, since the starting point of a cycle does not matter.)

The concept of 'subpaths' is useful:

$$Q = \{n_{i_0} a_{j_1} n_{i_1} \cdots a_{j_h} n_{i_h}\}$$

is a *subpath* of P (5.1), if Q is a path and $i_{r-1} < j_r \leq i_r$ for $r = 1, \ldots, h$. If $0 \leq s \leq t \leq k$, then the subpath of P (5.1),

$$S = \{n_s a_{s+1} n_{s+1} \cdots a_t n_t\},$$

is a *segment* of path P. Every subpath of a simple path is a segment.

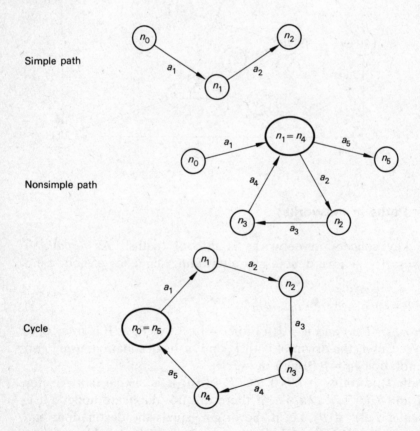

Simple path

Nonsimple path

Cycle

Fig. 5.3

Two paths

$$P = \{n_0 a_1 n_2 \cdots a_k n_k\},$$
$$\bar{P} = \{\bar{n}_0 \bar{a}_1 \bar{n}_2 \cdots \bar{a}_{\bar{k}} \bar{n}_{\bar{k}}\}$$

with

$$n_k = J(P) = I(\bar{P}) = \bar{n}_0$$

can be combined to form the *concatenation*

$$P + \bar{P} = \{n_0 a_1 \cdots a_k n_k = \bar{n}_0 \bar{a}_1 \cdots \bar{a}_{\bar{k}} \bar{n}_{\bar{k}}\}.$$

The original paths $P, \bar{P}$ are segments of $P + \bar{P}$.

If the indices $1, 2, \ldots, k$ associated with the arcs in path P (5.1) can be partitioned into several disjoint nonempty sets $S^{(h)} = \{i_1^{(h)} < i_2^{(h)} < \cdots < i_{f_h}^{(h)}\}$ such that the corresponding arcs define a path $P^{(h)}$ for each h, i.e. $J(a_{i_1}^{(h)}) = I(a_{i_2}^{(h)})$, then P has been *partitioned* into the subpaths $P^{(h)}$ (Figure 5.4).

We can now formulate the following

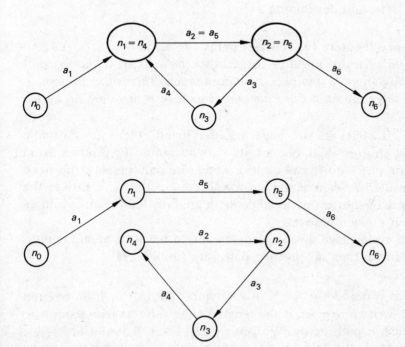

Fig. 5.4 Partition.

Path partition theorem *Every non-simple path P can be partitioned into a simple path P_s with the same origin and destination as P, $I(P_s) = I(P)$, $J(P_s) = J(P)$, and some cycles (at least one).*

It follows that every path has a simple subpath P_s the origin and destination of which agree with the origin and destination of P, respectively. We call P_s a *simplification* of P.

5.3 Shortest paths

We consider now networks (N, A) in which a real number, an *arc length* $l(a)$, has been specified for each arc $a \in A$. In this case, the *length* $l(P)$ of a path in network (N, A) can be defined as follows:

$$l(P) = \begin{cases} \displaystyle\sum_{i=1}^{k} l(a_i) & \text{if} \quad k > 0, \\ 0 & \text{if} \quad k = 0. \end{cases}$$

P is a *shortest path* if there are no paths of smaller length between origin $I(P)$ and destination $J(P)$.

Existence theorem for shortest paths *If the network (N, A) contains no cycles of negative length, then there exists a shortest path from any origin to any accessible destination. This is true in particular, if there are no arcs of negative length or if there are no cycles.*

Proof If cycles do not have negative length, then no nonsimple path is shorter than one of its simplifications P_s (follows from partition of P into P_s and cycles). Therefore only simple paths need be considered when searching for shortest paths. This proves the existence of shortest paths since there are only finitely many simple paths in a given network.

If all cycles have positive lengths, in particular, if all arc lengths are positive, then all shortest paths are simple. ∎

Given two nodes $n, \bar{n} \in N$ in a network (N, A), the *distance* from n to $\bar{n}$, written $d(n, \bar{n})$, is the length of the shortest path from n to $\bar{n}$, if such a path exists. We put $d(n, \bar{n}) = \infty$ if $\bar{n}$ is not accessible from n, and $d(n, \bar{n}) = -\infty$ if $\bar{n}$ is accessible from n, but a shortest path does not exist between these points.

If for three nodes $n, \bar{n}, \bar{\bar{n}}$, the distances $d(n, \bar{n})$ and $d(\bar{n}, \bar{\bar{n}})$ are finite then the *triangle inequality*

$$d(n, \bar{\bar{n}}) \leqslant d(n, \bar{n}) + d(\bar{n}, \bar{\bar{n}})$$

holds. With suitable interpretation, it holds also if some of the distances are not finite.

5.4 Finding shortest paths

Finding shortest paths is a finite problem: selecting the shortest path among the finite number of simple paths requires only a finite number of operations. Why not just determine all simple paths between two nodes and pick the shortest?

The answer is, that there are too many such paths, even in a moderately sized network, for such a procedure to be practical. To illustrate this point, we consider the network in Figure 5.5. It has 130 nodes and 256 arcs, which makes it a rather small network. The simple paths from n to $\bar{n}$ are characterized by 64-tupels of 0 and 1: 0 signalizes a 'left turn' and 1 a 'right turn'. There are therefore 2^{64} simple paths from n to $\bar{n}$. Evaluating one path per microsecond, it would require more than 500 000 years to scan all simple paths.

The first case study in Part II of this chapter will involve a network of 9000 nodes and 27 000 arcs. The number of candidate paths in such a network is unbelievably large. Yet the shortest path problem can be solved in a tolerable amount of computer time. The algorithms which accomplish this calculation are very powerful indeed!

There are two main classes of shortest path algorithms:

1. *matrix methods* (to find distances between all pairs of nodes);

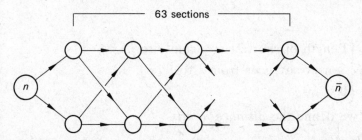

Fig. 5.5 A number of simple paths. The number of nodes is 130 and the number of arcs is 256: thus the number of simple paths from n to $\bar{n}$ is 2^{64}.

2. *labeling methods* (to find shortest paths from a given origin).

Labeling methods, in turn, partition into two subclasses:

1. *label correcting methods;*
2. *label setting methods.*

Matrix methods are theoretically interesting, but in their present form are of less practical importance than labeling methods.

5.5 Matrix methods

In this section, the nodes of a network (N, A) will be considered to be integer numbers between 1 and n:

$$N = \{1, 2, \ldots, n\}.$$

To each arc, $a \in A$, of the network there corresponds an ordered pair (i, j) of numbers (i, j), $i, j \in N$, where $i = I(a)$ is the origin and $j = J(a)$ is the destination of arc a. In other words, to each arc $a \in A$ there corresponds an entry into an $n \times n$ matrix. There may be *multiple arcs*, that is, arcs which have identical origin and destination and correspond therefore to the same entry in any node-by-node matrix. In a shortest path context, however, only the shortest arc in a bundle of multiple arcs is of interest. The diagonal entries (i, i) in a node-by-node matrix corresponds to *loops*, i.e. arcs that form a cycle. As far as shortest paths are concerned, loops are not interesting unless of negative length, in which case they cause a negative cycle.

In what follows, we will assume that there are *no loops* in (N, A).

If arc-lengths have been specified for a network (N, A) without loops, then the above considerations suggest the definition of an *arc-length matrix*

$$L = [l(i, j)]_{i,j \in N}$$

with

$$l(i, j) = \begin{cases} \text{Length of shortest arc from } i \text{ to } j, i \neq j, \\ \infty \text{ if no arc goes from } i \text{ to } j, i \neq j, \\ 0 \text{ if } i = j. \end{cases}$$

Similarly we define the *distance matrix*

$$D = [d(i, j)]_{i,j \in N}$$

simply as the matrix of distances $d(i, j)$, between nodes i and j.

Problem Given the arc-length matrix L, find the distance matrix D.

Necessary for D to be the distance matrix for L is that

$$d(i, j) = \min_{h} \, (d(i, h) + l(h, j))$$

as well as (triangle inequality)

$$d(i, j) = \min_{h} \, (d(i, h) + d(h, j)).$$

Observe that the above expressions have a structure analogous to that of a scalar product. They arise if we replace the multiplication of elements by their addition, and the addition of the products by their minimization. This modified definition of scalar products gives rise to a modified definition of matrix multiplication. Let

$$A = [a(i, h)]_{i,h \in N} \quad \text{and} \quad B = [b(h, j)]_{h,j \in N}$$

be matrices, then the 'product'

$$C = [c(i, j)]_{i,j \in N}$$

is given by

$$c(i, j) = \min_{h} \, (a(i, h) + b(h, j)).$$

The above relations for the arc-length matrix L and the distance matrix D can now be expressed as

$$D = D \times L, \quad D = D \times D.$$

An early suggestion for finding the distance matrix D was to use successive modified matrix multiplication to enforce the above relations. Indeed one can show that $L^n = D$. This procedure, however, is expensive, and there exist methods that are more efficient. Two of these methods, the ones by Dantzig and by Floyd, will be discussed in the two subsequent sections.

5.6 The method of Dantzig

Given a network (N, A) of n nodes. Then a new network $(\bar{N}, \bar{A})$ of $n + 1$ nodes can be created by adding a new node $n + 1$ together with new arcs from node $n + 1$ to and from the nodes of old network N (Figure 5.6).

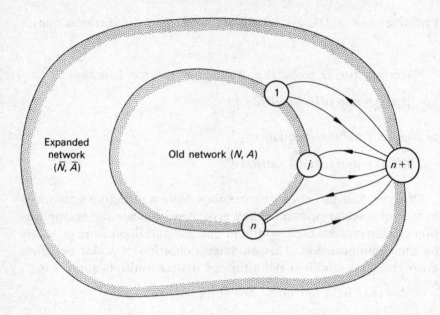

Expanded
network
$(\bar{N}, \bar{A})$

Old network (N, A)

1

j

$n+1$

n

Fig. 5.6

How does distance matrix $\bar{D}$ of $(\bar{N}, \bar{A})$ arise from distance matrix D of (N, A)? To answer this we observe that the shortest path from node i to node $n+1$ consists either of the arc from i to $n+1$ (length $= \bar{l}(i, n+1)$) or of the shortest path in N from node $i \leqslant n$ to node $j \leqslant n$ followed by the arc from j to $n+1$ (length $= d(i, j) + \bar{l}(j, n+1)$). Therefore

$$\bar{d}(i, n+1) = \min_{1 \leqslant j \leqslant n} (d(i, j) + \bar{l}(j, n+1)), \qquad 1 \leqslant i \leqslant n.$$

Symmetrically,

$$\bar{d}(n+1, i) = \min_{1 \leqslant j \leqslant n} (\bar{l}(n+1, j) + d(j, i)), \qquad 1 \leqslant i \leqslant n.$$

It may happen that a former shortest path in the old network N can now be improved upon by proceeding via the new node $n+1$. This happens precisely if

$$\bar{d}(i, n+1) + \bar{d}(n+1, j) < d(i, j).$$

Therefore

$$\bar{d}(i, j) = \min (d(i, j), \bar{d}(i, k+1) + \bar{d}(k+1, j)), \qquad 0 \leqslant i, j \leqslant n.$$

Dantzig's method [4] now starts with two nodes and expands successively by adding single nodes. New distances are created and old ones updated as described above (Figure 5.7).

If $\bar{d}(i, i) < 0$ at some point, then the shortest path problem does not have a solution for all pairs of nodes. If it is known to have a solution, then $d(i, i) = 0$ must hold. In this case, we do not have to worry about diagonal elements, and Dantzig's method will require precisely $n(n-1)(n-2)$ additions and comparisons.

5.7 The method of Floyd

Let $k \in N$ be a node in a network (N, A) with given arc lengths. We construct an appended network $(N, \bar{A})$ by adding, for each pair of nodes i, j with $i \neq k$, $j \neq k$, and $i \neq j$, a new arc of length $l(i, k) + l(k, j)$ from node i to node j whenever

$$l(i, k) + l(k, j) < l(i, j),$$

that is, whenever it pays to detour via k. We observe that

(i) (N, A) and $(N, \bar{A})$ have the same distances;

(ii) in $(N, \bar{A})$, all distances can be realized by shortest paths not containing k as an interior node;

(iii) the arc length matrix of $(N, \bar{A})$ is

$$\bar{l}(i, j) = \min \, (l(i, j), l(i, k) + l(k, i)).$$

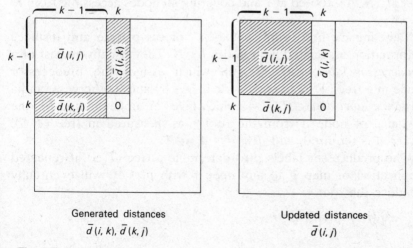

Generated distances
$\bar{d}(i, k), \bar{d}(k, j)$

Updated distances
$\bar{d}(i, j)$

Fig. 5.7

We say that we added *bypass arcs,* bypassing node k.

Floyd's algorithm [10] adds arcs bypassing node 1, thereby creating a new network $(N, A^{(1)})$ with arc length matrix $L^{(1)}$. Then it bypasses node 2, building network $(N, A^{(2)})$ with arc-length matrix $L^{(2)}$, and so on. The claim is

$$L^{(n)} = D.$$

Indeed, by construction, any $d(i, j)$ can be realized in $(N, A^{(n)})$ by a shortest path which does not contain any interior node, i.e. by a single arc. $L^{(n)}$ is therefore equal to the distance matrix of $(N, A^{(n)})$, namely D.

5.8 Labeling methods

In these methods, the origin (or, symmetrically, the destination) of the shortest paths is given. We call this fixed origin the *root r*. A network (T, S) is a *tree rooted at r*, if for each node $i \in T$ there exists in T a unique simple path† from r to i. In such a tree, every node $i \in T$, $i \neq r$, has a unique *predecessor arc* $a = q(i) \in S$ with $J(a) = i$, and a unique *predecessor node* $j = p(i) = I(a)$.

Subnetworks which are trees are particularly important. Let (T, S) be a tree rooted at r and contained in the network (N, A). Then (T, S) is a *shortest path tree* in (N, A) if every path in (T, S) is a shortest path $m(N, A)$.

Problem   Given node r in network (N, A). Find a shortest path tree in (N, A), rooted at r and covering all nodes accessible from r.

Labeling methods employ 'labels', pieces of tree and distance information associated with nodes $n \in N$. They usually consist of a *predecessor label* $p(n) \in N \cup \{0\}$, which assigns the predecessor node in a tree (T, S) to each node in $T - \{r\}$ and 0 otherwise, and a *distance label* $d(n) \in R \cup \{\infty\}$, which gives an upper bound for the distance of node n from the root r as measured in tree (T, S). $d(r) = 0$ is required, and $d(n) = \infty$ if $n \notin T$.

The predecessor labels $p(n)$ determine a tree (T, S), if repeated application of map p to any node t with $p(t) \neq 0$ will eventually produce the root r:

$$t, p(t), p(p(t)), \ldots, r.$$

† Counting the empty path from r to r.

The sequence of these nodes determines a simple path from r to t, because the arcs between these nodes are usually unique. If there are several possibilities, i.e. if there are multiple arcs, then a shortest arc is selected.

A labeling (p, d) is *sharp*, if the predecessor labeling p defines a tree (T, S), and if $d(t)$ is the actual distance within the tree (T, S) from the root r to node $t \in T$. In other words,

$$d(I(s)) + l(s) = d(J(s))$$

must hold for all arcs $s \in S$ in the tree.

A labeling (p, d) is *optimal* if the predecessor label p defines a shortest path tree (T, S) on all nodes in (N, A) that are accessible from the root r, and if the distance labels are sharp. In this case, the distance labels indicate the true distances from the root r.

We now have the

Optimality criterion *A labeling (p, d) is optimal, if the predecessor labels p define a tree in (N, A) and if*

$$d(I(a)) + l(a) \geqslant d(J(a)) \quad \text{for} \quad a \in A.$$

Proof First we will prove by induction that the labeling is sharp. Let (T_k, S_k), $k = 0, 1, \ldots$ be the sequence of trees which are contained in the tree (T, S) determined by p, and the nodes of which are not more than k arcs away from the root r within (T, S). As $d(r) = 0$, the proposition is true for (T_0, S_0), $T_0 = \{r\}$, S_0 empty. Suppose it is true for some (T_k, S_k) with $k \geqslant 0$, and let n be some node in $T_{k+1} - T_k$. Then $m = p(n) \in T_k$, and $d(m)$ is therefore the distance from r in both (T, S) and (N, A). By hypothesis,

$$d(m) + l(s) \geqslant d(n)$$

for each arc $s \in S$ with $m = I(s)$ and $n = J(s)$. Since $d(n)$ is an upper bound for the distance from r in (T, S) by definition of distance labels, it follows that

$$d(m) + l(s) = d(n).$$

The labeling is therefore sharp on (T_{k+1}, S_{k+1}), and by induction, on (T, S).

Let P be a shortest path in (N, A) from r to n, and assume it has a first arc $a \notin (T, S)$. Then substituting the tree path from r to $J(a)$ for the corresponding segment of P will, because of $d(I(a)) + l(a) \geqslant d(J(a))$, not increase the length of P: leaving the tree does not improve length. The tree (T, S) is therefore a shortest path tree and the labeling (p, d) is optimal. ■

5.9 Label correcting

The large class of *label correcting methods* (Moore [14], Bellman [1], etc.) start with an arbitrary labeling (p, d) which determines a tree in the network (N, A). (The simplest such labeling consists of the root r alone: $d(r) = 0$, $d(n) = \infty$ for $n \in N - \{r\}$, $p(n) = 0$ for $n \in N$.) They then check whether each arc $a \in A$ satisfies the optimality criterion

$$d(I(a)) + l(s) \geqslant d(J(a)).$$

If satisfied for each arc, the labeling is optimal and the desired shortest path tree has been found. If violated for some arc $a \in A$, redefine

$$d(J(a)) = d(I(a)) + l(a), \qquad p(J(a)) = I(a).$$

This results in a new labeling, provided there are no cycles of negative length in (N, A). The search for violations is then repeated.

5.10 Label setting

Let $(T, S) \subseteq (N, A)$ be a shortest path tree rooted at r and characterized by a sharp labeling (p, d). Consider the *cutset*

$$C(T) := \{a \in A \mid I(a) \in T, J(a) \notin T\}.$$

If $C(T)$ is empty, then T contains all nodes which are accessible from r, and therefore represents the desired tree. Otherwise, there exists $b \in C(T)$ such that

$$d(I(b)) + l(b) = \min \{d(I(a)) + l(a) \mid a \in C(T)\}.$$

We now add arc b and node $J(b)$ to the tree T, and extend the labeling (p, d) by putting

$$\hat{d}(J(b)) = d(I(b)) + l(b), \qquad \hat{p}(J(b)) = I(b).$$

It is readily seen that these definitions lead to an extended labeling $(\hat{p}, \hat{d})$ and an enlarged tree $(\hat{T}, \hat{S})$, for which we have the

Tree extension theorem *If all arc-lengths of arcs $a \in A$ in a network (N, A) are nonnegative, $l(a) \geqslant 0$, then the enlarged tree $(\hat{T}, \hat{S})$ is a shortest path tree, and the extended labeling $(\hat{p}, \hat{d})$ characterizes $(\hat{T}, \hat{S})$ and is sharp.*

Proof Figure 5.8 gives a schematic description: the 'island' (T, S) in the middle is surrounded by the 'moat' $C(T)$, which separates T from the remaining network. Let P be a shortest path from r to $J(b)$. It must cross some 'bridge' $a \in C(T)$, and its length up to node $J(a)$ is therefore at least equal to $d(I(a)) + l(a)$, which is not less than $\hat{d}(J(b))$ by definition of b. Since all arc lengths are nonnegative, the length of P does not improve on its last leg. Thus P cannot be shorter than $\hat{d}(J(b))$. ∎

An important difference between label setting and label correcting algorithms is that the former methods can be stopped once the

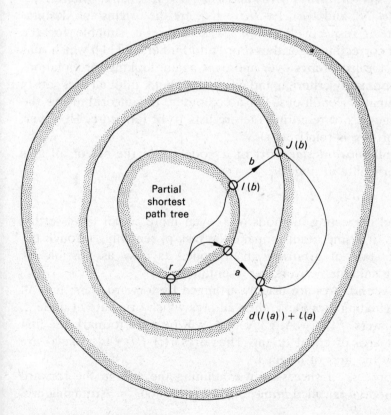

Fig. 5.8

destinations to which shortest paths are desired have been included into the shortest path tree. In many cases, it is therefore not necessary to grow the shortest path tree to the full extent possible. For label correcting algorithms, on the other hand, the full shortest path tree has to be found before any single shortest path is known with certainty.

5.11 Network representation

For purposes of computation, networks have to be represented by list structures. Usually, the nodes and arcs, respectively, are con-secutively numbered by positive integers starting with 1. The nodes and arcs are then represented by these node and arc numbers. The simplest list structure for representing a network then consists of the two lists (or 'arrays') $I(a)$ and $J(a)$, $a = 1, \ldots, |A|$, where $I(a)$, $1 \leq I(a) \leq |N|$, and $J(a)$, $1 \leq J(a) \leq |N|$, are the origins and destina-tions of a, respectively. This list structure is suitable for the simplest correcting algorithm (Ford and Fulkerson [11]) which runs through the list of arcs over and over again, looking for violations of the optimality criterion and correcting them, until all arcs satisfy the optimality conditions. On a computer, this algorithm has the advantage of not requiring the arc lists to fit into core. However, the algorithm is relatively slow.

We call *forward star* $F(n)$ of a node $n \in N$ the set of all arcs which originate at node n:

$$F(n) = \{a \in A \mid I(a) = n\}.$$

For label correcting methods and, even more so for label setting methods, it is important to make the task of searching through the forward stars of arbitrary given nodes as easy as possible by choosing suitable network representations.

To this end, arcs are usually arranged by forward stars: first all arcs originating at node 1, then all arcs which originate at node 2, etc. 'Pointers' $f \mid N \to A$, $g \mid N \to A$ will be used to mark the first and last arcs of equal origin. Thus arcs $f(i), f(i) + 1, \ldots, g(i)$ are precisely the arcs of origin i.†

The process of successively examining the arcs in the forward star of node n is called *branching out* from node n. Arranging arcs

---

† Special conventions are needed to indicate $F(n) = \phi$.

by forward stars and adding pointers facilitates the process of branching out. Note, however, that the above technique requires the entire information to be in core in order to be effective.

An example of the above network representation is given in Figure 5.9, which also illustrates the characterization of a tree by labels.

5.12 Sequencing

Label correcting methods are much improved by 'branching out' from already labeled nodes instead of blindly checking arcs in some 'fixed sequence'. Furthermore, once a node n has been branched out from, it need not be branched out from again until its label $d(n)$ is decreased. The idea suggests itself, to keep those nodes which are candidates for branching out on a list, or 'stack', which we call the *sequence list*.

Typically one starts with a sequence list containing just the root r. At each step one selects a node n from the sequence list for branching out. Those nodes in the forward star $F(n)$ which are labeled for the first time or in which labels have been corrected in the process of branching out are then entered in the sequence list, and so on. The algorithm terminates as soon as the sequence list is empty.

The performance of such stack-driven label correcting methods depends critically on the strategy of retrieving nodes from the sequence list. The most straightforward strategies are

LIFO = last in, first out;

FIFO = first in, first out.

For networks of a few thousand nodes and arcs the difference is already dramatic: LIFO may take minutes where FIFO takes a few seconds.

5.13 Dijkstra's method

When using a basic label setting method, repeated minimization over the cutset $C(T)$ will lead to repeated examination of arcs. This can be avoided by assigning temporary labels $d(t)$ to nodes t on the 'other side' of $C(T)$, that is, nodes $t = J(a)$ where $a \in C(T)$.

Node	f	g	p	d
1	1	1	–	0
2	2	3	–	∞
3	4	4	–	∞
4	5	5	1	13
5	6	8	4	17
6	9	9	5	35
7	10	10	–	∞
8	11	12	5	24
9	13	13	–	∞
10	14	14	–	∞
11	15	16	8	27
12	17	17	–	∞

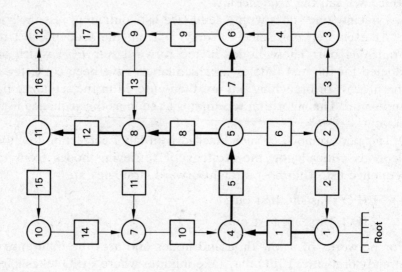

Arc	i	j
1	12	4
2	7	1
3	19	3
4	6	6
5	4	5
6	11	2
7	16	6
8	7	8
9	3	9
10	9	4
11	13	7
12	3	11
13	16	8
14	19	7
15	14	10
16	8	12
17	5	9

Fig. 5.9

Remember that all labels on 'this side' of $C(T)$ are 'permanent', because they represent the lengths of shortest paths already found. The temporary labels are defined as follows:

$$d(t) = \min \{d(I(a)) + l(a) \mid a \in C(T), J(a) = t\}.$$

Dijkstra [8] observed that cutset examinations can be replaced by setting and updating temporary labels, at each time branching out from the node of smallest temporary label. The smallest temporary label is the minimum of $d(I(a)) + l(a)$ for $a \in C(T)$. By the tree extension theorem, it is a permanent label, and the node need not be branched out from again. Every arc is examined *precisely once* in the resulting algorithm of Dijkstra.

If the temporarily labeled nodes are put on a sequence list, then Dijkstra's method is formally equivalent to a stack-driven label correcting method, its retrieval strategy being to select the smallest distance label from the sequence list. As a matter of fact, if there are some negative arc lengths then Dijkstra's method becomes a label correcting scheme since some nodes that have been branched out from before may reappear on the sequence list.

5.14 Dantzig's label setting method

Let again T denote the partial shortest path tree determined so far by a label setting method, and let $C(T)$ be its cut-set. If two arcs $a, b \in C(T)$ share their origin node, then

$$d(I(a)) + l(a) \leq d(I(b)) + l(b)$$

whenever

$$l(a) \leq l(b).$$

This means that only the shortest arc in each forward star $F(i)$ has to be considered for the purpose of defining temporary labels. Indeed, in the above example, the temporary label $d(I(b)) + l(b)$ can be excluded from the minimum search since $d(I(a)) + l(a)$ is at least as small. This observation leads to a variant of Dijkstra's algorithm. This variant is due to Dantzig [5].

Dantzig's variant presupposes that the arcs in each forward star are sorted by increasing length. One starts with $T = \{r\}$, $d(r) = 0$ and uses the shortest arc in the forward star $F(r)$ of the root r to set a single temporary label $d(i)$, which then becomes automatically permanent. A pointer then is moved to the second shortest arc in $F(r)$. If its destination is in T, then the next shortest arc in $F(r)$ is considered, and so on, until either $F(r)$ is exhausted or an arc in the cutset $C(T)$ is found. Similarly, the shortest arc in the forward star $F(i)$ of the new permanently labeled node i is considered. If its destination is in T, then the next arc in $F(i)$ is considered, until $F(i)$ is either exhausted or the shortest arc in $F(i) \cap C(T)$ is found. These arcs – at most two – are then employed to set temporary labels.

Thereafter, the smallest temporary label $d(j)$ characterizes a new permanently labeled node j, which is added to the tree T. Let $k = p(j)$ be the predecessor of node j. Then the shortest arcs in $F(k) \cap C(T)$ and $F(j) \cap C(T)$ are determined in the fashion described above. Of course, $F(k) \cap C(T)$ and/or $F(j) \cap C(T)$ may be empty, and k and/or j, respectively, need not be considered any more as a consequence. One determines the smallest temporary label, and so on.

There are two important advantages to Dantzig's label setting method: (1) there are fewer temporary labels to find the minimum of than in Dijkstra's method; (2) the method may actually terminate before all the arcs have been examined.

Because the forward stars have to be sorted at the outset, Dantzig's method is usually not recommended for a *single* determination of a shortest path tree. However, it has been found (Dial, Glover, Karney, and Klingman [7]; Spira [16]) to be quite effective if shortest path trees for *several* different roots are to be determined in the same network.

5.15   Sorting

The complexity of Dijkstra's algorithm is bounded by $O(n^2)$, the complexity of label correcting methods is bounded by $O(n^3)$, and cannot be bounded by $O(n^2)$. This, the fact that each arc is examined only once, and its mathematical neatness made Dijkstra's method look superior to label correcting methods. For quite some time, however, label correcting methods proved to be more efficient in practice than Dijkstra's method.

This was because it was not recognized right away that Dijkstra's method involves *sorting*, and that its efficiency was determined by the efficiency of the sorting algorithm it incorporated. Indeed, in order to avoid repeated minimum searches one has to keep the sequence list sorted.

So called 'bubble sort', where the sequence list is maintained in linear order and new labels are entered at the end and then rise like 'bubbles' – by successive place changes with bigger labels – until they find their place in the linear order, is $O(n^2)$ and inefficient. There are several sorting methods which are readily updated and of complexity $O(n \log n)$, the most popular being *heap sort* or *binary tree sort*.

In heap sorting, a partial order is imposed on the sequence list by specifying position k to be the 'father' of positions $2k$ and $2k + 1$, provided the latter are not too big to be on the sequence list. Thus 1 has sons 2 and 3, 2 has sons 4 and 5, etc. The sequence list is *heap ordered* – as opposed to linearly ordered – if the label in any father position does not exceed any of the labels in the corresponding son positions. Heap order imposes a weaker structure than linear order. However, it still guarantees that the minimum occupies position 1. After removing the node in top position, heap order can be restored, for instance, by moving the last entry into the top position and correcting violations of the heap order by suitable interchanges. The number of such interchanges will be $O(\log n)$. New labels may be added at the end, that is, the first unoccupied position of the sequence list, and violations of the heap order are again corrected by $O(\log n)$ interchanges. The same happens, when some label decreases in value.

Dijkstra's algorithm with heap sort, while fairly efficient, is hurt by a phenomenon we will explain shortly: the large number of temporary labels of equal value which are on the sequence list simultaneously in the case of integer arc lengths.

5.16 Dial's method

We call a shortest path tree *normal* if the temporary labels across its cutset are not less than the biggest 'permanent' label in the tree. The tree consisting of the root r alone is normal, and each step of Dijkstra's method preserves normality.

Temporary label theorem *For normal trees, all temporary labels differ from the largest permanent label – and therefore among themselves – at most by the largest arc length L in the network.*

Proof Let m be the tree node with largest (permanent) label. For any temporary label, $d(I(a)) + l(a) \geqslant d(m)$ because of normality. Since node $I(a)$ is in the tree, $d(I(a)) \leqslant d(m)$, thus $d(I(a)) + l(a) \leqslant d(m) + l(a)$, which proves the theorem because $l(a) \leqslant L$. ∎

This theorem explains the many 'ties', i.e. equal labels, one observes on the sequence list during Dijkstra's method. If L is a small integer, and the arc lengths are all integers, then there will often be fewer values available for temporary labels than there are nodes on the sequence list.

The temporary label theorem has been exploited to yield a particularly efficient variant of Dijkstra's method for integer arc lengths. Its development is mainly due to Dial [6]. The idea is to use *radix sort*.

Radix sort puts an integer label into the position given by its value, e.g. a label of value 32 into position 32 ('cubby hole sort'). The problems posed by radix sort are (1) the number of positions needed and (2) the accommodation of 'ties'.

The second problem is solved by linking all nodes of equal label in one or both directions and entering only the 'entrance pointers' to such a linked chain of labels into a position ('cubby hole') of the radix sort array. Thus only a single storage cell is needed for each cubby hole. The first problem is much reduced by conducting the *radix sort modulo* $L + 1$ on the basis of the temporary label theorem. Indeed, since the values on the radix list differ at each time by at most L, the label is uniquely determined by its remainder modulo $L + 1$, so that only $L + 1$ radix positions corresponding to these remainders need be provided.

Dial's algorithm has dominated the field for almost a decade, and in most situations it is clearly the best available method. Dijkstra's method with heap sort is occasionally useful, for instance, if labels are not numbers but lexicographically ordered pairs of numbers.

5.17 Pape's method

In a surprising recent development, it was found that for very *sparse* networks, i.e. networks with a very small number of arcs relative to the number of nodes, label correcting methods may still be superior to Dial's method [7]. Pape [15] proposes the following strategy: add nodes labeled for the first time at the bottom of the sequence list, and add nodes the label of which has been finite before and is now being updated, but which are not already on the sequence list, to the top of the latter.

In order to facilitate adding nodes to the top, Pape uses a *linked list* as a sequence list. Such a list is represented by a *link pointer*

$$h \mid N \rightarrow N \cup \{0\},$$

which points from each listed node to the next one in sequence. In addition, the first and last nodes are kept for reference. Adding a node i at the bottom of the sequence list consists of getting the last node j, putting $h(j) = i$ and noting that i is now the last node. Adding a node i at the top of the list is analogous.

In order to discuss Pape's method, we examine the effect of correcting the label $d(i) < \infty$ of a node in the present tree T; that is, a label which already had been changed to a finite label.

Let $a = g(i)$ be the predecessor arc of node i in tree T. Deleting the arc a from T will disconnect T into two components, one component which contains the root r of T, and one component which contains the root i, all its successor nodes, and all their successors, etc. We call the latter component the *branch* $B(i, T)$ of node i in tree T. In general, the above branch of node i is a subtree of T and rooted at i. If i is a dead-end of T, then $B(i, T)$ consists only of node i.

As is readily seen, correcting the label

$$d(i) \rightarrow \hat{d}(i) < d(i), \qquad p(i) \rightarrow \hat{p}(i)$$

of node i in T results in a new tree $\hat{T}$, and if $i \in T$, then the two branches of i coincide:

$$B(i, T) = B(i, \hat{T}).$$

Next we observe that if node i is not a *dead-end* of T (and $\hat{T}$), then the new labeling $(\hat{p}, \hat{d})$ will not be sharp (Section 5.8). Indeed, there exists in $B(i, T)$ a node j which immediately succeeds i in both T and $\hat{T}$:

$$\hat{p}(j) = p(j) = i.$$

Then

$$\hat{d}(j) = d(j) \geqslant d(i) + l(g(j)) = d(i) + l(\hat{g}(j)) > \hat{d}(i) + l(\hat{g}(j)).$$

If a labeling is to be kept sharp, then, whenever node $i \in T$ and is not a dead-end of T, then the entire branch of i requires updating by the same amount $\delta = d(i) - \hat{d}(i) > 0$:

$$\hat{d}(j) = d(j) - \delta \quad \text{for} \quad j \in B(i, T) = B(i, \hat{T}).$$

We call such a procedure *branch-correcting*. Complete branch-correcting requires additional pointers for identifying the nodes in a branch $B(i, T)$, and such techniques will be discussed later.

In this section, we will show that Pape's method amounts to a limited branch-correcting procedure. To this end, we call the label $d(i)$ of a node $i \in T$ *sharp with respect to the labeling* (p, d) if $d(i)$ equals the in-tree distance from root r to node i. If all nodes in T are sharp with respect to the labeling (p, d), then (p, d) is sharp in the sense of Section 5.8.

Observation *Pape's method always branches out from nodes the label of which is sharp.*

Proof Whenever a node i reappears on the sequence list, it will be at the top. It will be branched out from and removed in the next step unless some 'brother' nodes $i_1, \ldots, i_s$ will be updated concurrently from the same node as i and added to the top of the sequence list right after i had been added. Every node k found subsequently above i on the sequence list, until i has risen to the top again, will be in the branch of one of the brothers $i_1, \ldots, i_s$ of i. Thus $k \notin B(i, T)$.

k is a node on top of the sequence list, presently to be branched out from, with a non-sharp label. Let T be the current tree. Tracing backwards in T from k toward the root, one encounters a first tree arc a with

$$d(J(a)) > d(I(a)) + l(a).$$

Node $i \in I(a)$ has not been branched out from since the most recent time its label had been corrected: otherwise equality would hold in the above relation. Thus node i must be on the sequence list, contradicting $k \in B(i, T)$.

The fact that only nodes with sharp labels are branched out from is an essential ingredient accounting for the success of Pape's method.

5.18   Back-up storage

Complete branch-correcting (Section 5.17) amounts to whole sale label correcting. Being able to determine the branches $B(i, T)$, unfortunately, requires the use of additional pointers, which consume memory space and which themselves have to be updated as the tree T changes. The present consensus appears to be that the additional effort is therefore not worthwhile.

Recent investigations by Glover and Klingman [13], however, indicate that there is an important role to be played by branch-correcting in case the networks are so big as to require *back-up storage* when represented in a computer. This back-up storage is usually on magnetic tape or disc. The need for back-up storage implies that only part of the network information is readily available (*in core*) at any given point in time. Whenever information is needed which is not presently in core, then the information now in core must be moved back into back-up storage to make room for the needed information to be brought into core from back-up storage. This can be very costly if repeated frequently.

Coping with back-up storage poses a challenge for most combinatorial algorithms, and shortest path algorithms are no exceptions. Almost all methods discussed so far show a drastic loss of efficiency in an environment in which only parts of the network are readily available. In fact, this is the case for all label setting algorithms and for all those label correcting algorithms in which the sequence for branching out is determined during the course of the calculation. In this case, which covers all methods relying on sequence lists, the algorithm may require to branch out from a node whose forward star of arcs may not lie in the accessible portion of the network.

This leaves only such label correcting methods as those in which implementation is based on examining the arcs of the network in a predetermined sequence.

The most important case is the one in which the number of arcs is too large to store *arc-information* in core, and the number of nodes is still small enough so that *node-information*, that is, arrays in which length equals the number of nodes, can be stored in core. We will show in the next section that complete branch-correcting can be implemented using only node-information and can therefore be used in conjunction with label correcting methods which are geared to cope with limited access to arc-information. In this context, branch-correcting has an important function in offsetting some of the effects of limited accessibility.

5.19 Tree processing

The most common technique for describing branches of a tree T rooted at r is to define *sons* and *brothers*. Two nodes $i_1, i_2 \in T$ are *brothers* if they share the same predecessor node in the tree: $p(i_1) = p(i_2)$. If a node i is not a dead-end, then among the immediate successors of node i, a particular one is selected to be the *son* of i. Two pointers

$$s \mid N \to N \cup \{0\}, \qquad b \mid N \to N \cup \{0\}$$

describe these relationships: $s(i)$ is the son of i, if i has one, and 0, otherwise. $b(i)$ is a brother of i and 0, if i itself was the last brother. (Sometimes, it is useful to point back to the 'father' if there are no sons or if there are no further brothers.) The set of nodes

$$\{i_1 = s(i), \ i_2 = b(i_1), \ i_3 = b(i_2), \ldots\}$$

describes all immediate successors of node i. In this fashion, all nodes in the branch of i can be identified sequentially. This technique requires a *stack* on which those successor nodes are stored for which successors are yet to be processed.

A different technique for describing branches uses a *forward pointer* or *thread* (Gilsinn and Witzgall [12])

$$f \mid N \to N \cup \{0\}.$$

This thread imposes a *linear order*

$$i_1 = r, \qquad i_2 = f(i_1), \qquad i_3 = f(i_2), \ldots$$

on all nodes of the tree T. Moreover this linear order is *branch-compatible*. By this we mean that for each node $i \in T$ there exists a node $g(i) \in T$ such that the nodes which lie between i and $g(i)$ in the linear order are precisely the nodes j in the branch $B(i, T)$ of node i:

$$i \leqslant j \leqslant g(i) \Leftrightarrow j \in B(i, T).$$

Branch-compatible linear orders do exist. For instance, they can be constructed from son and brother pointers as follows. Start with the root, follow with its son, the son of its son, and so on, until a dead-end node is reached. Then back-track to the last node k – in terms of the linear order – which has a brother, i.e. for which $b(k) \neq 0$. If there is no such node k, then all nodes of the tree have been ordered. Otherwise continue the sequence with $b(k)$, its son, the son of its son, and so on, until renewed back-tracking becomes necessary. It is readily verified that such a sequence represents a branch-compatible linear order.

If a thread $f \mid N \to N \cup \{0\}$ is available, then, determining the nodes in a branch $B(i, T)$, proceeds as follows. Node i is marked as belonging to $B(i, T)$. Then consider $j \in f(i)$. If $j \in T$ and its predecessor $p(j)$ has been marked as belonging to $B(i, T)$, then j also belongs to $B(i, T)$ and is marked accordingly. Then consider $f(j)$ and proceed as before. As soon as $f(j) = 0$ or $p(f(j))$ is found not marked, then j is the last node of $B(i, T)$: all nodes between I and j belong to $B(i, T)$.

Additional pointers or counters can be introduced to speed up the process of determining branches based on a thread $f \mid N \to N \cup \{0\}$. An additional pointer is $g \mid N \to N$, which assigns to each node i the last node of $B(i, T)$ with respect to f. Alternatively, a count

$$b(i) = \text{cardinality } (B(i, T))$$

may be provided.

The thread techniques and the son–brother techniques are about equally efficient. The thread techniques have a slight advantage in that they do not require an additional stack. It is important to take the effort into account which is needed to update the respective pointers when the tree T changes, because the pointers are generated in this fashion along with the trees.

Problems

1. Is it possible to find a rooted tree spanning the entire network in Figure 5.2? Find a rooted tree in this network with the maximum number of nodes.

2. Solve the example of Figure 5.9 by label correcting from scratch ($d(1) = 0$, $d(i) = \infty$ for $i > 1$), examining the arcs in a fixed sequence by arc numbers.

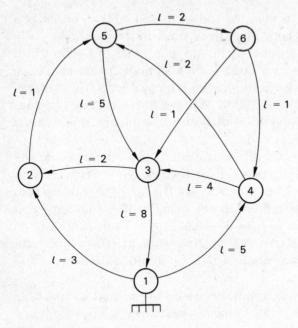

Fig. 5.10

3. Represent the network in Figure 5.10 by 'forward stars', i.e. arcs ordered by origin and corresponding pointers.

4. Solve the network in Figure 5.10 by LIFO label correcting.

5. Let (p, d) be an optimal labeling in network (N, A) with root r. Then the predecessor map p defines a shortest path tree T rooted at r.

   (a) Show that the shortest path tree T is unique if

$$d(I(s)) + l(s) > d(J(s))$$

   for all arcs $s \in A$ with $I(s)$ a node of T but s not an arc of T.
   (b) Let $s \in A$ be a nontree arc the ends of which are in T. How much can the length $l(s)$ of this arc be increased and how much can it be decreased while T remains a shortest path tree?

6. Given a rooted tree with predecessors and forward pointer. During the label correcting method, the following actions might be taken: (a) a new node is added to the tree; (b) an arc of the tree is replaced by some other arc, not previously in the tree, so that a new rooted tree

with a different predecessor map results. Describe methods for updating the forward pointer if any of the above actions is taken.

References

1   Bellman, R. On a routing problem, *Quart. Appl. Math.*, **16,** 87–90, 1958.
2   Berge, C. *Theory of Graphs and its Applications* (translated from French), Methuen, London, 1962.
3   Busacker, R. G. and Saaty, T. L. *Finite Graphs and Networks: An Introduction with Applications*, McGraw-Hill, New York, 1965.
4   Dantzig, G. B. All shortest routes in a graph, in *Theorie des Graphes*, International Symposium, Rome, 1966, Dunod, Paris, 1967.
5   Dantzig, G. B. On the shortest route through a network, *Management Sci.*, **6,** 187–190, 1960.
6   Dial, R. B. Algorithm 360, shortest path forest with topological ordering, *Comm. ACM.*, **12,** 632–633, 1969.
7   Dial, R. B., Glover, F., Karney, D. and Klingman, D. Shortest path forest with topological ordering. An algorithm description in SDL, Urban Mass Transit Administration, 1977 (to appear in *Networks*).
8   Dijkstra, E. W. A note on two problems in connexion with graphs, *Numer. Math.*, **1,** 269–271, 1959.
9   Dreyfus, S. E. An appraisal of some shortest-path algorithms, *Operations Res.*, **17,** 395–412, 1969.
10 Floyd, R. W. Algorithm 97, shortest path, *Comm. ACM.*, **5,** 345, 1962.
11 Ford, L. R., Jr and Fulkerson, D. R. *Flows in Networks*, Princeton University Press, Princeton, N.J., 1962.
12 Gilsinn, J. and Witzgall, C. A performance comparison of labeling algorithms for calculating shortest path trees, *National Bureau of Standards Technical Note* 772, 1973.
13 Glover, F. and Klingman, D. Oral communication, 1978.
14 Moore, E. F. The shortest path through a maze, in *Proceedings of an International Symposium on the Theory of Switching*, Part II, April 2–5, 1957, *The Annals of the Computation Laboratory of Harvard University* **30,** Harvard University Press, Cambridge, Mass., 1959.
15 Pape, U. Implementation and efficiency of Moore-algorithms for the shortest route problem, *Math. Programming*, **7,** 212–222, 1974.
16 Spira, P. M. A new algorithm for finding all shortest paths in a graph of positive arcs in average time $O(n^2 \log^2 n)$, *SIAM J. Comput.*, **2,** 28–32, 1973.
17 Wilson, R. J. *Introduction to Graph Theory*, Oliver and Boyd, Edinburgh, 1972.

Part II: **TWO CASE STUDIES**

5.20 Introduction

Part I of this chapter has discussed the background and basic methodology of shortest path algorithms. This part will focus on the use of those algorithms in two case studies and the associated problems of actually calculating paths in a computer.

The first case study involves work done by the National Bureau of Standards (NBS) for the Department of Transportation (DOT) in about 1970. The problem involved calculating 150 000 railroad distances for use by DOT in various analyses of freight movements in the USA. This particular example illustrates the difficulties of (1) coding and checking a large network and (2) dealing in the algorithm structure and computer implementation with the size of that network. Large problem size and the difficulties of handling and checking input data are common to many applied mathematics efforts, and their solutions often have as much or greater effect on problem resolution as the particular mathematical techniques used.

The second case study involves the design of specially tailored algorithms for use in automation of answering transit information inquiries. Transit companies in most large cities maintain facilities to help potential riders by providing individualized trip itineraries in response to telephone requests. This procedure is presently accomplished manually by transit company operators who use maps, route descriptions, and schedules to piece together the itineraries. Since this is a highly labor intensive operation, consideration is being given to automating this operation. General purpose shortest path algorithms do not address the discrete service aspects of a transit network, and preliminary estimates based on such algorithms indicate excessively large computation times. This case study illustrates a problem often arising in applications work, namely that the textbook approach must be modified, either because it does not include some important feature of the problem or because it cannot take advantage of special structure and is thus less efficient.

These two case studies have been chosen to demonstrate three situations which arise in actual applications, but which a student might not encounter in normal classroom work:

(a) the difficulties of dealing with data and ensuring its accuracy

and completeness;
(b) the impact of problem size on algorithm design; and
(c) the need for adapting general purpose algorithms to the particular application.

5.21 Railroad shortline distances

All Class 1 railroads (those with gross revenues exceeding $10 million a year) are required by law to send the Interstate Commerce Commission (ICC) copies of 1 percent of all waybills chosen at random. A waybill is a piece of paper accompanying each shipment and containing information such as the amount and commodity being shipped, the origin and destination (O and D) of the shipment, and sometimes the route or part of the route to be taken. The waybill sample is used to calculate various statistics, such as ton-miles of various commodities shipped by rail between various regions, for use in analyses of the effects of transportation policies such as rate setting and rule promulgation. Therefore a critical part of the analysis process is the ability to associate the miles traveled by each shipment in the waybill sample with that waybill sample. This arises since the total ton-miles m_k for commodity k is calculated as

$$m_k = \sum_i \sum_j t_{kij} d_{ij},$$

where t_{kij} is the amount of commodity k shipped from i to j and d_{ij} is the distance from i to j in the rail network. The actual distance traveled by a particular shipment may not be the shortest distance, either because the shipper specified another route or because the railroad chose to route the shipment along an alternate path to take advantage of train schedules, operational efficiencies, or otherwise to maximize its profit from the shipment. In spite of this the analysis procedures use the shortest distance, since it is repeatable and bears a more direct relationship to the rate charged for shipping.

The 1969 waybill sample contained about 150 000 waybills to be processed; that is, a distance was to be calculated for each waybill. The US rail network in which paths were to be calculated to obtain those distances contains approximately 60 000 stations, 9000 junctions, and 13 000 links. *Stations* are loading and unloading points such as terminals, sidings, mines, etc. *Junctions* are decision points in the network, points at which alternate routes are available. *Links* are pieces of track connecting two junctions. Links in the railroad network have no *a priori* direction, but the computer algorithms are designed for use in a directed network. Therefore the 13 000 links give rise to 26 000 *arcs* or ordered pairs of nodes. The computer implementation of the algorithms allows more than one arc between the same pair of nodes, but since any shortest path would only use the shortest arc between the pair, multiple arcs were eliminated early in the network processing.

The network nodes used in computing shortest paths were the junctions. Each station was connected to the two nearest junctions. An example of this procedure is illustrated in Figure 5.11. Stations *a* and *b* are along the line between junctions 1 and 2. Station *c* is

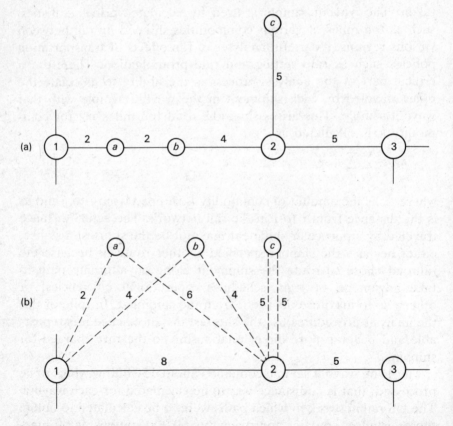

Fig. 5.11 Stations and junctions in the rail network. (a) Actual network; (b) coded network. Junctions are numbered and stations are lettered.

Table 5.1 Coded form of information in
Figure 5.11

Station	J_1	D_1	J_2	D_2
1	1	0	1	0
2	2	0	2	0
3	3	0	3	0
a	1	2	2	6
b	1	4	2	4
c	2	5	2	5

on a spur line, connected to the mainline only at junction 2. The
coded form of this information is given in Table 5.1, where J_1 and
J_2 are the two nearest junctions and D_1 and D_2 the distances to
those junctions, respectively. Note that most junctions were also
stations, that is, points of origin or destination of shipments. Thus
the distance d_{ij} between two points i and j is calculated as

$$d_{ij} = \min \begin{cases} D^*(i, J_1^i) + D(J_1^i, J_1^j) + D^*(J_1^j, j), \\ D^*(i, J_2^i) + D(J_2^i, J_1^j) + D^*(J_1^j, j), \\ D^*(i, J_1^i) + D(J_1^i, J_2^j) + D^*(J_2^j, j), \\ D^*(i, J_2^i) + D(J_2^i, J_2^j) + D^*(J_2^j, j), \end{cases}$$

where J_1^i is the first junction associated with i and J_2^i is the second,
$D(x, y)$ is the distance between the points x and y in the junction
network, and $D^*(i, J)$ is the distance between station i and the
appropriate nearest junction from the list above.

Most textbooks begin a section describing network algorithms
with a phrase such as 'Given a network . . .'; but just what form the
network appears in is critical to the network processing. In our
case, although the original project plan expected the network to be
available on computer tape, it was found that this information was
in fact only available in 45 notebooks which had originally been
compiled in the 1930s and 1940s. These notebooks, one per state,
except for several state combinations in the West and New Eng-
land, listed each link in the junction network and the distances of
stations along that link to the end junction points. Each of the
junction nodes was coded as a five digit number, the first two digits
of which described the book (thus in most cases the state) in which
that node appeared.

The work on the project involved four steps:

1. Edit the waybill sample.
2. Encode the network.
3. Check the network.
4. Compute network distances.

Only the first and fourth of these steps were included in the original plan of work, since it was not realized that the network was not available on magnetic tape. However, the bulk of the time and effort expended on this project was on steps 2 and 3. The 150 000 waybills in the initial sample were reduced to about 130 000 because of coding errors and incomplete or unreadable information. The 130 000 good waybills were then examined to see how many distinct origin–destination pairs were represented, since the distance would have to be computed only once for several shipments having the same origin and destination stations. This process reduced the number of distances to be calculated to about 90 000.

5.21.1 Coding the network

Although it was necessary in the railroad project to put the network data in a form directly accessible to the computer, we did not have to start from scratch in coding the network and were thus saved much additional work. The nodes were already identified with node codes which contained within them geographical identification. The books from which the computerized data base was produced contained the basic link data required.

Although the d_{ij} referred to in the previous section indicates that the network arc distances are stored in a matrix, this would require much too much computer storage for a network with 9000 nodes. Instead each link is coded as a triple consisting of origin, destination, and link length. The list of all links is then sorted so that all links with the same origin appear together. One then does not need to store the origin node of each link but only a pointer to where the data for the links for that origin are located. This process can be illustrated by referring to the example in Figure 5.12. The link triples are listed in the table at the left for the seven arcs in the network. (Bidirectional links have two arrows in the network diagram.) The column of the link table labeled 'Origin' can be replaced by the column labeled 'Arc' in the other table,

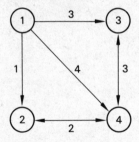

Arc	Origin	Destination	Length
1	1	2	1
2	1	3	3
3	1	4	4
4	2	4	2
5	3	4	3
6	4	2	2
7	4	3	3

Node	Arc
1	3
2	4
3	5
4	7

Fig. 5.12 Network representation.

since whenever we wish to know the origin of an arc we can see which numbers in the right-hand list it lies between. The right-hand list gives for each node the last arc the origin of which is that node. Thus since arc 7 lies between arcs 5 and 7, it must have node 4 as its origin. Since in practice the number of arcs is considerably larger than the number of nodes, this representation scheme can save important computer storage.

Additional efforts may also be made to reduce network size by simplifying network structure. One such a reduction comes about from eliminating serial nodes at which no true decision actually exists. In the example in Figure 5.13, node 2 can be removed and the two links combined into one longer link from node 1 to node 3, since all traffic either goes through 2 to 1 or 3 or else starts or ends at node 2. A second type of network reduction is the elimination of parallel arcs. Since in computing shortest paths we would always choose only the shortest link of several parallels, the others may be eliminated. (We would not eliminate them if we were concerned

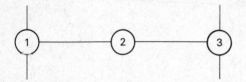

Fig. 5.13

with capacity.) A final network reduction possibility occurs with zero-length arcs. They may be eliminated and the endpoints consolidated into one node.

5.21.2 Checking the network

Once the network was put into machine-readable form, it was necessary to check that it was correct. In spite of the fact that many checks were performed on the network links as they were copied and keypunched, some errors were not detected by these checks. This is an inevitable situation which must be anticipated and planned for. The railroad network occupied seven boxes of computer cards, and to have expected perfection in 13 000 cards, each of which contained about 15 characters of data, is unreasonable.

The consequences of errors in the network coding are far-reaching and insidious. If a node number is miscoded this can introduce a new node into the network or can result in an improper connection because the erroneous node number duplicated another node. If an arc length is miscoded two nodes will be either further apart or closer than they should be. If an arc or a node is omitted the network may become disconnected, or if not disconnected distances may still be increased, or a dead-end node may be created which traffic can enter but not leave.

Coding errors are not the only source of incorrect network information. The source data itself may contain errors or inconsistencies, it may not be complete, and it may be out of date. Examples of all of these situations were uncovered while checking the US railroad network.

Figure 5.14 shows how two common types of error affect the calculation of one distance in the rail network. The initially calculated distance from Los Angeles to St Louis was about 800 miles and the path chosen was the unusual path shown in the figure, going by way of Washington and Idaho. Two short links in this path resulted from coding errors. The first connected a Los

Angeles suburb and a point in the state of Washington. This arose because data on a punched card was displaced one position and a node which should have been numbered 04162 was interpreted as 41620, which was a real node in Vancouver, Washington. The second error arose because the state designator codes used in describing nodes were the two-letter postal codes. Someone mistook IA, which is the code for Iowa, for the code for Idaho and used the first two digits of the node number appropriate for Idaho rather than Iowa.

The example described above illustrates how even a few coding errors can affect the calculation of many seemingly unrelated distances. Since computing shortest paths in a network involves operations similar to taking powers of a matrix, it is not surprising that an error in one entry affects many other entries of the power matrix. Of the 13 000 links of the rail network, errors were discovered in about 300 or 2.3 percent, but these errors substantially affected the calculation of over half the distances.

Systematic checking of the network is both possible and necessary. Initial reasonability checking can be performed early as the network is first available in machine-readable form. This might include checking that the node number is in range, that the node degree is in range (less than four for most ground transportation

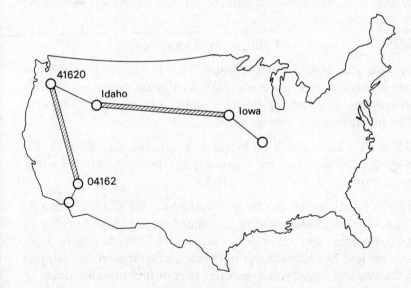

Fig. 5.14 Example of coding error.

systems, for example), and that the in-degree equals the out-degree. This latter was not important in our application, since it was assured by the process of coding the link in one arbitrary direction and replicating the opposite direction arc from it. Checks which may be performed on arcs include ensuring the arc length is in range, checking for sources of multiple arcs, and examining inter-regional arcs for reasonableness. More sophisticated network checking involves computing a set of shortest paths which cover most of the whole network and are fairly long. The paths may then be displayed on a map (automatically if the nodes are geo-coded in some fashion or manually if not). If the straight line distance between the endpoints is known, it may be compared with the network distance and unusually circuitous or short paths may be discovered. Whatever combination of checking methods is used, it is a long and tedious task, requiring some ingenuity and *a priori* knowledge of the network to devise appropriate procedures. The checks listed here, together with the examples of errors uncovered in coding the rail network, give a flavor of such a task, but are not exhaustive of the techniques which could be employed.

5.21.3 Partitioning the network

The railroad network was a very large network. With 9000 nodes and 26 000 arcs, the network storage scheme described in Section 5.21.1 requires

$$9000 + 2 \times 26\,000 = 61\,000 \text{ storage locations}$$

just to store the basic network. In addition the algorithms require working storage and storage for path and distance output. Let N be the number of nodes, A be the number of arcs, and D be one plus the maximum arc length, then

$6N + 2A + 1D$ is required by the best label-setting algorithm,
$4N + 2A$ is required by a minimum storage label-correcting algorithm,

or 106 500 locations for the fastest algorithm and 88 000 locations for a slower algorithm requiring minimum storage for the railroad network. Because our computer only had 65 000 words of core storage, we had to partition the network and computations in such a way that we only needed to consider part of it at any one time.

To partition the railroad network we divided it into the four subregions (which I will call *zones*) shown in Figure 5.15. The

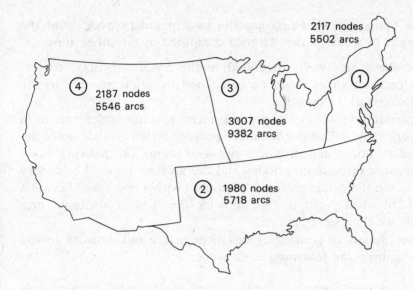

Fig. 5.15 Partitioned US rail network.

desire was to compute all distances within a zone, so that obtaining intrazonal distances simply involved looking up the answer in a table. Interzonal distances were computed by referring to the tables and adding appropriate table entries.

The first obstacle to this approach arose because the shortest distance between two points within one zone sometimes involved a path which went outside of that zone. This was solved by augmenting the arcs within a zone by a set of pseudo-arcs each of which is a path in a neighboring zone between boundary nodes of the first region. A *boundary* node is one which is the endpoint of an interzonal arc. To minimize the total number of boundary nodes, they were chosen so that, as much as possible, only one node of any interzonal arc would be a boundary node. The interzonal arcs thus had to be included in each zonal network whenever the boundary node end of the arc was not in that zone.

The network augmentation process was performed in the following steps:

1. Compute intrazonal distances between all boundary nodes within each zone.
2. Compare distances between the same two boundary nodes, calculated in different zones.
3. To that zone in which the distance is greater, append an arc

the endpoints of which are the two boundary nodes and the length of which is the distance computed in the other zone.

Once these arcs were appended to the zonal networks, correct intrazonal distances could be calculated by referring only to the single network in question.

Computation of interzonal distances requires reference to a network to be called the *boundary network* which is made up of the boundary nodes and distances between them. The network node set consists of boundary nodes and the arcs are pairs of boundary nodes and the distances (each computed within one zone) between them. Shortest paths in this network thus have constituent arcs which are themselves paths.

The process of computing distances in the rail network in the end required the following eight steps:

1. Compute distances between boundary nodes within each zonal network.
2. Augment zonal networks as needed.
3. Compute intrazonal distances to obtain actual shortest path distances, between all pairs of nodes in the same zone.
4. Construct the boundary node network, from distances between boundary nodes from step 3.
5. Compute distances between all boundary nodes.
6. Divide waybills into two classes: those for which the origin and destination lie within a zone and those requiring an interzonal trip.
7. For those waybills the origin and destination of which lie in one zone, look up the intrazonal distance.
8. For those waybills the origin and destination of which lie in different zones, compute the distance as

$$\min_{\substack{b_1 \in B_1 \\ b_2 \in B_2}} \{d(\text{origin}, b_1) + D(b_1, b_2) + d(b_2, \text{destination})\},$$

where B_1 is the set of boundary nodes of the region containing the origin and B_2 is the corresponding set for the destination, d is an intrazonal distance and D is a distance in the boundary network.

The actual computations were somewhat more complicated since most of the time the origin and destination were stations, not located at junctions. The computations in steps 7 and 8 then had to be performed for the four pairs of distances among nearest junctions with the station-to-junction distances added. The desired distance is the minimum of these four distances.

In concluding this section we would like to indicate the size of the effort involved in the solution of the railroad distance calculations. The final partition sizes are shown on Figure 5.15. The boundary node set had 131 nodes in it. The project required about three man-years work divided evenly among programming (and production runs), network encoding, and network checking. The final production run, exclusive of editing way bills and network checking, including only steps 1–8 above, required about 4.5 h on the UNIVAC 1108 under the EXEC II operating system. This was a batch processing system, so although input/output time plays a significant role, multiprogramming was not a factor. We have estimated that the whole project required more than 25 h of computer time, whereas original estimates had allotted that 25 h for the production run itself. Thus efficient processing was very important in the completion of the work. Network checking, which was not originally included in the plan, required a significant proportion of the manpower allocated to the task, and greatly expanded the work required from initial plans.

5.22 Transit information systems

Most transit companies provide telephone information facilities to answer patron requests for route and schedule information about specific planned trips. Smaller systems delegate this responsibility to one or two people along with other duties. Larger systems may employ up to 80 specially trained operators whose only job is to answer telephone information requests. In this very labor-intensive process the operators in most systems in use today consult route descriptions and schedules to piece together trips to answer caller queries.

Average call length varies from system to system and is a function not only of the size of the transit system, but of its complexity and variability. It varies from less than 1 min in a small city to more than 4 min for large complex systems. On a typical call, the operator spends about one-third of the call in ascertaining specifically what trip the caller is requesting, the origin and destination, desired arrival or departure time, day of travel, etc. A second third of the call is spent in piecing together an appropriate trip. The final third is spent in relaying the trip description back to the caller. Because the information center requires many people to answer calls and labor costs are rising faster than other costs, the process has become a candidate for automation. As an initial step only the route-finding middle-third of the call process is being considered for automation. This part of the call is a variant of the shortest route problem which may be stated as 'find the best route from A to B at time C'.

Critical factors which must be considered include the fact that the transit system provides discrete service, so the best routing is time-dependent and making connections very important. A second critical factor is that decisions must be made in real time, while the caller is on the phone, and several callers must be serviced, if not simultaneously, at least within seconds of one another. Another important factor is the size of major transportation systems. Washington, DC, for instance, has a fairly large transit system which consists of more than 9000 transit stops, about 850 separate routes, over 2000 buses which make 16 000 runs a day, and the system is growing with the construction of a fixed rail network to supplement bus service.

The initial question posed to NBS by Department of Transportation's Urban Mass Transit Administration (UMTA) was: is automation of the route-finding portion of a transit information call feasible? This question arose because of conflicting information available on the subject. One DOT contractor had estimated, using available general-purpose algorithms, similar to those described in Section 5.21, that for larger transit systems, a single response could require from 30 to 300 s of time on a large IBM 360 computer. A PhD thesis done at Stanford developed a method for computing paths in a discrete service network. This method was run on an IBM 360/67, requiring 0.2 s for a 40–50 node network. The author estimated that the computation time increased as the square of the network size. In addition, storage space is required for $N^2 \times T$ locations, where N is the number of nodes and T the number of time points in the day at which vehicles depart or arrive. On the other hand, everyone was not as pessimistic as these two groups. Two companies were actively marketing computer-based transit information systems. One had even demonstrated its system in Santa Monica, California. Although neither system had been run on a large-scale test case, both claimed that the computation time for their algorithms increased linearly with network size. Both companies viewed their algorithms as proprietary and were unwilling to disclose details. Thus UMTA asked NBS to investigate more carefully the feasibility of automation to reconcile these two differing opinions.

The transit information example discussed here illustrates graphically the problems with general-purpose algorithms, the algorithms upon which the conservative – it won't work – recommendations described above were based. Because they cannot take advantage of special problem structure they are less efficient and require greater computation time. But computation time can be very important in any real-time situation, and costs money whatever the application. A second difficulty is that general purpose algorithms are seldom designed to handle most efficiently the situation found in many large problems where the problem and data base are too large to be resident completely in computer core storage at one time. In this case organizing the algorithm so that it processes data sequentially to facilitate efficient paging of the data may be more important than actual algorithm design.

Another drawback to general purpose algorithms is that they may not provide information at the desired level of detail. One of the approaches suggested for transit information system use was the application of procedures now used for transportation planning. These procedures involve computing paths using standard shortest path algorithms on a network the nodes of which are transit stops, the arcs of which are sections of routes between stops, and with the disutility associated with an arc being the sum of an average vehicle travel time and half the headway between vehicles. This assumes that when transferring to a vehicle arriving every half hour, people must wait on the average 15 min. Transit companies, however, do not want to base the itineraries they provide to customers on such average and iffy information, since they know actual bus arrival and departure times. Thus the transportation planning approach is too general to be applied to the information system problem and we started to investigate modifications to the general purpose algorithms to tailor them for the specific application in mind.

One of the first questions that arose was the selection of an appropriate criterion of bestness in choice of path. Least time in the traditional sense was inappropriate, since travel time varies depending on time of day. In different circumstances both the departure time and the arrival time can be critical, and in other instances only general time of day is important. After examining a number of possibilities for appropriateness and ease of use two criteria were selected: *departure-oriented* (arrive soonest while departing after a desired departure time) and *arrival-oriented* (depart latest to arrive before a desired arrival time). An example of the first would be arranging a trip home after class, and an example of the second is arranging to get to class. Fares might also be considered in the optimization, but flat fares and zone fare structure would not differentiate among paths. The number of transfers was recognized to be an important factor, and indeed is used in the design of one of the algorithms below, but we did not know the trade-off between shorter trip time and an extra transfer. This factor might vary from person to person and for the same person from trip to trip. Thus the two criteria above were adopted for use in the algorithm.

In our search for algorithms, we identified three algorithms based on two different approaches as candidates for use in an automated transit information system. The algorithms depend on special network structuring and data handling to achieve their efficiency. The next section, which is in some ways a digression, provides the background needed to understand the first of the two approaches.

5.22.1 Acyclic networks

A *cycle* in a network is a simple path the origin and destination of which are the same node. An *acyclic network* is one which contains no cycles. We will call a node which is not the destination of any arc a *pure source*. Then we have the following theorem:

Theorem *A directed network without a pure source contains a cycle.*

To understand this theorem, since every node is the destination of some arc, let v_1 be any node. Then pick an arc with v_1 as destination. Let v_2 be its origin. Since v_2 is the destination of some arc, let v_3 be the origin of that arc, etc. At some point this process will run out of new nodes. Once some node is repeated $v_k = v_l$ for some $k \neq l$, creating a cycle.

The contrapositive of this theorem guarantees that every acyclic network contains at least one pure source. This ensures that the nodes in an acyclic network can be numbered consecutively so that the origin of any arc has a lower number than the destination of the arc. The procedure is as follows:

1. Find a pure source v and number it node 1.
2. Delete the arcs originating at v. The resulting network is still acyclic since removing arcs cannot introduce a cycle.
3. Again find a pure source and number it with the next highest number.

Repeat steps 2 and 3 until all nodes are numbered.

The advantage of an acyclic network and this numbering scheme is that it leads to a very efficient shortest path algorithm which requires only one pass, rather than the several iterations normally required by general purpose algorithms. The algorithm steps are given below, where $F(u)$, the *forward star* of u, is the set of all arcs originating at u.

Initialization $d(v) = \infty$ for all v, $d(\text{origin}) = 0$.

1. $u \leftarrow$ origin.
2. $d(v) = \min \{d(v), d(u) + l(u, v) \mid (u, v) \in F(u)\}$.
3. If $u < N$, $u \leftarrow u + 1$ and go to step 2.
4. STOP.

5.22.2   Time-expanded network algorithm

This approach considers the nodes of the network to be geographical transit stops at points in time. This means that 8th and Elm at 8:00 is a separate node from 8th and Elm at 8:01. Arcs in the network are vehicle trip segments; that is, the bus leaving 8th and Elm at 8:00 and arriving at 10th and Elm at 8:10 gives rise to one network arc. The resulting network is acyclic since each arc goes forward in time. In fact we do not even need the elaborate algorithm for numbering network nodes, since they can be numbered using time alone, with ties broken arbitrarily. Because the network is acyclic we can use the acyclic network algorithm from the previous section to compute shortest paths.

An example of the process of time-expanding the network is given in Figures 5.16 and 5.17. There are three routes, one a local route from node 1 to node 2 to node 3, a second express from node 1 to node 3, and a third from node 3 to node 4. Schedules for each are given in Figure 5.16. The time-expanded form of this

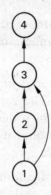

Route 1:	1	2	3
	9:00	9:05	9:10
	9:10	9:15	9:20
	9:20	9:25	9:30

Route 2:	1	3
	9:15	9:23

Route 3:	3	4
	9:15	9:20
	9:20	9:25
	9:25	9:30

Fig. 5.16 Example routes and schedules.

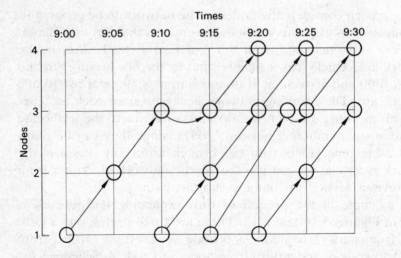

Fig. 5.17 Examples of a time-expanded network.

network is given in Figure 5.17. Note that transfer arcs have been included at node 3, to connect up the routes.

There are several advantages to this algorithm over the general purpose approach. It uses a one-pass algorithm rather than an iterative approach. Because the network can be sorted once and for all on arrival time at a node, and because it is processed in this order, the approach allows an efficient paging scheme which can be very important for large transit networks. A disadvantage to the time-expanded approach is that it greatly enlarges the network and because of the need to store transfer arcs explicitly, it requires significantly more storage to gain the one-pass advantage.

One problem which has arisen in examining paths produced in transit networks is generally termed the *overtake problem*. It occurs when a vehicle which departs later at one node overtakes and passes a vehicle which departs earlier at the first node. This often occurs with express and local service on the same line. Two paths may be equivalent by one of the criteria discussed earlier, for example since by the departure-oriented criteria they arrive at the same time, but one path may require more transfers and thus be less desirable. An example appears in Figure 5.18. The first path starts out on the first departure from node 1 and transfers to route

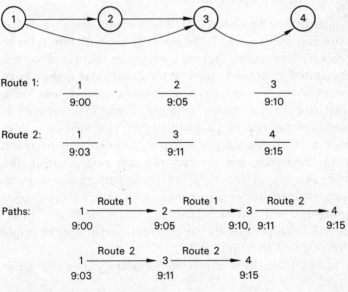

Fig. 5.18 Overtake problem example.

2 at node 3. The second path takes route 2 all the way. Both arrive at node 4 at the same time and so are equally acceptable under the criterion defined earlier, but the second path requires no transfers and is thus more desirable.

One special feature of this situation should be noted. The best path from node 1 to node 3 uses route 1, but this path is not the best first part of the best path to node 4. Most shortest path approaches require that if the best path from node a to node c goes through node b, then the subpath from node a to node b should be the best path between those nodes. This is not the case for the better path in Figure 5.18, and some means must be available for distinguishing the two paths. Although the time-expanded network scheme, in theory, provides such a means since (node 3 at 9:10) and (node 3 at 9:11) are distinct nodes in the time-expanded network, in practice overtake does occur because of the necessity of applying path choice rules based on information about the most recent arc in the path. There is no good way to decide whether it was more desirable to get to node 3 from node 1 or node 2 when aiming for node 4. The algorithm described below will improve this situation by permitting easy look-back along a whole route.

5.22.3 Bipartite route/stop algorithms

For the two algorithms considered below we will design another special network representation. To begin with, we will only refer to the route structure and define network nodes in two classes. One of these is the set of all transit stops; the second class is the set of all transit routes. Arcs connect any transit route to the stops on it and any transit stop to the routes stopping there. This network is *bipartite*, since its nodes can be partitioned into two disjoint sets in such a manner that an arc may connect a node in one partition with a node in the other, but no arcs connect nodes within the same partition. A path in the bipartite route/stop network is an alternating sequence of nodes and routes with the route between two nodes being one which travels from the one node to the other. The bipartite route/stop network representation for the example in Figure 5.16 is given in Figure 5.19.

The steps in the basic bipartite route/stop algorithm are given below:

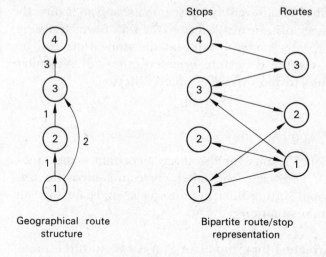

Stops   Routes

Geographical route
structure

Bipartite route/stop
representation

Fig. 5.19 Example of a bipartite route/stop network.

Initialization $T(i) = \infty$ for all i; $T(\text{origin}) = $ desired departure time.

1. $i \leftarrow$ origin. Let r be the first route from i.
2. Search the schedule of route r for the first departure at or after $T(i)$.
3. For each stop j on this vehicle run (after stop i), compare the arrival time of route r at that stop with $T(j)$. If the arrival time by route r is better, put it in $T(j)$.
4. Let r be the next route stopping at i. Go to step 2. If none go to step 5.
5. Let i be the 'next node'. If 'next node' is destination, stop. Otherwise go to step 2.

Two different algorithms arise from two different approaches to calculating the 'next node'. When the nodes i are ordered by the value of $T(i)$, that is by the arrival time of the best path so far, the resulting algorithm is a label setting algorithm with a distance list ordering, usually the fastest algorithm for most networks with small node degrees.

When the 'next node' list is ordered by cardinality distance, that is, the number of links from the origin, a label correcting algorithm results. This latter ordering has special advantages, since in this bipartite route/stop structure the number of links from the origin is just twice the number of different route segments, and so is directly related to the number of transfers. Since paths with fewer transfers are examined first, later paths arriving at the same time can be discarded when using the departure oriented criterion. A similar decision rule applies to the arrival oriented criterion.

5.22.4 Algorithm comparisons

Recent computational results for the three algorithms – the time-expanded network approach, the label correcting bipartite approach, and the label setting bipartite approach – indicate that all have merit in certain situations:

1. The label correcting bipartite algorithm is two to three times slower than the fastest algorithm, but always produces the path with fewest transfers.
2. The label setting bipartite algorithm is fastest for smaller networks and ones with frequent service over a simple network structure.
3. The time-expanded network algorithm is fastest for larger, complex networks.

A 225-node grid network required about 50 ms per path computation. Regression analysis indicates that computation time for all three algorithms is primarily a function of the number of network nodes (stops) and grows linearly (with a slope of less than 1 for the label setting bipartite and time-expanded algorithms). Estimates of the computation time for networks in cities the size of Washington clearly indicate acceptably low computation times for automation of on-line transit information service.

This analysis has clearly indicated the need for specially tailored algorithms which can utilize the particular structure of an application. The general purpose algorithms would not have solved the problem. The specially designed ones described above do. Washington, DC is currently in the process of purchasing a computerized transit route-finder to automate that part of its information system. Whether the actual algorithms used are the ones described here or others, the exercise described above contributed to UMTA's willingness to fund the venture based on a clear demonstration of its feasibility.

Problems

1. (a) Number the nodes in the network in Figure 5.20 so that each arc
      goes from a smaller to a larger numbered node.
   (b) Find the shortest path between the black nodes.

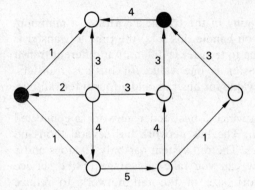

Fig. 5.20

2. The bus network in Figure 5.21 has the following schedule. Horizontal
   routes run every 5 min, starting at 9:00; each segment is 4 min long.

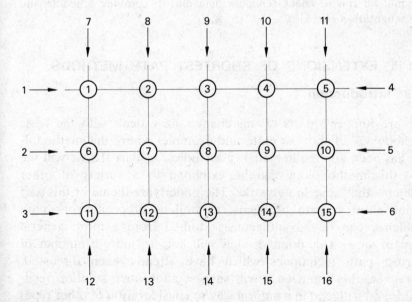

Fig. 5.21

Vertical routes run every 7 min, starting at 9:02; each segment is 4 min long. Find the best path from node 1 to node 14, starting at or after 9:03.

3. Devise an example for which the bipartite route/stop scheme does *not* produce a minimum transfer path and explain why.

4. Suggest a method incorporating in the transit algorithms a minimum transfer time. How would you handle this if (a) the time to transfer is just one number, (b) the time to transfer is different at different transit stops, (c) the time to transfer is one value for bus/bus transfers, another for rail/rail, a third value for bus/rail, and a fourth for rail/bus.

5. Consider a transit system in which a bus feeder network is connected to a high speed rail system. The bus network has several thousand stops and irregular schedules. The rail system has only 20 stops and a very regular schedule. How can you take advantage of the service regularity and small network size of the rail network to reduce computation, since most trips involve at least one bus/rail or rail/bus transfer?

6. Suggest methods of checking out a transit network. Remember that the methods used for the railroad network were primarily oriented toward ensuring proper network connections. What additional tests could be run to check schedule data and to combine schedule and configuration checking?

Part III: **EXTENSIONS OF SHORTEST PATH METHODS**

5.23 Introduction

The previous two parts of this chapter have dealt with the basic methodology of shortest paths and examples where this methodology has been applied in actual case studies. In Part III, we will see how this methodology can be extended to a variety of other problems that arise in networks. The underlying theme of this part is that shortest path problems, as well as other network path problems, can be advantageously studied from a more general point of view. This point of view will help to unify a number of shortest path techniques which have already been discussed. Moreover, this framework will suggest alternative solution techniques and will lead in a natural way to consideration of other types of network problems.

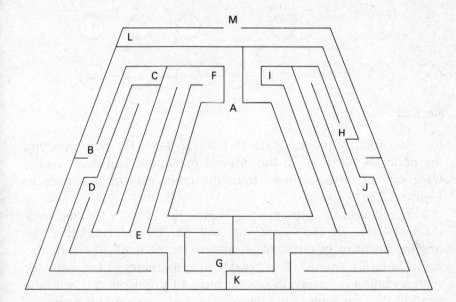

Fig. 5.22

Let us begin by looking at two rather different situations where a certain type of shortest path problem arises. The first instance transports us back to historic Hampton Court, the Tudor palace built by Cardinal Wolsey and presented as a gift to Henry VIII. Further additions were made to the palace during the reign (1689–1702) of William III, including a magnificent collection of gardens and a maze formed by a series of hedges (*see* Figure 5.22). The challenge of this maze was, of course, to start in the inner portion (A in the diagram) and find one's way to the outside (M in the diagram).

As a matter of fact, important characteristics of this maze can be captured using a network representation: namely, the nodes (shown by letters A, B, ..., M, in Figure 5.22) indicate 'decision points' where two or more passageways meet; 'dead-ends' are also designated by nodes. In this context, an edge (indicating two oppositely directed arcs) represents a passageway connecting two nodes. The original maze of Figure 5.22 can thus be depicted as the network of Figure 5.23. Clearly, the original problem of tracing out an escape from the maze translates into the problem of finding a path from A to M in the corresponding network. It is quite easy to locate such a path in Figure 5.23 (in fact, there are several):

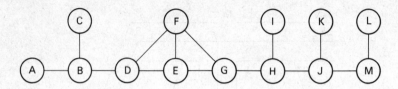

Fig. 5.23

e.g. the node sequence A–B–D–E–G–H–J–M. By reinterpreting the nodes as locations in the original maze, one can then readily trace out an 'escape route' from the inner part of the maze in Figure 5.22.

Notice that in the present case, we are not actually looking for a shortest path; in fact, any path will do. By reformulating the original problem in terms of an underlying network, the required route is easily found. To illustrate the usefulness of a network representation in resolving certain types of problems, we will now consider the much more modern example of a compiler for computer programs. During the compilation of a series of programs and subprograms, it is necessary to keep track of which subprograms *call* (make reference to) other subprograms. For example, suppose that

subprogram A calls subprogram D;
subprogram B calls subprograms A, C, E;
subprogram C calls subprogram E;
subprogram D calls subprogram C;
subprogram E calls subprogram D.

This collection of subprograms and their relations to one another are represented by the network in Figure 5.24. Here, nodes correspond to subprograms and an arc (i, j) joins node i to node j if subprogram i calls subprogram j. Two relevant questions can

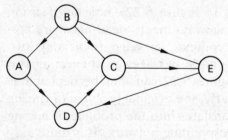

Fig. 5.24

now be answered:

1. Which subprograms will (potentially) be called by subprogram A, either directly or indirectly? (Such a question arises in resolving all external references generated by subprogram A.)
2. Which subprograms are recursive – i.e. ultimately call themselves? (Recursiveness is checked, for example, by ALGOL compilers.)

In question 1, what is really required then is to find all nodes *accessible* (by a path) from node A. From Figure 5.24, it is clear that C, D, and E are the only nodes accessible from A. Accordingly, subprograms C, D, and E have to be included together with subprogram A in order for execution to be successful. In question 2, one seeks all nodes i such that a path exists in Figure 5.24 from node i to itself. In other words, it is required to find all nodes which lie on a cycle: namely, nodes C, D, and E. Therefore, the only recursive subprograms here are subprograms C, D, and E.

The above two examples serve to illustrate three important points. First, networks can arise in the most unsuspected places! More generally, whenever one encounters systems of interconnected elements there may well be a network lurking underneath. Second, the underlying network may not always represent a true physical system of connections. Indeed, a network can often portray (as in the compiler example) the logical, rather than the physical, characteristics of a system. Third, in both of the above examples, we were mainly concerned with simply finding a path between nodes, rather than a shortest one. This type of problem, where the nodes accessible from given nodes need to be determined, is sometimes referred to as the *transitive closure problem*.

The transitive closure problem, while conceptually simpler than the shortest path problem, is intimately related to the latter problem. Moreover, solution techniques for the shortest path problem can be suitably modified for the transitive closure problem, as we will later see. In order to pursue the connections between these and other problems, let us now return to shortest path problems, but this time viewed from a slightly different perspective.

5.24 Shortest paths revisited

We begin by considering the network in Figure 5.25, and suppose that the shortest path from node 1 to node 5 is required. To find

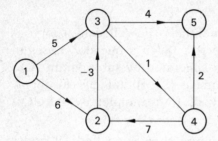

Fig. 5.25

such a path, we adopt the following philosophy: successively reduce the given network problem to smaller and simpler problems
until the solution is obvious.

In order to proceed, we propose three reasonable *rules of
reduction*. First, if two *parallel* arcs extend between two nodes,
then certainly the arc with smaller length should be used when
following a shortest path; that is to say, two parallel arcs of lengths
a and b, respectively, can be replaced by a single arc of length
$\min (a, b) = $ the minimum of a and b. This first rule is illustrated in
Figure 5.26. Rule 2 simply says that a pair of arcs (i, k) and (k, j) in
series can be replaced by a single arc from i to j having as its

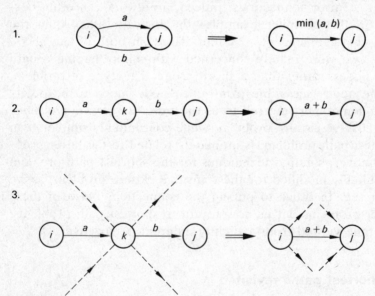

Fig. 5.26 The three rules of reduction. Rule 3 is known as the rule of
superposition.

length the sum of the arc lengths of the two series arcs. This second rule is also shown in Figure 5.26. Finally, we require a 'rule of superposition' (*see* Figure 5.26) that allows us to apply Rule 2 simultaneously for several pairs of arcs entering and leaving a given node k.

The use of these rules is illustrated in Figure 5.27, where we successively reduce the network by eliminating nodes 2, 3, and 4 in turn. Note that after node 3 has been eliminated, we obtain a *loop* of length 5 on node 4. Since a shortest path will never take an excursion around this loop (it would only increase its length, and needlessly), we can without harm eliminate this loop as well. Finally, we end up with a very simple network (the last network in Figure 5.27), in which the shortest path from 1 to 5 can easily be identified. In fact, there is only *one* path in the last network from node 1 to node 5, and this path has length 6. It can also be readily verified that the shortest path in the original network does indeed have length 6, too.

Actually, it is easy to trace backwards from the reduced network to the original network (*see* Figure 5.28) in order to find a corresponding shortest path with length 6: namely, the node sequence 1–2–3–4–5. This reduction technique is a perfectly general and valid method for finding shortest paths – of course, as long as there are no cycles of negative length in the network. Notice that this requirement about the length of cycles manifests itself during our reduction process; that is, the loop of length 5 we encountered corresponds precisely to the cycle 2–3–4–2 having length $7 - 3 + 1 = 5$: the fact that there are no cycles of negative length allows us to remove with impunity the (nonnegative length) loop arising during the elimination of node 3 from the network.

To understand better why this reduction procedure works, let us consider again the first two rules of reduction (Figure 5.26). There appear to be two essential operations underlying the reduction process: namely, taking the minimum of two lengths, and adding together two lengths. For convenience, these two essential operations will be abbreviated by

$$\oplus = \text{minimum}, \qquad \otimes = \text{ordinary addition}.$$

Rephrased in these terms, the first two rules can be reformulated as in Figure 5.29, where parallel arcs now 'add' and series arcs 'multiply'.

Furthermore, we can now use these new operations $\oplus$ and $\otimes$ to

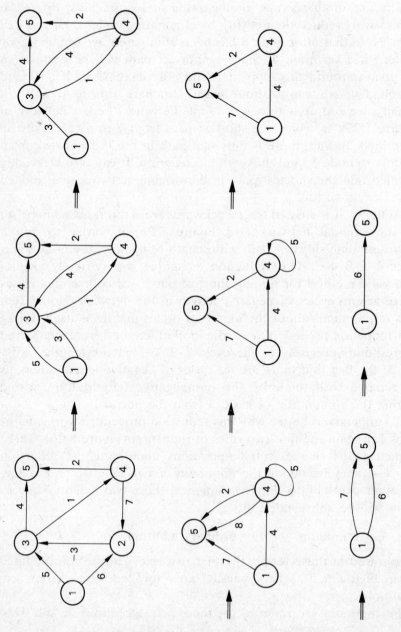

Fig. 5.27

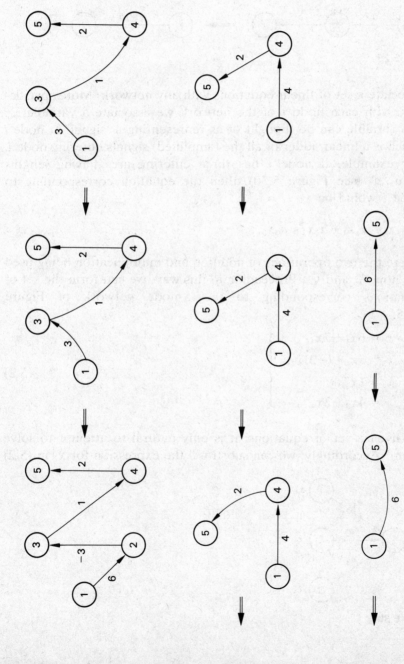

Fig. 5.28

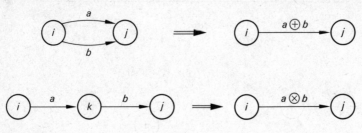

Fig. 5.29

associate a set of linear equations with any network. More specifically, with each node i of the network we associate a variable x_i;
this variable can be thought of as representing a 'signal' at node i
which is a linear adder of all the (amplified) signals entering node i.
For example, if node i has three entering arcs having lengths
a_1, a_2, a_3 (see Figure 5.30), then the equation corresponding to
node i would be

$$x_i = a_1 x_1 + a_2 x_2 + a_3 x_3,$$

where the two operations of addition and multiplication being used
are now $\oplus$ and $\otimes$. Proceeding in this way, we can form the set of
equations corresponding to the 5-node network of Figure
5.25:

$$\left.\begin{aligned}
x_2 &= 6x_1 + 7x_4, \\
x_3 &= 5x_1 + (-3)x_2, \\
x_4 &= 1x_3, \\
x_5 &= 4x_3 + 2x_4.
\end{aligned}\right\} \tag{5.2}$$

Given a set of equations, it is only natural to attempt to solve
them! Accordingly, we can substitute the expression for x_2 in (5.2)

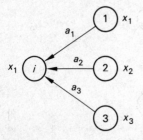

Fig. 5.30

into the other equations, obtaining

$$x_3 = 5x_1 + (-3)[6x_1 + 7x_4] = 5x_1 + 3x_1 + 4x_4 = 3x_1 + 4x_4,$$

$$x_4 = 1x_3,$$

$$x_5 = 4x_3 + 2x_4. \tag{5.3}$$

Of course we have used such facts as $(-3)(6) = (-3) \otimes 6 = 3$ and $5 \oplus 3 = 3$ in simplifying certain expressions. In the end, though, we have succeeded in eliminating x_2 from the original set of equations. Notice that equations (5.3) bear a special relationship to our original network: namely, they correspond exactly to the network obtained by eliminating node 2 from the original network (*see* Figure 5.27)!

We can continue to solve equations (5.3), now by eliminating x_3:

$$x_4 = 1[3x_1 + 4x_4] = 4x_1 + 5x_4,$$

$$x_5 = 4[3x_1 + 4x_4] + 2x_4 = 7x_1 + 8x_4 + 2x_4 = 7x_1 + 2x_4.$$

Again, these equations correspond exactly to the network obtained after eliminating node 3 in Figure 5.27. Note, however, that we were able to ignore the loop present on node 4 in Figure 5.27. Accordingly, we will ignore the term $5x_4$ in the above equation for x_4, with the result

$$x_4 = 4x_1,$$

$$x_5 = 7x_1 + 2x_4. \tag{5.4}$$

Finally, we can substitute for x_4 into the expression for x_5 in (5.4), to obtain

$$x_5 = 7x_1 + 2[4x_1] = 7x_1 + 6x_1 = 6x_1. \tag{5.5}$$

Again, this final equation (5.5) corresponds to the final reduced network in Figure 5.27. Moreover, the coefficient of x_1 in (5.5) gives us the length of a shortest path from node 1 to node 5 in the original network.

It is seen, therefore, that eliminating a node from the network is tantamount to eliminating a variable from a system of equations, now 'linear' in two operations $\oplus$ and $\otimes$. This observation is perfectly general and serves to suggest an analogy between network problems and the solution of linear equations.

Using this equation viewpoint, it is possible to find the lengths of shortest paths from node 1 to *all* nodes of the network. In fact, the value of the variable x_i can be interpreted as the length of a shortest path from node 1 to node i. Naturally, once we are at node 1 it is not necessary to go anywhere in order to reach node 1: i.e. $x_1 = 0$. To find the remaining values for x_i, we collect the following equations from (5.2)–(5.5):

$$\left. \begin{aligned}
x_5 &= 6x_1 = 6 \times 0 = 6, \\
x_4 &= 4x_1 = 4 \times 0 = 4, \\
x_3 &= 3x_1 + 4x_4 = 3 \times 0 + 4 \times 4 = 3, \\
x_2 &= 6x_1 + 7x_4 = 6 \times 0 + 7 \times 4 = 6.
\end{aligned} \right\} \tag{5.6}$$

Using the above calculations, we have indeed found the shortest path lengths from node 1 to all other nodes of the network; for example, a shortest path from node 1 to node 4 has length $x_4 = 4$.

The actual procedure used to solve equations (5.2) corresponds to the method termed 'Gaussian elimination and back substitution' in the context of solving ordinary linear equations. Here, we have adapted this method to solve the 'linear' equations associated with a network (and thus determine the lengths of shortest paths). However, there are many ways to solve ordinary linear equations, and so it should come as no surprise to find that there are many ways to solve shortest path problems. An alternative way, suggested by the arrangement of equations in (5.2), is to use an *iterative* technique. The basic idea of such a technique is to guess an initial solution to the equations, and then to generate a sequence of approximate solutions (even better guesses), until some sort of convergence to the true solution is achieved.

To illustrate, consider the network of Figure 5.25 for which the corresponding equations are given by (5.2). We can indicate our complete ignorance of the solution by using the initial approximation:

$$x_1^{(0)} = 0,$$
$$x_j^{(0)} = \infty \qquad j \neq 1.$$

Then improved estimates $x_j^{(1)}$ are available by substituting into the right-hand side of equations (5.2):

$$x_2^{(1)} = 6x_1^{(0)} + 7x_4^{(0)} = 6,$$
$$x_3^{(1)} = 5x_1^{(0)} + (-3)x_2^{(0)} = 5,$$
$$x_4^{(1)} = 1x_3^{(0)} = \infty,$$
$$x_5^{(1)} = 4x_3^{(0)} + 2x_4^{(0)} = \infty.$$

Table 5.2

	Iteration					
x_i	0	1	2	3	4	5
x_1	0	0	0	0	0	0
x_2	∞	6	6	6	6	6
x_3	∞	5	3	3	3	3
x_4	∞	∞	6	4	4	4
x_5	∞	∞	9	7	6	6

We can continue in this way, substituting the current estimates at iteration $k-1$ into (5.2), thus generating the next estimates at iteration k. This process is repeated until two successive estimates are identical, at which point a solution to (5.2) will actually have been found. The details of this procedure are shown in Table 5.2, where convergence is established at the fifth iteration. The shortest path lengths x_i from node 1 to node i are thus found from the last column: $x_1 = 0$, $x_2 = 6$, $x_3 = 3$, $x_4 = 4$, $x_5 = 6$. Notice that these are precisely the same values found in (5.6).

The general approach followed in this iterative technique should be reminiscent of what is done in label correcting techniques for finding shortest paths, where node labels are continually revised until no further changes are possible. In fact, one can show that this iterative technique actually corresponds to a form of label correcting. Likewise, other shortest path techniques we have already encountered have counterparts in appropriate techniques for solving linear equations. Thus, the equation point of view adopted here serves to unify our current inventory of shortest path techniques. Moreover, this point of view can lead to newer, and sometimes more appropriate, techniques for performing shortest path calculations (e.g. methods for decomposition in networks).

To summarize, two essential operations on arc lengths were first identified in the context of shortest path problems. By means of these operations, it was possible to associate a system of equations (linear in these operations) with every network. In this way, it became clear that the determination of shortest paths in the original network was equivalent to solving this system of linear equations. Thus, by appropriate reformulation, this network problem has in fact been converted into a problem (equation solving) which is much more familiar and for which there already exists a substantial arsenal of solution techniques.

5.25 Other network problems

In this section, our attention will be broadened beyond the concerns of shortest paths to other network problems. We will be aided in this task by continual use of the equation point of view developed in Section 5.24. The basic idea here is to formulate these other network problems in such a way that they assume a more familiar form. Solution techniques can then be easily found, by appropriately adapting existing methods.

The first example to be considered here is that of the *maximum capacity path problem*. Such a problem can arise, for instance, in a transportation network, where each road of the network has a *capacity* indicating the maximum number of vehicles per hour that can flow along the road. Here, as in the case of pipes of different diameters joined together, the total rate of flow along some route is determined by its 'weakest link': i.e. its arc of smallest capacity. Also, in the industrial setting of a job shop, the flow of work that must pass through several successive stages is determined by the 'bottleneck' stage – the one with the slowest production rate.

Thus, it is reasonable to define the capacity of a path in a network by the minimum arc capacity along that path. In this context, the maximum capacity path problem is to find, among all paths from i to j, a path having maximum rate of flow between the given nodes in the system.

In order to study this problem it is useful to see what properties a maximum capacity path should have in two simple cases. First, when two arcs are in parallel (see Figure 5.29), they can be replaced by a single arc with the larger of the two arc capacities; after all, it is the *maximum* capacity path that we are interested in. Second, when two arcs occur in series, they can be replaced by an arc having as capacity the smaller of the two constituent arc capacities. In other words, the two operations appropriate for combining parallel and series arcs in Figure 5.29 are simply $\oplus =$ maximum and $\otimes =$ minimum.

Just as in the case of shortest paths, we can proceed to reduce any

given network using our rules of reduction (which are now formulated in terms of two new operations). For example, suppose that
the maximum capacity path is required from node 1 to node 5 in
the first network of Figure 5.31. We can, in turn, eliminate nodes
2, 3, and 4 from the network, eventually resulting in a single arc of
capacity 6 between nodes 1 and 5. As a matter of fact, a maximum
capacity path from 1 to 5 in the original network does have
capacity 6; no larger capacity can be found for any path joining
these two nodes.

So the reduction technique generalizes to this situation as well.
Note that during the reduction process (Figure 5.31) we ignored
the loop on node 1. (Why?) Moreover, it is easy to trace backwards
in Figure 5.31 to recover an actual maximum capacity path; in this
case, the required path is given by the node sequence 1–2–4–5.
Furthermore, it is also possible to set up a system of equations,
now linear in the two new operations, and solve them as before –
thus producing the maximum capacity paths from node 1 to all
other nodes of the network.

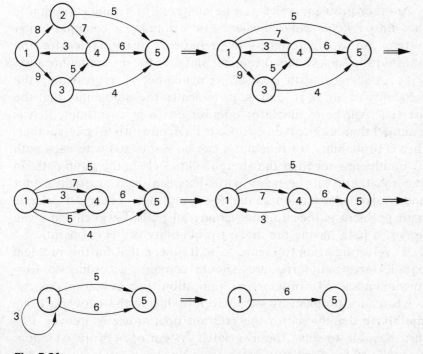

Fig. 5.31

In addition, the usual labeling algorithms discussed in Part I can be suitably modified for the current problem of finding maximum capacity paths. The following procedure will eventually produce labels $d(i)$ representing the maximum capacity of a path from node 1 to node i; in this procedure, c_{ij} represents the capacity of arc (i, j) in the network.

Modified label correcting procedure:

1. Label the origin 1 with $d(1) = \infty$. Set $d(j) = -\infty$ for $j \neq 1$.
2. For each arc (i, j), perform the labeling

$$d(j) \leftarrow \max\{d(j), \min[c_{ij}, d(i)]\}.$$

3. Continue until there are no changes in the current labels.

Notice that once the final labels have been found, it is possible to trace out a maximum capacity path to any node by working backwards from that node. Alternatively, it is possible to use a predecessor index which is continually updated (whenever a label is changed) and which upon termination of the algorithm will define a tree containing maximum capacity paths from the origin node.

Another problem which can be analyzed in a similar fashion is the *most reliable path problem*. For example, a communication system can be represented by a network using nodes for the transmitting (or switching) centers, and arcs for the communication links. Associated with each arc is a number p_{ij} representing the reliability of arc (i, j); that is, p_{ij} indicates the probability that the arc (i, j) will be available or operating at a given instant. If it is assumed that arc breakdowns occur independently of one another, then a probability (or reliability) can be associated with each path by multiplying together the arc reliabilities along the given path. In general, there will be many paths between a given origin center and a given destination center for a message. The most reliable path problem is then to find, among all paths between the given nodes, a path having the highest probability of being operative.

By referring again to Figure 5.29, it is seen that for this problem parallel arcs and series arcs should combine according to $\oplus = $ maximum and $\otimes = $ ordinary multiplication. Just as before, one can solve such a problem by successively reducing the network, using the above definitions for the relevant operations. Moreover, it is also possible to solve the associated system of network equations to find the most reliable paths from an origin node to all other nodes. Alternatively, it is easy to modify existing techniques to obtain a label correcting procedure for the most reliable path problem.

Modified label correcting procedure:

1. Label the origin node 1 with $d(1) = 1$. Set $d(j) = -\infty$ for $j \neq 1$.
2. For each arc (i, j) perform the labeling

$$d(j) \leftarrow \max \{d(j), p_{ij}d(i)\}.$$

3. Continue until there are no changes in the current labels.

The above procedure will upon termination produce values for the $d(j)$ which give the greatest reliability of any path from node 1 to node j. To illustrate the procedure, consider the network of Figure 5.32. We will find most reliable paths from the origin node 1 in this network. To begin, all nodes are given the label $-\infty$, except for node 1, which has 1 as its label. Consider next the arc $(1, 2)$; the label $d(2)$ can be improved (increased) to $d(2) = 1(0.8) = 0.8$. Using the arc $(1, 3)$, node 3 can be relabeled with $d(3) = 0.9$. Continuing in this manner to relabel nodes, we eventually reach the situation where no node label can be further improved. These labels $d(i)$ are given by

$$d(1) = 1.0, \qquad d(2) = 0.8, \qquad d(3) = 0.9,$$
$$d(4) = 0.72, \qquad d(5) = 0.8, \qquad d(6) = 0.72,$$
$$d(7) = 0.36.$$

For example, the most reliable path from 1 to 7 passes through nodes 1, 2, 5, 4, 6, 7 and has a reliability $= d(7) = 0.36$.

A final type of problem to be discussed in this section can be illustrated by the following chessboard example. Suppose one places a knight at the lower left square of the chessboard shown in

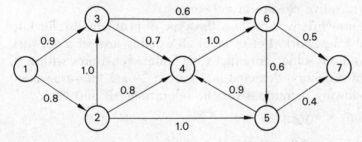

Fig. 5.32

START   FINISH

Fig. 5.33

Figure 5.33. The knight of course moves in an L-shaped fashion (two squares in one direction, and one in the perpendicular direction). If the knight is not allowed to land on any of the shaded squares, is it possible to describe a series of moves so that the knight ends up at the lower right square? More generally, which squares can the knight visit, starting from the lower left position?

Underlying this problem is a network the nodes of which correspond to (unshaded) squares and the arcs of which correspond to single moves of the knight. The first question above then translates into the following: is there a path in the network from the START node to the FINISH node? Likewise, the second chessboard question has the network analogue: what nodes are accessible from the START node? The questions are really problems of determining the transitive closure (relative to a given node) in a certain network. Recall, in this connection, the first two problems discussed in Section 5.23; those problems were also ones pertaining to accessibility and transitive closure in networks.

We shall now briefly show how this type of problem also fits into our general framework. Let us label all existing arcs of a network with a 1, and any other potential (but nonexistent) arcs with a 0. The rules of reduction depicted in Figure 5.29 are then translated into the following definitions for the operations $\oplus$ and $\otimes$:

$$0 \oplus 0 = 0, \qquad 0 \otimes 0 = 0,$$
$$0 \oplus 1 = 1, \qquad 0 \otimes 1 = 0,$$
$$1 \oplus 1 = 1, \qquad 1 \otimes 1 = 1.$$

For example, $0 \otimes 1 = 0$ conveys the requirement that a nonexistent arc in series with an existing arc does not produce an existing arc between the two nodes. The above definitions for $\oplus$ and $\otimes$ actually correspond to operations in the 'two-element Boolean algebra' – an important mathematical structure for analyzing electrical networks. The essential point here is that again one can find two essential operations that specify the given problem.

The previous reduction procedures and solution methods for linear systems are also applicable in the present case. Perhaps the simplest technique for systematically determining 'accessibility' is a modification of the label setting technique for shortest paths.

Modified label setting procedure:

1. Label the origin node 1.
2. Label any unlabeled node which is at the end of an arc from a labeled node.
3. Continue until no more new labels are possible.

Upon termination of this procedure, all labeled nodes correspond to those nodes accessible (reachable by a path) from the origin node 1. The unlabeled nodes cannot be reached from node 1. We shall now apply this procedure to our chessboard example, with one slight modification: namely, instead of using a single symbol to label each node, we shall label the origin node with a '0', all (unlabeled) nodes at the end of an arc from a '0' node will be labeled with a '1', and so forth. To illustrate this, we return to Figure 5.33. Instead of explicitly writing out the underlying network, labels will be directly attached to the squares of this figure. To begin, the lower left node is labeled with 0. As it turns out, only one node can be labeled 1 from here, while three nodes can be labeled 2 from the node labeled 1. This procedure is continued until no further labels can be added, with the final labels indicated in Figure 5.34.

Therefore, since the FINISH node is labeled with a 7, we know that the lower right corner can be reached in seven moves. The reason for using successive integers as labels is now becoming clear, since these labels can now be used to trace out a path from START to FINISH. More explicitly, working backwards from the circled 7, we must have been able to reach this square from a square labeled 6; this square is now itself circled. Continuing in this fashion, we eventually reach the START node and in the process we have identified a path from START to FINISH. Thus,

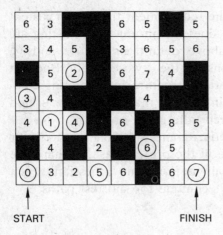

START   FINISH

Fig. 5.34

by following the circled numbers a knight can make the required journey.

In addition, since all squares except one are eventually labeled, we can say that every square except that particular one is reachable from the START position. We have shown, therefore, that it is *impossible* to reach this one (unlabeled) square from the lower left corner. The fact that we can make such a definite statement about the impossibility of a particular type of journey serves to point out the value of labeling methods in resolving a combinatorial problem.

5.26 Nearly optimal paths

Another type of network problem that is especially important in analyzing transportation networks will be discussed in this section. To begin, the basic methodological approaches for finding *nearly optimal paths* will be described and illustrated. In addition, the use of these concepts will be discussed in relation to real-world modeling problems.

In order to focus more clearly on the problem of nearly optimal paths, consider the simple four-node network of Figure 5.35. Suppose we are interested in alternative ways of sending goods from location 1 to location 4 in this network; that is, we are interested in examining paths from 1 to 4. There are numerous paths

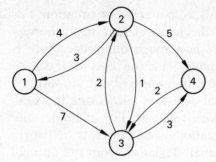

Fig. 5.35

between the given nodes including the following:

Path	Node sequence	Length
P_1	1–2–3–4	8
P_2	1–2–4	9
P_3	1–3–4	10
⋮	⋮	⋮
P_9	1–3–2–4	14
⋮	⋮	⋮

As is easily verified, path P_1 is a shortest path from 1 to 4; in other words, P_1 is a path having the shortest length from node 1 to node 4 in the network. Similarly, path P_2 is a path having the second shortest length, while path P_3 is a path having the third shortest length. Also, path P_9 (as it turns out) is a path having the seventh shortest length among all paths extending from node 1 to node 4.

More generally, a *k*th *shortest path* between two nodes in a network is defined to be a path having the *k*th shortest length between the two nodes. The problem of finding 'nearly optimal paths' – which this section addresses – is precisely that of finding *k*th shortest paths in a given network. This sort of problem arises in several different types of situations; in fact, the use of nearly optimal paths is especially relevant to assessing and making more realistic a given mathematical model.

To be specific, the calculation of nearly optimal paths allows one to conduct a form of sensitivity analysis in a network situation. For example, the difference between the shortest and next shortest path lengths gives an indication of how much difference there is between 'optimality' and 'suboptimality' – i.e. the 'cost' of less than optimal decision making. In addition, the sensitivity of the shortest path's length to possibly suboptimal decisions allows one to assess how good one's model of a network really is. For example, one sometimes models a continuous situation using a discrete (network) approximation. In this context, a small deviation from the optimal sequence of decisions should not cause a disproportionate change in the length of a shortest path. If a large difference between the shortest path length and the next shortest path lengths is observed (and if one does not expect on intuitive grounds this to be the case), then an indication is given that possibly the given model is *too* discrete; that is, a finer approximation to the continuous phenomenon being studied may be warranted. This type of valuable information can be conveyed if it is possible and practical to calculate nearly optimal (kth shortest) paths in the underlying network.

Another use of nearly optimal paths arises when one is interested in not just a single best path, but rather several good paths. Put in another way, one may well be interested in a class of good solutions, and not just the best. In the traffic assignment example discussed at the end of this section, the need for a number of *alternative* good routes for vehicular traffic is required and calculation of kth shortest paths appears appropriate.

One further use of nearly optimal paths can be seen in the construction of mathematical models, which often simplify the true complexity of an actual system. Thus, there are sometimes additional constraints on the problem, which for the sake of simplicity and tractability have not been included in the current formulation. As an example, it may turn out that the calculated shortest path in a network is simply unavailable at the time it is needed, and so an alternative route must be sought. In fact, this alternative route can be sought among the second, third, ... shortest paths between the required origin and destination. One instance of this can be seen in the street network of Figure 5.36, where the shortest path A–B–F from junction A to junction F involves a left-hand turn; if such a left-hand turn is prohibited, then the path A–B–C–D–E–B–F provides an alternative (albeit longer) path which does obey this additional constraint.

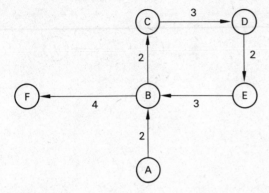

Fig. 5.36

The network of Figure 5.36 also provides an instance where the second shortest path contains a cycle. Because there are instances where paths with embedded cycles are admissible and because it is computationally more difficult to include only simple paths, we shall allow a kth shortest path to return to the same node twice. Thus, there are in general an infinite number of paths that are candidates for kth shortest paths! How then are we to determine kth shortest paths systematically and efficiently? That is, we need a method which is systematic, in the sense of allowing us to remember which paths have – as well as which have not – been examined already. In addition, the method should be efficient, in the sense of requiring us to explore only a small, finite number of possibilities out of the infinite number of paths that are available.

In order to find such methods, let us return (once again) to our rules of reduction in Figure 5.29. In this case, the objects a and b are not single scalar quantities, but are in fact k-vectors of numbers. After all, we are interested in not simply the length of a shortest path, but that of a second, third, ..., kth shortest path, and so it is not unreasonable to work with a 'bundle' of k items of information now. Accordingly, we will write

$$a = (a_1, a_2, \ldots, a_k), \qquad a_1 < a_2 < \cdots < a_k,$$

where the a_i are scalars. Moreover, if we think about how parallel arcs should combine in the case of kth shortest paths, it becomes clear that the operation $\oplus$ should have the effect of selecting the k shortest lengths out of $a_1, \ldots, a_k, b_1, \ldots, b_k$; that is, $a \oplus b = c$ means that c_j is the jth smallest element among $\{a_1, \ldots, a_k, b_1, \ldots, b_k\}$. Likewise, 'multiplication' of series arcs

(a)

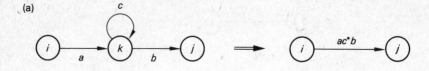

(b)

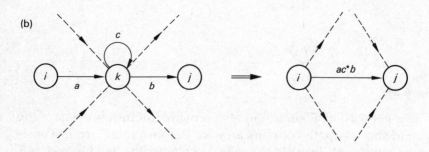

Fig. 5.37   (a) Generalized rule 2. (b) Rule of superposition.

should have the effect of selecting the k smallest composite paths from i to j that pass through some intermediate node; that is, $a \otimes b = c$ means that c_j is the jth smallest element among $\{a_s + b_t : s, t = 1, \ldots, k\}$.

In addition to these two basic rules for combining parallel and series arcs, we also need a more general version of Rule 2. Since loops on nodes cannot now be ignored, Figure 5.37(a) shows how series arcs can be combined in the presence of loops. In this case, the designation c^* represents the effect of going around the loop any number of (including zero) times. It is also possible to express c^* in terms of the operations $\oplus$ and $\otimes$ (now abbreviated to $+$ and juxtaposition):

$$c^* = e + c + c^2 + c^3 + \cdots,$$

where $e = (0, \infty, \ldots, \infty)$ has the effect of including the empty path (zero traversals of the loop). For example, if $k = 3$ and $c = (3, \infty, \infty)$, then

$$c^* = (0, \infty, \infty) + (3, \infty, \infty) + (3, \infty, \infty)(3, \infty, \infty) + \cdots$$
$$= (0, \infty, \infty) + (3, \infty, \infty) + (6, \infty, \infty) + \cdots$$
$$= (0, 3, 6).$$

The rule of superposition, which allows us to combine simultaneously all arcs entering a node with all arcs leaving a node, is also applicable here; *see* Figure 5.37(b). We are now just about ready to begin reducing networks using these rules. The only missing item concerns how to assign initial k-vectors to each arc. This is done in a straightforward fashion by assigning to arc (i, j) having length a_{ij} the k-vector

$$(a_{ij}, \infty, \infty, \ldots, \infty) \equiv (a_{ij}).$$

Here, as a shorthand device, we have chosen to abbreviate k-vectors by only listing their noninfinite components.

By using these rules of reduction we can find the $k = 4$ shortest path lengths from node 1 to node 4 in the network of Figure 5.35. As an illustration, Figure 5.38 shows this reduction process applied to the original network, where nodes 2 and 3 are successively eliminated. Note that in the elimination of node 3, the generalized

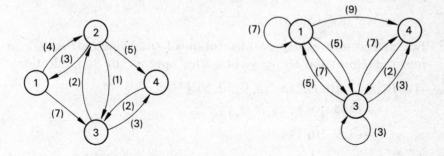

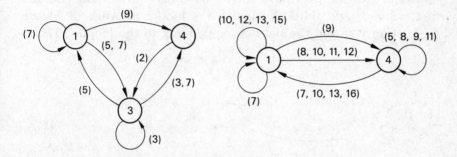

Fig. 5.38

second rule is used in producing the 4-vectors:

$$(5, 7)(3)^*(3, 7) = (8, 10, 11, 12),$$
$$(5, 7)(3)^*(5) = (10, 12, 13, 15),$$
$$(2)(3)^*(3, 7) = (5, 8, 9, 11),$$
$$(2)(3)^*(5) = (7, 10, 13, 16).$$

As a result of these manipulations, we have reduced the original problem to a two-node problem. The final step that remains is to produce the solution to a two-node problem, such as the one depicted in Figure 5.39; in our particular case,

$$a = (8, 9, 10, 11),$$
$$b = (7, 10, 13, 16),$$
$$c = (7, 10, 12, 13),$$
$$d = (5, 8, 9, 11).$$

While not immediately obvious, it can be shown that the k shortest path lengths from i to j in Figure 5.39 are given by

$$L_{ij} = c^*a(d + bc^*a)^*.$$

For the present example, substitution of the values for a, b, c, d into the expression above yields, after appropriate simplification,

$$L_{14} = (7, 10, 12, 13)^*(8, 9, 10, 11)[\cdots]^*$$
$$= (8, 9, 10, 11)(5, 8, 9, 11)^*$$
$$= (8, 9, 10, 11).$$

Thus, it is claimed that the $k = 4$ shortest path lengths from 1 to 4 in the original network are 8, 9, 10, and 11, respectively. As a matter of fact, our previously identified paths P_1, P_2, and P_3 are the first, second, and third shortest paths in the network of Figure 5.35. (Can you find the path corresponding to the length 11?)

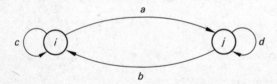

Fig. 5.39

The above calculation of kth shortest path lengths, while straightforward, has been somewhat tedious. A more effective method of solution can be found by exploiting the analogy between solving network problems and solving systems of linear equations. As before, let us associate a 'variable' x_i with each node i of Figure 5.35. In the present situation, x_i represents a k-vector of path lengths from node 1 to node i. The following network equations are obtained in the usual way:

$$x_1 = (3)x_2 + (0),$$
$$x_2 = (4)x_1 + (2)x_3,$$
$$x_3 = (7)x_1 + (1)x_2 + (2)x_4,$$
$$x_4 = (5)x_2 + (3)x_3.$$

Note that in the above, $(3) = (3, \infty, \infty, \infty)$ and so forth. In addition, since the empty path always exists from node 1 to itself, we had better include $(0) = (0, \infty, \infty, \infty)$ on the right-hand side of the equation for x_1.

Let us try to solve the above system iteratively, with the initial approximation

$$x_1^{(0)} = (0, \infty, \infty, \infty) = (0),$$
$$x_j^{(0)} = (\infty, \infty, \infty, \infty) = (\cdot), \qquad j \neq 1.$$

At iteration 1, we obtain

$$x_1^{(1)} = (3)(\cdot) + (0) = (0),$$
$$x_2^{(1)} = (4)(0) + (2)(\cdot) = (4),$$
$$x_3^{(1)} = (7)(0) + (1)(\cdot) + (2)(\cdot) = (7),$$
$$x_4^{(1)} = (5)(\cdot) + (3)(\cdot) = (\cdot).$$

Continuing in this way, we obtain at the second iteration

$$x_1^{(2)} = (3)(4) + (0) = (0, 7),$$
$$x_2^{(2)} = (4)(0) + (2)(7) = (4, 9),$$
$$x_3^{(2)} = (7)(0) + (1)(4) + (2)(\cdot) = (5, 7),$$
$$x_4^{(2)} = (5)(4) + (3)(7) = (9, 10).$$

This process is continued until convergence is obtained (*see* Table 5.3) at the sixth iteration. At that point, we have found (last column of Table 5.3) the $k = 4$ shortest path lengths from node 1 to all nodes of the network. In order to recover the paths that

Table 5.3

	Iteration				
x_i	0 1	2	3	4	5 = 6
x_1	(0) (0)	(0, 7)	(0, 7, 12)	(0, 7, 10, 12)	(0, 7, 10, 12)
x_2	(·) (4)	(4, 9)	(4, 7, 9, 11)	(4, 7, 9, 11)	(4, 7, 9, 10)
x_3	(·) (7)	(5, 7)	(5, 7, 10, 11)	(5, 7, 8, 10)	(5, 7, 8, 10)
x_4	(·) (·)	(9, 10)	(8, 9, 10, 14)	(8, 9, 10, 12)	(8, 9, 10, 11)

correspond to these lengths, it is useful to label the network with the k-vectors of path lengths just obtained, as done in Figure 5.40. Suppose we are interested in finding one of the $k = 4$ shortest paths from node 1 to node 4. In this task, we are aided by the following important results.

Theorem *Any subpath of a shortest path is also a shortest path (between its respective origin and destination).*

Proof Suppose a shortest path P from node A to node D passes through node B and node C, as shown in Figure 5.41. We need to show that the subpath P_0 of P extending from B to C is also a shortest path between these two nodes. Assume, to the contrary, that this is not the case: i.e. P_0 is not a shortest path from B to C. Thus, if Q_0 is a shortest path from B to C, then Q_0 has a smaller

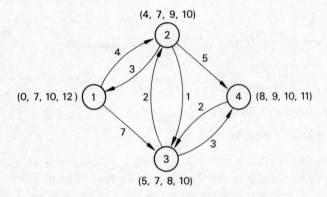

Fig. 5.40

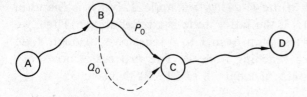

Fig. 5.41

length than P_0. But the path Q which follows path P from A to B, then follows Q_0 from B to C, and finally follows P from C to D would therefore have a smaller total length than path P, contradicting the fact that P is a shortest path. As a result, then, the subpath P_0 must be a shortest path (from B to C) in the network. ■

The above result forms the basis, in one way or another, for all shortest path algorithms. The following result (which can be proved in a similar way) generalizes the theorem above to the case of kth shortest paths.

Extension *Any subpath of a kth shortest path is a tth shortest path for* $1 \leqslant t \leqslant k$.

This latter result allows us to trace out kth shortest *paths* from the vectors of kth shortest path *lengths* that have been already found. Namely, suppose a kth shortest path P is required from node 1 to node n; let l denote the length of path P. Now, if j denotes the penultimate node on path P – i.e. arc (j, n) is the final arc of this path – then by the above result the subpath P_0 of P extending from 1 to j is a tth shortest path from 1 to j, with $1 \leqslant t \leqslant k$. Hence, $l - a_{jn}$ must be a tth shortest path length from 1 to j, where a_{jn} denotes the length of arc (j, n). In other words, $l - a_{jn}$ must appear as a length on the k-vector for node j. By repeating this procedure, we can eventually trace out the required path.

For example, in order to trace out a 4th shortest path of length 11 from node 1 to node 4 in Figure 5.40, we first calculate the values $l - a_{jn} = 11 - a_{j4}$ for all arcs $(j, 4)$:

$$11 - 5 = 6, \qquad j = 2,$$
$$11 - 3 = 8, \qquad j = ③.$$

Since 6 is not found in the k-vector for node 2, but 8 is found in the k-vector for node 3, the latter node is circled above. Thus, we know that a 4th shortest path from 1 to 4 must pass through node 3 immediately before reaching node 4. The process is now continued by finding a path of length 8 ($=11-3$) to node 3:

$$8-2=6, \qquad j=4,$$
$$8-7=1, \qquad j=1,$$
$$8-1=7, \qquad j=②.$$

The next node, occurring immediately before node 3, must be node 2 since 7 occurs in the k-vector for node 2. The process is successively repeated until the origin node 1 is reached with $l=0$. The details of this procedure are spelled out in Table 5.4. From the calculations in this table, it is seen (using the circled nodes read in reverse order) that the 4th shortest path of length 11 from node 1 to node 4 is given by the node sequence 1–2–3–2–3–4. Note that this path is not simple.

The above procedure is perfectly general and can be used to retrieve actual paths in the network, when desired. The essential point to be made here is that such paths can be easily constructed from the path length information contained in the calculated k-vectors. Moreover, if there are several paths having the same length, they can also be found using this procedure; in such a case, there will be several circled nodes occurring at some step of the procedure shown in Table 5.4.

The final portion of this section discusses how the calculation of kth shortest paths finds application in the realm of transportation networks. In this application, a network is used to model the macroscopic movement of vehicular traffic (e.g. autos, buses, subways). More specifically, a node now represents the centroid of a

Table 5.4

---

11 ④	$11-5=6$					
	$11-3=8$ ③	$8-2=6$				
		$8-7=1$				
		$8-1=7$ ②	$7-4=3$			
			$7-2=5$ ③	$5-2=3$		
				$5-7=-2$		
				$5-1=4$ ②	$4-2=2$	
					$4-4=0$ ①	

---

geographical zone; all traffic emanating from or entering a given zone is assumed to be generated from or attracted to the centroid of that zone. An arc may represent, for example, a main road along which such traffic flows.

The general scope of the *transportation planning process* (used by municipal, state, and federal planning agencies) is to develop long-range transportation plans and alternatives for a given area. The types of questions that have to be addressed in this process include:

(a) *How much traffic*? That is, what will be the magnitude of traffic needing to use the transportation system in (say) 15 years, according to different traffic modes (e.g. autos, buses)?

(b) *How distributed*? That is, how is the total traffic by modes distributed according to the various origin/destination pairs?

(c) *Which systems*? That is, which of several proposed transportation systems will best serve the predicted travel patterns?

In this last category, one finds the important phase called *traffic assignment*, which is used to describe the anticipated traffic flow patterns. This phase makes extensive use of shortest path procedures and has provided a practical (and important) stimulus to the study of efficient shortest path routines. The basic tenet that guides (at least to a first approximation) this study of traffic patterns is that in an 'equilibrium' situation, no driver of a vehicle can reduce his travel time by choosing a new route; that is, he will travel by (in some sense) a shortest path between his origin and destination.

A simple way of assigning traffic to a network is called the 'all-or-nothing' assignment method. This method proceeds by first calculating shortest path trees from each centroid and then loading onto the network vehicle trips between the origin centroid and all other centroids. Thus, all forecasted traffic which will travel between an origin and destination (estimated in resolving question (b) above) is assumed to travel by a *single* shortest path between those nodes. Once the loading process has been done for each node as a base centroid, the entire traffic has been loaded onto the given system and traffic flows are established.

Certainly, this assignment procedure (which assigns *all* traffic between a given origin and destination to a single path) is only a crude first approximation to reality, and several modifications to this technique have been made. One way to improve the realism of this assignment procedure is through the use of *multiple* paths between a given origin and destination; that is, if one could find a class of good paths between the origin and destination, one could assign traffic to a number of paths and not just one designated as the 'shortest'. In this way, the excessive congestion that often results with an all-or-nothing assignment (arcs with small traversal times will be quickly overloaded) can be reduced, and a further touch of realism can be added (not every driver has the same criterion for what constitutes a shortest path). Therefore, the calculation of nearly optimal paths can find a ready application to this portion of the transportation planning process.

It should be pointed out that once the traffic assignment phase has been completed, the testing out of alternative transportation systems can then proceed. Different transportation designs and policies can therefore be tested using a network model with calculated traffic flows. This application clearly points out the essence of mathematical modeling: namely, it is much, much easier to test modifications on a mathematical model than to construct actual large-scale transportation systems in order to assess the appropriateness of various options. Even when the underlying model is only (as it sometimes is) a rather crude approximation to reality, it can provide valuable (and relatively inexpensive) information about the consequences of alternative policy decisions.

Problems

1. In the communications example shown in Figure 5.42, we seek a path from A to B that has the greatest probability of being operative (link reliabilities are shown in the figure).

    (a) Find the most reliable path from A to B, using the network reduction technique.

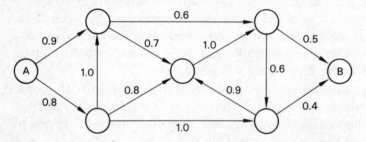

Fig. 5.42

(b) Find the most reliable path from A to B, this time using the modified label correcting technique.

2. Consider the network shown in Figure 5.43.

(a) Find all $k = 3$ shortest path lengths from node 1 to all nodes in this network. (Use the iterative, linear equation procedure.)

(b) Find all *paths* corresponding to the three shortest path lengths, found in (a), from node 1 to node 5.

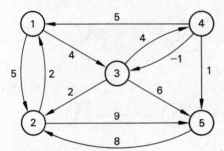

Fig. 5.43

Random networks Suppose we have a network G with n nodes. Associated with each arc (i, j) of G is a *probability* α of traversal: that is, the probability of reaching node j directly from node i. Typically, the probabilities on all arcs leaving a given node sum to 1. In addition, a *length* (or time delay) A is associated with each arc.

In the example below (Figure 5.44), the three nodes represent the types of weather observed on any given day in a particular city: W (wet), S (sunny), or C (cold). The probability α and length A are shown as the pair (α, A) on each arc. For example, the long-run probability of a sunny day following a cold day is shown as 0.35. (Note that all lengths are 1 in this example.)

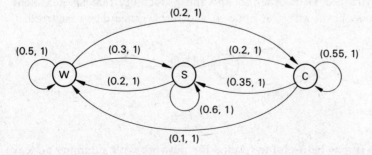

Fig. 5.44

We are interested in calculating two characteristics of such networks:

(a) the probability of eventually reaching one node (say n) from another node (say 1);

(b) the average path length (time delay) required for the journey from 1 to n, given that we have indeed arrived at node n.

3. *Rules of reduction.* Find an equivalent expression for each of the series/parallel situations shown in Figure 5.45.

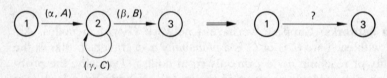

Fig. 5.45

Note: In the expressions (δ, D) to be found above, δ represents the probability of traversing the arc or path, and D is the conditional average length of the arc or path (a weighted average path length, with weights summing to 1).

4. Apply the rules of reduction to the network in Figure 5.46 (where all arc lengths are 1) in order to find the probability that an item sent from node 1 will arrive at node 4, and the average delay incurred.

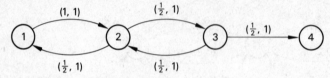

Fig. 5.46

Hint: It may be useful to 'prefix' the network with a dummy node x and dummy arc (having probability $= 1$, length $= 0$), obtaining the form

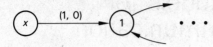

Fig. 5.47

shown in Figure 5.47. Equivalently, then, you can reduce the network to one involving nodes x and 4 only.

5. The problem formulated in Problem 4 is sometimes more colorfully described as the 'drunkard's walk'. An individual begins at lamppost 1 (the tavern) and wishes to arrive at lamppost 4 (home). However, considering his inebriated state, when the drunkard is at some inter-mediate lamppost i, he is just as likely to go backward (to $i-1$) as forward (to $i+1$). In Problem 4, you should have discovered that under these circumstances the drunkard will eventually (with probabil-ity 1) reach home, but after an average delay of nine time units.

(a) Find the average delay for the analogous situation when there are five lampposts.

(b) Can you suggest a general formula for the average delay when there are n lampposts?

6 Mathematical models for computer data communication

ALAN G KONHEIM *IBM Thomas J. Watson Research Center*

6.1 What is data communications?

The field of computer communications has witnessed rapid growth and technological innovations in recent years. By the term *computer communications* we loosely imply a variety of user-to-computer, or computer-to-computer interfaces realized by communication links. They range from various forms of *teleprocessing* seen in today's data processing industry, *time-sharing systems* between collections of terminals and central computers, to the burgeoning *computer-to-computer communication networks* typified by the AR-PANET. A number of books and articles have been written on various aspects of this increasingly important subject area. The reader is referred, for example, to books by Abramson and Kuo [2], Chu [20], Davies and Barber [33], Green and Lucky [52], Grimsdale and Kuo [55], Martin [105], and articles by Green and Tang [53], Schwartz, Boorstyn, and Pickholtz [137] among many others.

With the increasing complexity and sophistication of computer communication systems, *modeling and performance evaluation* is becoming one of the critical issues in the design and operation of such systems. It is apparent that for a cost-effective design we must be equipped with systematic methods of predicting quantitative relations between system resource parameters, system workloads, and measures of system performance. Any computer communication system is, in essence, composed of an organized collection of resources – hardware, software, and combinations thereof – which are usually shared by multiple users, messages, or processes. The shareable resources are, for instance, communication links, computational resources of remotely located computers, file systems, and data bases in a distributed system.

The communication links are a major cost component in a data transmission system. In addition to the conventional multiplexing methods, such as frequency-division multiplexing (FDM) and synchronous time-division multiplexing (STDM), a number of new forms of channel-sharing have been proposed to achieve more efficient and flexible usage of communication media by a large number of terminal-based users. The most successful development in this direction is a random-access multiplexing method which has been devised and implemented by the ALOHA system project at the University of Hawaii (*see* Abramson [1], Kuo and Binder [99]). This multiplexing technique, known as the *ALOHA technique* or ALOHA channel, is particularly suited to a packet communication system which uses a radio or satellite channel. Another form of statistical and dynamic sharing of a channel is the asynchronous time-division multiplexing (ATDM) technique studied by Chu [21, 22], Rudin [134], and others.

Multiplexing of a central computer is the key idea of time-sharing systems, which have grown tremendously in their number and sophistication within the last decade. Many of today's computing systems which support the teleprocessing applications are quite complicated: they are often multiprogrammed virtual-storage systems. More frequently than not, a teleprocessing system is one of the many application subsystems built on a common machine and operating system. Scheduling and allocation of resources of a central processing system (not just the sharing of CPU time, but sharing of all of the system resources including memory, auxiliary storage, devices, and supporting hardware) is certainly a major component in any computer communication system. Modeling of a computer system/subsystem has been pursued by a great number of people, and recent results on analytic models are found, for example, in Kleinrock [78], Kobayashi [86], and in a number of references cited therein.

The most recent development in computer communications is the increasing interest and development efforts found in *intercomputer-communication nets* such as the ARPANET and its descendents. In a computer network the primary resources to be shared are geographically separated computers (often called *host* computers), the program library, and data bases attached to them. In order to support efficient and flexible sharing of these resources, such novel techniques as message-switching and packet-switching multiplexing have been introduced, at the expense of additional complexity of system structure: that is, a set of message-switching processors (called interface message processors or IMPs) now constitute the highest level of the network below which groups of hosts exist and are attached to the corresponding IMPs. As a consequence, buffer spaces of the individual IMPs, as well as message-switching processors themselves and communication links connected to them, contribute to the list of critical resources to be considered in the design and operation of the network.

Whenever there is a sharing of a scarce resource, contention for the resource will arise. Flows of messages or data generated by user terminals, multiplexors, concentrators, or by host computers, are not steady streams. On the contrary, occurrences of messages are often sporadic and bursty. The amount of resource usage demanded by the messages or processes is often unpredictable and consequently is viewed as stochastic in nature; for example, the length of messages or data to be transferred or stored; the time required in processing transactions; the amount of main memory or buffer pool to be allocated to processes. In intercomputer communication nets another dimension is added to the stochastic nature of the workloads, namely the *destination IMPs or hosts* of messages are also assumed to be random variables, and we face such new issues as routing and flow control of messages.

Because of the unpredictable nature of the work demands placed on the resources, congestion occurs (occasionally or frequently depending upon the workload level), queues will be formed, and delays introduced at critical resources. In the performance analysis of a computer communication system/subsystem, we must therefore take these queues into consideration. One of the major issues, which concerns designers of complex information processing systems, is the lack of our capability to predict performance measures such as response time, throughput, and resource utilization. A problem of similar nature will be faced by those who *configurate* (*see* Green and Tang [53]) a system, given a set of candidate components or subsystems, such as communication links of various capacities, central processors of different speeds, memory and buffer storage of different capacities, various types of topologies connecting terminals to local processors. Of course, performance prediction is not the only major technical issue in design of computer communication systems. However, such well discussed issues as routing and flow control, link capacity assignment, concentrator placement, allocation and distribution of data base, are certainly not separable from the performance analysis. The problem of link capacity assignment, for example, has been successfully formulated by Kleinrock [74] and others, as an optimization or mathematical programming problem based on the average delay formula derived from queueing analysis. How to schedule and allocate resources effectively among competing requests is certainly in the realm of congestion or queueing theory in a broader sense. Therefore, it is clear that queueing models provide a basic framework and the mathematical tools for dealing with a large class of system design issues. Several other disciplines of applied mathematics such as graph theory, mathematical programming, optimization techniques, and reliability theory must augment the queueing analysis in order to cope with the overall design and analysis issues. A survey article by Green and Tang [53] addresses a number of the specific technical problems that concern professionals engaged in design, configuration, and maintenance of tele-processing systems.

The intent of this chapter is to review that portion of queueing theory which is relevant to modeling and performance evaluation of computer communication systems and subsystems. Of course there are a number of circumstances in which the currently available techniques cannot provide a satisfactory solution. In such circumstances, a simulation model is often the only viable alternative. Even when a decision is made for simulation, an analytic solution, however crude it may be, should be sought. An analytic model can serve as a guideline in narrowing down a range of system configuration and parameters under which a simulation runs. It also could save a considerable amount of modeling effects, by detecting possible errors introduced in the design and implementation phases of a simulator. There are a large number of books and articles on queueing theory: Bhat [7], Cox and Smith [31], Feller [39], Gnedenko and Kovalenko [48], Kleinrock [79], Newell [113], Riordan [129], and Syski [143]. Due to space limitations, our treatment is not as broad as some readers might wish to see. An extensive bibliography at the end (and the books cited above) will hopefully direct the reader to fundamental and collateral reading.

6.2 Preliminaries

6.2.1 Counting processes

We begin with the notion of a *counting process*. We suppose that at randomly determined times $T_1, T_2, \ldots, T_n, \ldots$ *events* occur. An *event* – within the context of applications to data processing – might be the start of the transmission of a message from a terminal. We denote by N_t the number of events which have occurred in the interval $(0, t]$; it is convenient to set $N_0 = 0$. The function N_t is a nondecreasing (right-continuous) nonnegative-integer-valued random variable defined on some probability space $(\Omega, \mathbf{E}, \text{Pr})$. The family of random variables $\mathbf{N} = \{N_t : 0 \leq t < \infty\}$ is called a *counting process*. If $0 \leq a \leq b$, then the difference $\mathbf{N}_{(a,b]} - N_b - N_a$ is the number of events in the interval $(a, b]$. $N_{(a,b]}$ is called the *increment* of N_t over $(a, b]$. The *principal function* of $\mathbf{N}$, denoted by $\Lambda(t)$, is the expectation $E\{N_t\}$. A counting process may satisfy one of the following properties:

1. *Stationary increments.* If

$$0 \leq a_1 \leq b_1 \leq a_2 \leq b_2 \leq \cdots \leq a_n \leq b_n < \infty,$$

then the two n-dimensional vector-valued random variables

$$(N_{(a_1, b_1]}, \ldots, N_{(a_n, b_n]}), \qquad (N_{(a_1+h, b_1+h]}, \ldots, N_{(a_n+h, b_n+h]})$$

are identically distributed.
2. *Independent increments.* If

$$0 \leq a_1 \leq b_1 \leq a_2 \leq b_2 \leq \cdots \leq a_n \leq b_n < \infty,$$

then the n random variables $\{N_{(a_i, b_i]} : 1 \leq i \leq n\}$ are independent.
3. *Orderliness – absence of after-effects.* $\text{Pr}\{X_{t+h} - X_t > 1\} = o(h)$ as $h \downarrow 0$.

Lemma 6.2.1   *If $f : [0, a) \to [0, \infty)$ is nondecreasing and subadditive*

$$f(x + y) \leq f(x) + f(y) \qquad (0 \leq x, y, x + y < a),$$

then

$$\lim_{x \downarrow 0} f(x)/x = f^*$$

exists with $0 \leq f^* \leq \infty$; $f^* = 0$ if and only if $f(a) = 0$.

Proof   By subadditivity $f(x) \leq mf(x/m)$ for $0 \leq x < a$ and hence

$$\frac{f(x/m)}{x/m} \geq \frac{f(x)}{x}.$$

Thus

$$f^* = \limsup_{h \downarrow 0} f(h)/h \geqslant f(x)/x$$

for every x, $0 \leqslant x < a$. There are two cases to consider.

Case 1: $f^* < \infty$. Given $\varepsilon > 0$, determine $x_0 = x_0(\varepsilon)$ such that $f(x_0)/x_0 > f^* - \varepsilon$. For x in $(0, x_0)$ let m be determined by

$$x_0/m \leqslant x \leqslant x_0/(m - 1).$$

The monotonicity of f then yields

$$\frac{f(x)}{x} \geqslant \frac{f(x_0/m)}{x_0/(m-1)} \geqslant \frac{m-1}{m} \frac{f(x_0)}{x_0} \geqslant (1 - 1/m)(f^* - \varepsilon),$$

which implies

$$\lim_{x \downarrow 0} f(x)/x = f^*.$$

We leave the proof for the case $f^* = \infty$ to the reader. ∎

Define

$$p_k(s, t) = \Pr \{N_{(s, t]} = k\}$$

and

$$\pi_k(s, t) = \Pr \{N_{(s, t]} \geqslant k\}$$

for $k = 0, 1, \ldots$ and $0 \leqslant s \leqslant t < \infty$. If **N** has stationary increments, the functions $p_k(s, t)$ and $\pi_k(s, t)$ depend only the *difference* $t - s$ and in this case we write $p_k(t - s) = p_k(s, t)$ and $\pi_k(t - s) = \pi_k(s, t)$.

Theorem 6.2.2 *If* **N** *has stationary increments, then*

$$\lim_{t \downarrow 0} t^{-1} \pi_1(t) = \lambda$$

with $0 \leqslant \lambda \leqslant \infty$. λ *is called the* rate *of the counting process.*

Proof Since the random variable N_t is nondecreasing in t, it follows that $\pi_1(t)$ is likewise nondecreasing in t. If $p_0(t) = 1$ (for all t) the counting process **N** is degenerate and the above limit clearly exists with $\lambda = 0$. If **N** is not degenerate then a t_0 exists with $\pi_1(t_0) > 0$. But

$$\{N_{t_1 + t_2} \geqslant 1\} \cup \{N_{t_1} \geqslant 1\} \supseteq \{N_{(t_1, t_1 + t_2]} \geqslant 1\},$$

so that by the stationarity of the increments

$$\pi_1(t_1 + t_2) \leqslant \pi_1(t_1) + \pi_1(t_2)$$

and the result now is a consequence of Lemma 6.2.1. ∎

Remark 1 The conclusion of the theorem may be restated in the form

$$\pi_1(t) = \lambda t + o(t)$$

which implies that

$$p_0(t) = 1 - \lambda t + o(t).$$

Remark 2 If **N** is orderly and has stationary increments, then

$$p_k(t) = o(t) \qquad (1 < k < \infty),$$
$$\pi_k(t) = o(t) \qquad (1 < k < \infty),$$

because

$$P(X_{t+\bar{h}} - X_t > 1) = o(h)$$

by orderliness.

so that

$$p_1(t) = \lambda t + o(t).$$

Definition 6.2.3 A Poisson process *is an orderly counting process with stationary and independent increments.*

Theorem 6.2.4 *If* **N** *is a Poisson process with rate* λ *then* $\Lambda(t) = \lambda t$ *and*

$$p_k(t) = (\lambda t)^k e^{-\lambda t}/k! \qquad (0 \leqslant k < \infty).$$

Proof For $h > 0$,

$$p_k(t+h) = \sum_{0 \leqslant j \leqslant k} \Pr\{X_t = j, X_{t+h} - X_t = k - j\}$$

$$= \sum_{0 \leqslant j \leqslant k} \Pr\{X_t = j\} \Pr\{X_{t+h} - X_t = k - j\}$$

$$= \sum_{0 \leqslant j \leqslant k} p_j(t) p_{k-j}(h),$$

the first equality due to the independence of increments and the second due to the stationarity of the increments. Thus

$$[p_k(t+h) - p_k(t)] = \sum_{0 \leqslant j < k} p_j(t) p_{k-j}(h) + [-1 + p_0(h)]p_k(t).$$

Since $p_{k-j}(h) = o(h)$ for $0 \le j < k-1$ and $\pi_1(h) = \lambda h + o(h)$, it follows that $p_1(h) = \lambda h + o(h)$, so that

$$(d/dt)p_k(t) = \begin{cases} -\lambda p_k(t) & \text{if } k = 0, \\ -\lambda p_k(t) + \lambda p_{k-1}(t) & \text{if } 1 \le k < \infty, \end{cases}$$

from which the theorem follows immediately. ∎

Theorem 6.2.5 *If N is orderly with independent increments and if the limit*

$$\lim_{h \downarrow 0} (1/h)p_1(t, t+h) = \lambda(t)$$

exists with $\lambda(t)$ locally Lebesgue integrable, then

$$p_k(t_1, t_2) = \{\Lambda(t_1, t_2)\}^k/k! \, \exp^{-\Lambda(t_1, t_2)}$$

with

$$\Lambda(t_1, t_2) = \int_{t_1}^{t_2} \lambda(u) \, du.$$

We say that $\lambda(t)$ is the instantaneous rate *of the nonstationary Poisson process. The principal function of N is equal to $\Lambda(0, t)$.*

Proof The proof is similar to that of Theorem 6.2.4. Begin by observing that

$$p_k(t_1, t_2 + h) = \sum_{0 \le j \le k} \Pr\{N_{(t_1, t_2]} = j, N_{(t_2, t_2+h]} = k - j\}$$

$$= \sum_{0 \le j \le k} p_j(t_1, t_2)p_{k-j}(t_2, t_2 + h)$$

since **N** has independent increments. Rearranging this equation we obtain

$$[p_k(t_1, t_2 + h) - p_k(t_1, t_2)] = p_k(t_1, t_2)[-1 + p_0(t_1, t_2 + h)]$$

$$+ \sum_{0 \le j < k} p_j(t_1, t_2)p_{k-j}(t_2, t_2 + h).$$

Dividing by h and allowing $h \downarrow 0$,

$$(\partial/\partial t_2)p_k(t_1, t_2) = \begin{cases} -\lambda(t_2)p_0(t_1, t_2) & \text{if } k = 0, \\ \lambda(t_2)[p_{k-1}(t_1, t_2) - p_k(t_1, t_2)] & \text{if } 1 \le k < \infty. \end{cases}$$

$$\tag{6.1}$$

Introduce the generating function $F(z:t_1, t_2)$ of the sequence $\{p_k(t_1, t_2): 0 \le k < \infty\}$,

$$F(z:t_1, t_2) = \sum_{0 \le k < \infty} p_k(t_1, t_2) z^k,$$

which converges in $|z| \le 1$ and is analytic in $|z| < 1$. From (6.1) we deduce that $F(z:t_1, t_2)$ satisfies the partial differential equation

$$(\partial/\partial t_2) F(z:t_1, t_2) = (z-1)\lambda(t_2) F(z:t_1, t_2),$$

from which we may conclude that

$$F(z:t_1, t_2) = C \exp\left[(z-1) \int_{t_1}^{t_2} \lambda(u)\, du \right].$$

Since $p_k(t_1, t_1) = 0$ for $k \neq 0$, we must have $C = 1$. ∎

There is an alternative characterization of the Poisson process which is appropriate to note at this point. If $T_1, T_2, \ldots, T_n, \ldots$ are the times of *events*, let

$$\tau_k = T_k - T_{k-1} \qquad (1 \le k < \infty, T_0 = 0)$$

be the *interevent times*. The statements $\{T_k \le t\}$ and $\{N_t \ge k\}$ are identical. Moreover,

$$\Pr\{t_k \le \tau_k < t_k + dt_k, 1 \le k \le n\}$$
$$\approx \Pr\{N_{(s_{k-1}, s_{k-1}+t_k]} = 0, N_{(s_{k-1}+t_k, s_{k-1}+t_k+dt_k]} = 1, 1 \le k \le n\}, \quad (6.2)$$

where $s_k = (t_1 + dt_1) + \cdots + (t_k + dt_k)$. The probability on the right-hand side of (6.2) is

$$\prod_{1 \le k \le n} [\lambda e^{-\lambda t_k}\, dt_k] \tag{6.3}$$

while the probability on the left-hand side of (6.2) is

$$\prod_{1 \le k \le n} f_k(t_k)\, dt_k, \tag{6.4}$$

where f_k is the density of τ_k. We conclude from (6.3) and (6.4) that the $\{\tau_k : 1 \le k < \infty\}$ are independent and identically distributed with the common *exponential distribution*

$$\Pr\{\tau_k \le t\} = 1 - e^{-\lambda t} \qquad (0 \le t < \infty). \tag{6.5}$$

Finally, from the identity of the events $\{N_t \ge k\}$ and $\{T_k \le t\}$, it follows that

$$(\mathrm{d}/\mathrm{d}t)\,\mathrm{Pr}\,\{T_k \leqslant t\} = (\mathrm{d}/\mathrm{d}t)\,\mathrm{Pr}\,\{\tau_1 + \cdots + \tau_k \leqslant t\}$$
$$= \lambda(\lambda t)^{k-1}/k!\,e^{-\lambda t} \qquad (0 \leqslant t < \infty). \qquad (6.6)$$

Conversely, starting with a sequence $\{\tau_k : 1 \leqslant k < \infty\}$ of independent and identically distributed nonnegative random variables with the exponential distribution and setting

$$T_k = \tau_1 + \cdots + \tau_k,$$

we obtain the Poisson counting process $\mathbf{N}$ of event times $\{T_k\}$.

This construction suggests a generalization of the Poisson process: the *renewal process*. A renewal process is a sequence $\{\tau_k\}$ of nonnegative independent and identically distributed random variables. The $\{\tau_k\}$ are interpreted as the interevent times. The renewal process determines a counting process by defining

$$N_t = \max\,\{k : \tau_1 + \cdots + \tau_k \leqslant t\}.$$

For the Poisson process these interevent times are exponentially distributed and $\Lambda(t) = E\{N_t\} = \lambda t$. For the general renewal process this equality is replaced by the asymptotic result

$$\lim_{t \to 0} (1/t)E\{N_t\} = 1/E\{\tau_1\}.$$

This limit is referred to as the *renewal theorem* [138]. The simpler result

$$\lim_{t \to \infty} N_t/t = 1/E\{\tau_1\}$$

is a direct consequence of the law of large numbers.

Let $\{\mathbf{N}^{(i)} : 1 \leqslant i \leqslant n\}$ be independent Poisson processes with rates $\{\lambda^{(i)}\}$. The counting process

$$\mathbf{N} = \sum \mathbf{N}^{(i)}$$

which counts *all* events

$$N_t = N_t^{(1)} + \cdots + N_t^{(n)}$$

is also a Poisson process with rate $\lambda = \lambda^{(1)} + \cdots + \lambda^{(n)}$. $\mathbf{N}$ is the *join* or *sum* of the individual processes. Conversely, starting with a Poisson process $\mathbf{N}$ of rate λ and a sequence of independent and identically distributed random variables $\{X_k : 1 \leqslant k < \infty\}$,

$$\mathrm{Pr}\,\{X_k = j\} = q_j \qquad (1 \leqslant j \leqslant n),$$

$$q_1 + q_2 + \cdots + q_n = 1,$$

we may *split* $\mathbf{N}$ into n processes $\{\mathbf{N}^{(i)}\}$,

$$\mathbf{N}^{(i)} = \{N_t^{(i)}\}, \qquad N_t^{(i)} = \sum_k \chi_{(T_k \leqslant t)} \chi_{(X_k = i)},$$

where χ_E is the *characteristic* or *indicator* function of the condition E; 1 if the condition holds and 0 otherwise. An event of $\mathbf{N}$ is counted in $\mathbf{N}^{(i)}$ if and only if $X_k = i$. The Poisson process $\mathbf{N}$ is thus *split* into n subprocesses. We leave the details of proof to the reader.

One final extension – let $\mathbf{N}$ be a Poisson process of rate λ. We let $\mathbf{N}$ fix the *times* of events while the number of events will be determined by a second and independent process

$$\mathbf{X} = \{X_k : 1 \leqslant k < \infty\},$$

where $q_j = \Pr\{X_k = j\}$ $(1 \leqslant j < \infty)$. At the time T_k, generated by the Poisson process $\mathbf{N}$, X_k events are recorded. We assume that the $\{X_k\}$ are independent random variables. The superposition of the two random processes $\mathbf{N}$ and $\mathbf{X}$ is the compound process $\mathbf{N}[\mathbf{X}]$. If

$$p_k(t) = \Pr\{N[X]_t = k\},$$

then

$$p_k(t) = \sum_{0 \leqslant j < \infty} \Pr\{N_t = j\} \Pr\{X_1 + \cdots + X_j = k\}, \tag{6.7}$$

so that

$$\sum_{0 \leqslant k < \infty} p_k(t) z^k = \exp^{-\lambda t (1 - \Phi(z))}, \tag{6.8}$$

where

$$\Phi(z) = \sum_{1 \leqslant k < \infty} q_k z^k.$$

6.2.2 Generating functions

Definition 6.2.6 *The generating function of the sequence $\{a_n : 0 \leqslant n < \infty\}$ is the function*

$$A(z) = \sum_{0 \leqslant n < \infty} a_n z^n. \tag{6.9}$$

Remarks The 'series' in (6.9) may be viewed as a 'formal' power series with no notion of convergence required. On the other hand, the great power of generating functions (z-transforms, Laplace transforms) derives from the fact that properties of the sequence $\{a_n\}$ are reflected in the behavior of the function $A(z)$. We shall use generating functions in connection with probability distributions. Thus, if X is a random variable assuming nonnegative integer values with probability distribution

$$p_j = \Pr\{X = j\}$$

then the *generating function* (of the probability distribution) of X is the function

$$P(z) = \sum_{0 \leq j < \infty} p_j z^j. \tag{6.10}$$

The series (6.10) converges *at least* for $|z| \leq 1$ and is analytic *at least* in $|z| < 1$.

The moments of a random variable X with distribution $\{p_k\}$ are expressible in terms of derivatives of the probability generating function. If $E\{X^k\} < \infty$, then $(\mathrm{d}^k/\mathrm{d}z^k)P(z)|_{z=1}$ exists and

$$E\{X(X-1)(X-2) \cdots (X-(r-1))\} = (\mathrm{d}^r/\mathrm{d}z^r)P(z)|_{z=1} \tag{6.11}$$

$$(1 \leq r \leq k).$$

Some examples are as follows:

Example 2.1 Poisson process

$$p_k = \lambda^k e^{-\lambda}/k! \qquad (0 \leq k < \infty);$$
$$P(z) = e^{\lambda(z-1)} \qquad (|z| < \infty).$$

Example 2.2 Geometric distribution

$$p_k = \rho^k(1-\rho) \qquad (0 \leq k < \infty);$$
$$P(z) = (1-\rho)/(1-\rho z) \qquad (|z| < \rho^{-1}).$$

One of the most useful technical theorems in queueing theory is Rouché's theorem [3]. If $f(z)$ and $g(z)$ are analytic in a domain Ω with $|f(z)| < |g(z)|$ on $bd(\Omega)$, then $f(z) - g(z)$ and $g(z)$ have the same number of zeros inside Ω. As an application we prove

Theorem 6.2.7 *If $P(z)$ is the probability generating function (of some nonnegative integer-valued random variable) and w is a complex number of modulus at most 1, then the equation*

$$z^n - wP(z) = 0 \tag{6.12}$$

has n roots, $\theta_1(w), \ldots, \theta_n(w)$ inside the unit disk $\{z: |z| < 1\}$. When $n = 1$, $\theta(w)$ is itself the probability generating function of a nonnegative integer-valued random variable,

$$\theta(w) = \sum_{1 \le n < \infty} w^n/n! \, (d^{n-1}/dz^{n-1}) P^n(z)|_{z=0}. \tag{6.13}$$

If $\mu = (d/dz)P(z)|_{z=1} < 1$, then $\theta(w) \to 1$ as $w \to 1$.

Proof Since $|P(z)| \le P(|z|) \le P(1) = 1$, we have $|wP(z)| < |z^n|$ on the circle $\{z: |z| = 1\}$ and hence, by Rouché's theorem, equation (6.12) has as many roots as z^n has, namely n. Equation (6.13) is a direct consequence of Lagrange's theorem [148]. Finally, if $\theta(w) \to \theta < 1$ as $w \to 1$, then the equation $\psi(z) = z - P(z) = 0$ has two roots $z = 1$ and $z = \theta$. Thus, by Rolle's theorem, the derivative of $\psi(z)$ vanishes at some point z_0 in $(0, 1)$,

$$0 = 1 - (d/dz)P(z)|_{z=z_0},$$

and this implies that

$$1 = (d/dz)P(z)|_{z=z_0} < (d/dz)P(z)|_{z=1} = \mu,$$

which yields a contradiction. ∎

We conclude this section with a brief discussion of so-called *Tauberian* theorems for power series. Let us recall Abel's theorem on the convergence of power series:

Abel's theorem *If $\sum b_n$ converges, then*

$$\lim_{z \to 1} \sum_{0 \le n < \infty} b_n z^n = \sum b_n.$$

Corollary of Abel's theorem *If $a = \lim_{n \to \infty} a_n$, then, by setting $b_n = a_n - a_{n-1}$,*

$$a = \lim_{z \to 1} \sum_{0 \le n < \infty} b_n z^n = \lim_{z \to 1} (1 - z) \sum_{0 \le n < \infty} a_n z^n,$$

so that

$$A(z) = \sum_{0 \le n < \infty} a_n z^n \sim a(1 - z)^{-1}$$

as $z \to 1$.

This is an *Abelian* theorem; it deduces from the behavior of the sequence $\{a_n\}$ at ∞ the behavior of the generating function of $\{a_n\}$

near $z = 1$. Converses of Abelian theorems are called Tauberian theorems. Note that from

$$A(z) \sim a(1-z)^{-1} \quad \text{as} \quad z \to 1$$

one *cannot* conclude that $a_n \to a$. This converse of the Corollary to Abel's theorem is false.

A function L defined on $[0, \infty)$ is *slowly varying* at ∞ if for every fixed x

$$\frac{L(tx)}{L(t)} \to 1 \quad \text{as} \quad t \to \infty.$$

A converse to Abel's theorem is

Theorem 6.2.8 *If L is slowly varying, $a_n \geq 0$ and $A(z)$ converges for $|z| \leq 1$, then*

$$A(z) \sim (1-z)^{-k} L((1-z)^{-1}) \quad \text{as} \quad z \to 1- \tag{6.14}$$

with $0 \leq k < \infty$ is equivalent to

$$\sum_{0 \leq n \leq N} a_n \sim N^k L(N)/\Gamma(k+1) \quad \text{as} \quad N \to \infty, \tag{6.15}$$

where $\Gamma(x)$ is the gamma function

$$\Gamma(x) = \int_0^\infty t^{x-1} e^{-t} \, dt.$$

Moreover, if $\{a_n\}$ is eventually monotonic, (6.12) is equivalent to

$$a_n \sim n^{k-1} L(n)/\Gamma(k) \quad \text{as} \quad n \to \infty. \tag{6.16}$$

Note that a constant is a slowly varying function so that

$$A(z) \sim a/(1-z) \quad \text{as} \quad z \to 1-$$

if and only if

$$(1/N) \sum_{0 \leq n \leq N} a_n \to a \quad \text{as} \quad N \to \infty.$$

Furthermore, if $\{a_n\}$ is (ultimately) monotonic, then $a_n \to a$.

Problems

1. Prove that the *join* of independent Poisson processes is a Poisson process.

2. Prove that the *split* of a Poisson process yields independent Poisson processes.

3. If $\{X_i : 1 \leqslant i \leqslant n\}$ are independent *Bernoulli* random variables

$$\Pr\{X_i = 0\} = 1 - p_n, \qquad \Pr\{X_i = 1\} = p_n \qquad (1 \leqslant i \leqslant n),$$

prove that $S_n = X_1 + \cdots + X_n$ converges in distribution to the Poisson law as $n \to \infty$ if $np_n \to \lambda$.

4. If **N** is Poisson with rate λ, show that the conditional distribution of $T_1, T_2, \ldots, T_n$, given $N_t = n$, is *uniform* on $(0, t]$.

6.3 Exponential systems

In this section we consider the behavior of *exponential service systems* which are used to model data communication networks. The emphasis will be on methods used in obtaining the behavior of the system. A service system is the mathematical model for a system which performs some type of service operation. The simplest example is a checkout counter at a supermarket. Customers arrive at the *service facility* – the checkout counter – and require service from the *server* at this facility. The service facility might consist of several (parallel) checkout counters each provided with a server. Service is usually measured in units of time; the time required to complete the service of a customer.

The main ingredients of a service system are

(i)   the manner by which customers enter the system,
(ii) the amount of service they require,
(iii) the rules by which the facility processes requests.

We describe the entry of customers into the system in terms of an *arrival process* **A** and the amounts of service required by a *service process* **S**. The interaction between customers and servers will be specified by a *service policy* or *queue discipline*. These three items define a service system.

In Figure 6.1 we picture the simplest service system. We shall

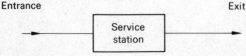

Entrance   Exit

Service
station

Fig. 6.1

assume that customers arrive singly at the facility and let $\mathbf{T} = \{T_k : 1 \leqslant k < \infty\}$ denote their arrival times. The *service time* of the kth customer will be denoted by S_k. The service discipline is *first-come-first-served* or service in order of arrival. We further assume

(i) the arrival times $\mathbf{T}$ constitute a Poisson process of rate λ;

(ii) the service process $\mathbf{S} = \{S_k : 1 \leqslant k < \infty\}$ consists of independent and identically distributed random variables with the common distribution

$$\Pr\{S_k \leqslant t\} = 1 - e^{-\mu t} \qquad (0 \leqslant t < \infty);$$

(iii) the service and arrival processes are independent.

In our applications the *server* will be a transmission channel and the *customer* a message. The customer will present a *service demand* W to the service facility. This demand may have units [bit], [byte], [character], or [packet] depending upon the application. The service facility will process these requests for service at a *service rate* C. The units of C are [bps] (bits per second), [kbps] (kilo bits per second). C is sometimes called the *bandwidth* of the channel or line. The ratio

$$S = \frac{W}{C} \text{ [seconds]}$$

is called the *service time*.

Finally, we must describe the method by which the *system* serves the customers – the *queue discipline*. We shall assume for simplicity that service is 'in order of arrival' (FIFO) – *first-come-first-served*. However, many of the results which we will describe are valid for a larger class of service disciplines called *work-conserving* [75, 148]. A discipline is work-conserving if

(i) the service demand W of each job is not affected by the queue discipline;

(ii) the queue discipline does not take advantage of knowledge about service demands (or times) and/or arrival times of individual jobs;

(iii) the service is not idle when there are jobs waiting for service.

The disciplines

(i) first-come-first-served (FIFO),

(ii) last-come-first-served (LIFO),

(iii) random,
(iv) round-robin (RR),
(v) processor-sharing (PS)

are all examples of work-conserving queue disciplines.

We now turn to the analysis of the queueing system referred to in the literature as the M/M/1 queueing system. The first step is to describe the state of the system. We let X_t denote the number of customers either in service or waiting for service at time t. The important observation is that the *future* X_{t+s} is conditionally independent of the *past* $[X_u : 0 \leq u < t]$ given the *present* X_t:

$$\Pr\{X_{s+t} = k/[X_u : 0 \leq u \leq t]\} = \Pr\{X_{s+t} = k/X_t\}. \tag{6.17}$$

This is the *Markovian property* and $\mathbf{X} = \{X_t : 0 \leq t < \infty\}$ is a *Markov process*. The proof of (6.17) for the M/M/1 system is easy to demonstrate. First, the arrival process is Poisson; hence if τ is the waiting time to the *next* arrival, then τ is exponentially distributed *independent* of how much time has elapsed since the last arrival. Furthermore, if a customer is in service at time t, then the remaining amount of service is also independent of the amount of service already given. Thus at time t the future evolution of the system is independent of what has transpired up to time t given the state X_t.

Let

$$\pi_{i,j}(t) = \Pr\{X_t = j/X_0 = i\} \qquad (0 \leq i, j < \infty, 0 \leq t < \infty),$$

$$\Pi(t) = (\pi_{i,j}(t)).$$

$\pi_{i,j}(t)$ is the *transition* probability of the process $\{X_t\}$. The transition probabilities, $\Pi(t)$, together with an *initial* distribution

$$\xi_i = \Pr\{X_0 = i\} \qquad (0 \leq i < \infty)$$

determine the state probabilities $p_j(t) = \Pr\{X_t = j\}$ according to

$$p_j(t) = \sum_i \xi_i \pi_{i,j}(t). \tag{6.18}$$

Thus the study of a system like the M/M/1 queue requires an examination of the properties of the matrix $\Pi(t)$. Let I denote the identity matrix and consider the limits

$$q_{i,j} = \lim_{t \to 0} t^{-1}[\pi_{i,j}(t) - \delta_{i,j}] \qquad (\delta_{i,j} = \text{Kronecker symbol}), \tag{6.19}$$

$$Q = (q_{i,j}) = \lim_{t \to 0} t^{-1}[\Pi(t) - I]. \tag{6.20}$$

Assume that the limits ((6.19)–(6.20)) exist; it follows that

$$\pi_{i,i}(t) = 1 - q_{i,i}t + o(t) \quad (\text{as } t \to 0), \tag{6.21}$$

$$\pi_{i,j}(t) = q_{i,j}t + o(t) \quad (\text{as } t \to 0) \quad \text{if} \quad i \neq j. \tag{6.22}$$

Note also that

$$q_{i,j} \geq 0, \quad i \neq j, \quad q_{i,i} = -\sum_{j:j \neq i} q_{i,j}. \tag{6.23}$$

The matrix $Q = (q_{i,j})$ is called the *infinitesimal generator* of the Markov process.

The parameters Q have a simple interpretation; the state process $\{X_t\}$ wanders around the state space $S = \{0, 1, 2, \ldots\}$ remaining or *sojourning* in a state for some random amount of time. The *sojourn* time in state i is exponentially distributed:

$$\Pr\{\text{SOJOURN}_i \leq t\} = 1 - \exp(-q_{ii}t).$$

When X_t *leaves* state i it makes a transition to state j with probability $-q_{i,j}/q_{i,i}$. The mathematical details can be found in Cohen [26]. For a *practitioner*, a Markov process (with discrete state space) is really the matrix Q. The matrix is defined in accordance with our understanding of the nature of the physical system. Starting from Q, a Markov process $\{X_t\}$ can be constructed having Q as the infinitesimal generator.

For the M/M/1 system the matrix Q is

$$q_{i,j} = \begin{cases} -[\lambda + \mu\chi_{(i>0)}] & \text{if} \quad j = i, \\ \lambda & \text{if} \quad j = i+1, \\ \mu\chi_{(i>0)} & \text{if} \quad j = i-1, \\ 0 & \text{if} \quad j \neq i-1, i, i+1, \end{cases} \tag{6.24}$$

where χ_E is the *characteristic function* of the event E: 1 if E is true and 0 otherwise.

The transition probabilities $\Pi(t)$ satisfy two systems of equations, called the *forward* and *backward* equations:

$$(d/dt)\Pi(t) = \Pi(t)Q \quad (\text{\textit{forward} equation}), \tag{6.25}$$

$$(d/dt)\Pi(t) = Q\Pi(t) \quad (\text{\textit{backward} equation}). \tag{6.26}$$

The state probabilities $\{p_i(t)\}$ of (6.18) also satisfy the forward equation

$$(d/dt)p_j(t) = \sum_i p_i(t)q_{i,j}. \tag{6.27}$$

The derivation of (6.25)–(6.26) employs a standard and important idea. For the forward equation we consider the changes of the state $i \rightarrow j$ which take place over the interval $(0, t+h]$ when h is small and classify them according to what happens during the interval $(t, t+h]$. There are three possibilities:

(i)   the state at time t is j and no change in state takes place in $(t, t+h]$;
(ii) the state at time t is $j-1$ and an arrival occurs in $(t, t+h]$;
(iii) the state at time t is $j+1$ and a service completion occurs in $(t, t+h]$.

The probability of more than one 'change' – service completion or arrival – is an event of probability $o(h)$ as $h \rightarrow 0$. From (6.24),

$$\pi_{i,j}(t+h) = [1 - (\lambda + \mu\chi_{(j>0)})h + o(h)]\pi_{i,j}(t)$$
$$+ (\lambda\chi_{(j>0)}h + o(h))\pi_{i,j-1}(t)$$
$$+ (\mu h + o(h))\pi_{i,j+1}(t), \qquad (6.28)$$

from which we obtain the forward equation (6.25). A similar proof is used to derive the backward equation (6.26).

If the Markov process is *irreducible* – $\pi_{i,j}(t) > 0$ (for some $t = t(i, j) > 0$) for *every* i, j – meaning that it is possible to move between any two states, then

$$p_j = \lim_{t \to \infty} p_j(t)$$

exists for *any* choice of the *initial* distribution $\{p_j(0)\}$ and the limit is *independent* of $\{p_j(0)\}$. We say that $\{p_j\}$ is the *stationary* or *equilibrium* distribution. It may be that $p_j \equiv 0$ and we say that $\{X_t\}$ is a *transient* process. Otherwise, $\{p_j\}$ is a *bona fide* probability distribution, $p_j > 0$ (for *all* j) and $\mathbf{p} = (p_0, p_1, \ldots)$ satisfies

$$\mathbf{p}Q = \mathbf{0}, \qquad (6.29)$$
$$Q\mathbf{p} = \mathbf{0}. \qquad (6.30)$$

In this case we say that $\{X_t\}$ is *recurrent*.

Foster's theorem [40] provides a converse; if $\mathbf{p} = (p_0, p_1, \ldots)$ exists satisfying

$$\mathbf{p}Q = \mathbf{0}, \qquad (6.31)$$
$$\sum_i |p_i| < \infty, \qquad (6.32)$$

then a stationary distribution exists and **p** will have *positive* components. As a consequence of (6.25), (6.31) we conclude that $p_i(t)$ given by (6.28) is *independent* of t if $\xi_i = \Pr\{X_0 = i\} = p_i$. This justifies the use of the term stationary!

For the M/M/1 system we have

$$[\lambda + \mu\chi_{(j>0)}]p_j = \lambda\chi_{(j>0)}p_{j-1} + \mu p_{j+1}. \tag{6.33}$$

It is simple to verify that

$$p_j = \rho^j(1-\rho) \tag{6.34}$$

with $\rho = \lambda/\mu$ satisfies (6.33) and hence, according to Foster's theorem, (6.34) is *the* stationary solution, provided

$$\sum_j p_j < \infty. \qquad \rho = \text{utilization of system,}$$
$$\text{fraction of time server is busy.}$$

This necessitates $\rho < 1$. Note that $1/\lambda = E\{T_i - T_{i-1}\}$ = the expectation of the interarrival times and $1/\mu = E\{S_i\}$ = the expectation of the service time. Thus $\{X_t\}$ is recurrent provided $\lambda < \mu$. This condition is intuitively clear; the average interval between arrivals is $1/\lambda$ while the average interval between departures is $1/\mu$, so that $1/\lambda > 1/\mu$ is necessary if the queue before the server is not to become infinitely long (implying that $p_\infty = 1$ and $p_j = 0$ for $j < \infty$). The ratio ρ is called the *utilization* of the system. It is easy to prove that

$$\rho = \lim_{T\to\infty} (1/T) \int_0^T \chi_{(X_u>0)} \, du,$$

so that ρ may be interpreted as the limiting fraction of time the state is nonzero; that is, the fraction of time the server is busy (being utilized).

When we model complicated data networks we shall encounter systems which are composed of many service facilities (like the M/M/1) which are interconnected. Thus the *output* of a service facility will be the *input* to some other service facility. What is the nature of the output process? Reich [125] and Burke [8] independently gave the answer:

Theorem 6.3.1 *The output process of an M/M/1 queueing system in which*

(i) *the initial distribution is the stationary distribution,*
(ii) *service is according to the discipline order of arrival,*

is Poisson. Moreover, the state of the system X_t, and the number of departures in $(0, t]$, are independent.

The conclusion remains valid for any work-conserving discipline. This *output* theorem implies that with an arbitrary initial distribution, the output process 'converges' to the Poisson distribution.

There is a much more general setting in which these results concerning the M/M/1 system hold. A Markov process $\mathbf{X} = \{X_t : 0 \leqslant t < \infty\}$ in which the *state space* S is $\{0, 1, 2, \ldots\}$ is called a *birth and death process* provided that the only *infinitesimal changes* allowed are

$$i \to i+1 \qquad (birth)$$

and

$$i \to i-1 \qquad (death).$$

The transition probabilities $\pi_{i,j}(h) = \Pr\{X_{t+h} = j / X_t = i\}$ satisfy

$$\pi_{i,j}(h) = \begin{cases} 1 - [\mu_i + \lambda_i]h + o(h) & \text{if } j = i, \\ \mu_i h + o(h) & \text{if } j = i-1, \\ \lambda_i h + o(h) & \text{if } j = i+1, \\ o(h) & \text{if } j \neq i-1, i, i+1. \end{cases} \tag{6.35}$$

We call $\{\lambda_i\}$ and $\{\mu_i\}$ the *birth and death rates*.

Some examples are as follows:

Example 3.1 M/M/1 queue

$$\lambda_i = \lambda,$$

$$\mu_i = \mu \chi_{(i>0)}.$$

Example 3.2 M/M/s queue – s servers

$$\lambda_i = \lambda,$$

$$\mu_i = \text{Min}(i, s)\mu.$$

Example 3.3 M/M with processor sharing

$$\lambda_i = \lambda,$$

$$\mu_i = \begin{cases} \mu/i & \text{if } i > 0, \\ 0 & \text{if } i = 0. \end{cases}$$

Example 3.4 M/M/∞

$$\lambda_i = \lambda,$$

$$\mu_i = i\mu.$$

For a birth and death process set $\pi_0 = 1$ and

$$\pi_j = \frac{\lambda_0 \lambda_1 \cdots \lambda_{j-1}}{\mu_1 \mu_2 \cdots \mu_j}. \tag{6.36}$$

The birth and death process $\mathbf{X} = \{X_t\}$ with transition function (6.35) is recurrent,

$$p_k = \lim_{t \to \infty} \Pr\{X_t = k\} > 0, \tag{6.37}$$

provided

$$\sum_j \pi_j < \infty, \tag{6.38}$$

and when (6.38) holds,

$$p_j = \pi_j \Big/ \sum_i \pi_i. \tag{6.39}$$

Equation (6.39) (and the recurrence condition (6.38)) provide the formulas for the stationary state probabilities in each of the examples given as well as for other models of the M/M type in which the service and/or arrival rates may be state-dependent.

The output theorem (Theorem 6.3.1) is generalized as follows:

Theorem 6.3.2 *If* $\mathbf{X}$ *is a birth and death process satisfying* Output of BD process.

(i) $\lambda_i = \lambda,$

(ii) $\sum_i \pi_i < \infty,$

(iii) *the initial distribution,* $\Pr\{X_0 = i\}$ *is given by* (6.39),

then the sequence of death times forms a Poisson process of rate λ *and the number of deaths in* $(0, t]$ *and the state* X_t *at time t are independent.*

Proof Let

$$a_{k,j}(t) = \Pr\{k \text{ deaths in } (0, t] \text{ and } X_t = j\}.$$

Then, by considering the possible changes in the state during the interval $(t, t+h]$, we derive the formula

$$a_{k,j}(t+h) = [1-(\lambda+\mu_j)h+o(h)]a_{k,j}(t)+\mu_{j+1}ha_{k-1,j+1}(t)$$
$$+\lambda ha_{k,j-1}(t)+o(h),$$

which yields the differential equation

$$(d/dt)a_{k,j}(t) = -[\lambda+\mu_j]a_{k,j}(t)+\mu_{j+1}a_{k-1,j+1}(t)+\lambda a_{k,j-1}(t). \quad (6.40)$$

It is now simple to show by direct substitution that $a_{k,j}(t) = p_j(\lambda t)^k e^{-\lambda t}/k!$ is a solution to (6.40). ∎

The output theorem has very important consequences in the study of networks of M/M queues – the so-called *Markovian* networks. The simplest such network is shown in Figure 6.2. Customers enter the network at the first node (or stage), queue for service, and upon completion of service immediately join the queue at the second node. The state of the system is the two-dimensional vector-valued random process $\mathbf{X} = \{X_t = (X_{t,1}, X_{t,2}) : 0 \leqslant t < \infty\}$, where $X_{t,i}$ is the number of customers queued or in service at the ith-node. If

   (i)   the arrival process (to stage 1) is Poisson (with rate λ),
   (ii) the service processes are independent and exponential (with rates μ_i, $i = 1, 2$),
  (iii) the queue discipline in each stage is work-conserving,
  (iv) the service and arrival processes are independent,

then the output process of stage 1 will be asymptotically Poisson (as $t \to \infty$) and we may apply the analysis for the M/M/1 queue to obtain the joint distribution of the number of customers waiting (or in service) at each stage, obtaining

$$p_{i,j} = \lim_{t \to \infty} \Pr\{X_t = (i, j)\} = \rho_1^i \rho_2^j (1-\rho_1)(1-\rho_2), \quad (6.41)$$

where

$$\rho_i = \lambda/\mu_i \quad (i = 1, 2) \quad (6.42)$$

provided that $\max(\rho_1, \rho_2) < 1$.

Fig. 6.2 Two-stage tandem queueing network.

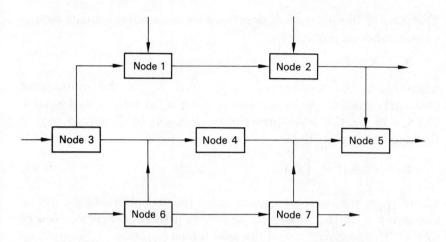

Fig. 6.3 Service network.

The analysis of the two-stage network of Figure 6.2 was generalized by Jackson [65]. Start with a graph **G** of nodes and edges; nodes represent service stations and edges paths linking the stations (Figure 6.3). For our applications, the service stations are message-switching nodes and the links transmission channels. Customers enter the system at the nodes; the *external* arrival process at node $\mathbf{n}_i$ is a Poisson process of rate λ_i. The ith node is a service station with s_i servers each offering service according to the exponential distribution with parameter μ_i. After service is completed at node $\mathbf{n}_i$, the customer either immediately joins the queue at the jth node with probability $\theta_{i,j}$ or leaves the system with probability

$$\theta_i = 1 - \sum_j \theta_{i,j}.$$

The flow into $\mathbf{n}_i$ is composed of

(i) the external flow with rate λ_i,
(ii) the flow from node j $(1 \leq j \leq n)$.

If we denote by Γ_i the *net flow* into $\mathbf{n}_i$, then this second flow must have rate $\Gamma_j \theta_{j,i}$ since the proportion $\theta_{j,i}$ of the output of $\mathbf{n}_j$ is diverted to the input of $\mathbf{n}_i$. The flows $\{\Gamma_i\}$ must then satisfy the *conservation equation*

$$\Gamma_j = \lambda_j + \sum_i \Gamma_i \theta_{i,j}. \tag{6.43}$$

The state of the network is described by the n-dimensional vector-valued random process

$$\mathbf{X} = \{X_t = (X_{t,1}, X_{t,2}, \ldots, X_{t,n}) : 0 \le t < \infty\},$$

where n is the number of nodes and $X_{t,i}$ is the number of customers queued or in service at node $\mathbf{n}_i$ at time t. Let $p_k(t) = \Pr\{X_t = \mathbf{k}\}$ be the state probability. Jackson [65] proved that if $\Gamma_i < s_i \mu_i$ $(1 \le i \le n)$, then

$$p_k = \lim_{t \to \infty} p_k(t) = \prod_{1 \le i \le n} p_{i,k_i}, \qquad (6.44)$$

where p_{i,k_i} is the stationary solution for the probability of the queue size being k_i in the M/M/s_i system with arrival process Poisson of rate Γ_i. The *product form* of the solution to equation (6.44) *suggests* that these individual components of the network of Figure 6.3 act independently and as if their input processes were Poisson with rates $\{\Gamma_i\}$.

[margin note: $S_i =$ #of servers]

First, let us consider equation (6.43). When does it have a solution? Let Θ be the matrix $(\theta_{i,j})$. Assume that for some n, Θ^n has row sums bounded away from 1. This implies that after some number of state transitions $i \to j$ there is a positive probability that a customer will depart from the system. This condition suffices to guarantee the existence of a positive solution to (6.43). The matter of independence is a much deeper question. If as before $a_{\mathbf{k},j}(t)$ is the probability that

(i) there have been $\mathbf{k}$ departures in $(0, t]$ (k_i from $\mathbf{n}_i$),
(ii) the state at time t is j,

then $a_{\mathbf{k},j}(t)$ is *not* the product of the state probability (6.44) and a Poisson distribution. The output theorem does not hold in this case even though the state probability (6.44) has the form which would result if it were true.

Jackson's result assumes that the rate of service at node $\mathbf{n}_i$ depends only upon the state of the queue at that node. In many systems the service rate at a node is influenced by the state of other nodes. For example, in the tandem network of Figure 6.2 we may admit the possibility of *blocking*. The server in the first stage will be blocked whenever M or more requests are queued or in service at the second stage. Obtaining the stationary state probabilities for Markovian networks operating under various blocking disciplines poses formidable analytical problems. For the two-stage tandem network (Figure 6.2), these state probabilies are *not* separable as in the Jackson model. Konheim and Reiser [96] give a closed form solution for the exponential case (exponentially distributed service times and Poisson arrivals); earlier results may be found in a paper of Neuts [110].

Gordon and Newell [51] considered a variant of the Jackson model in which the total number of customers (messages) is fixed. The state of this *closed* network may be described as in Jackson's model by the n-dimensional vector-valued random process $\mathbf{X} = \{X_t = (X_{t,1}, \ldots, X_{t,n})\}$. In the Gordon–Newell model the state space (the set of values assumed by the variables X_t) is the set

$$\left\{ \mathbf{k} = (k_1, \ldots, k_n) : k_i \geqslant 0, \sum_i k_i = M \right\},$$

where M is the number of customers (messages) allowed in the system. The closed model is particularly appealing when modeling an I/O-processor configuration, in which case M is the degree of multiprogramming. Since the random process $\mathbf{X}$ has a finite state space the general theory of Markov chains assures that it has a stationary distribution provided that the process is irreducible. Gordon and Newell proved that, like Jackson's result, the stationary distribution is of 'product' form:

$$p_k = \lim_{t \to \infty} p_k(t) = \lim_{t \to \infty} \Pr\{X_t = \mathbf{k}\} = C \prod_{1 \leqslant i \leqslant n} p_{i,k_i}, \qquad (6.45)$$

where $p_{i,k_i} = \rho_i^{k_i}(1 - \rho_i^{k_i})$ and the normalizing constant C is chosen so that the probabilities in (6.45) when summed over the state space equals unity. In general the determination of the normalizing constant C is not straightforward. The parameters $\{\rho_i\}$ may be quite general functions of i and the number of states large. The numerical aspects of the determination of the normalization constant have been examined by Reiser and Kobayashi [127, 128] and Buzen [10].

One final remark: in computer communications applications in which messages are transmitted between nodes in a network, the service time depends upon (i) the length of the message and (ii) the line speed. Evidently the service time of the same message at different nodes is dependent. We have pretended that these service times are chosen independently for the same message! Indeed not only are the service times dependent but the interarrival time between this message (when it enters externally into a node) and the next message are dependent. Kleinrock [74] recognized this defect in the modeling and called the assumption we make in the analysis the *message independence condition*. It is claimed that there is evidence to support the viability of this assumption [80].

Problems

1. Consider a service station the waiting room of which has *capacity M*. Customers trying to enter when there are M customers waiting or in service are turned away. Set up the differential equations for

   $$p_j(t) = \Pr\{j \text{ customers in system at time } t\} \qquad (0 \leqslant j \leqslant M)$$

   and find the equilibrium distribution.

2. Find the equilibrium distribution for the M/M/s system.

3. Find the equilibrium distribution for the M/M processor sharing model.

4. Find the equilibrium distribution for the M/M/∞ system.

5. Consider the closed system shown in Figure 6.4, in which the two stages are single server systems with exponentially distributed service times having parameters μ_i $(i = 1, 2)$. A total of M customers are in the system. Let $p_j(t)$ be the probability of j at the first stage (and hence $M - j$ at the second stage), $0 \leqslant j \leqslant M$. Write the differential equations for $\{p_j(t)\}$ and find the equilibrium distribution.

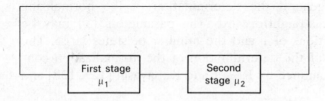

First stage μ_1

Second stage μ_2

Fig. 6.4

6.4 The buffer process

As a first step in understanding the problem of flow of *data* in a computing system we must consider the nature of data. A

program – in the sense of computation – is a sequence of instructions which are represented in machine readable form as a string of
0s and 1s. For example, the APL (or FORTRAN) expression

$$A \leftarrow B - 1$$

$$(A = B - 1),$$

meaning that the variable A is assigned the value of the variable
$B - 1$, is encoded by EBCDIC character-set into the binary string

11000001 10101011 11000010 01100000 11110001

using the encoding

$A = 11000001,$ $\leftarrow = 10101011,$

$B = 11000010,$ $- = 01100000.$

$1 = 11110000,$

Each symbol in the programming language is given a representation as a sequence of eight 0s and 1s; we call an 8-tuple of 0s and
1s a *byte*. Thus a program is translated into a sequence of bytes.
When we transmit a program to the central processing unit we are
sending some sequence of bytes. It is frequently more convenient
to break up a program into 'larger' units. Thus the sequence of
bytes is broken into segments of some fixed length. We call these
segments *packets, data units, frames, pages* depending upon the
context. Thus data when stored on a disk or drum of a computing
system is stored in units called *pages*. A page might consist of 4096
bytes. We will adopt the terminology *packet* and say that a
message consists of n packets. We begin by constructing a model
of the most primitive type of data collection device – a *buffer*. A
buffer is a temporary storage device (*see* Figure 6.5). This buffer is

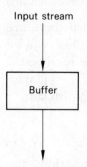

Input stream

Buffer

Fig. 6.5

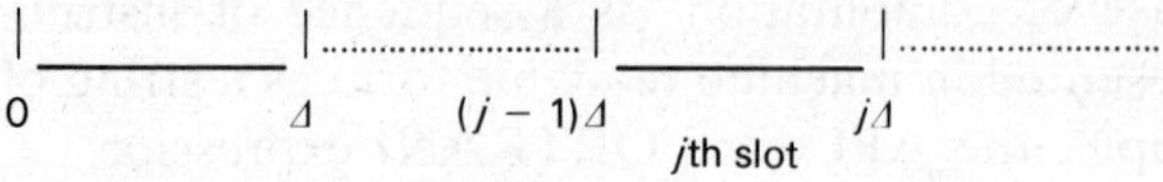

```
|_____.|......................|_____|.........................
0          Δ       (j − 1)Δ              jΔ
                       jth slot
```

Fig. 6.6

to receive data. Let us divide the time axis into intervals (Figure 6.6). We shall call the interval $[(j-1)\Delta, j\Delta)$ the jth *slot* and shall assume that data arrives at the buffer according to a random process

$$\mathbf{X} = \{X_j : 1 \leqslant j < \infty\},$$

where X_j is the number of packets arriving in the jth slot. We shall assume that $E\{X_j\} < 1$. The random process $\mathbf{X}$ is assumed to be a *renewal process*; that is, the random variables $\{X_j\}$ are independent and identically distributed.

Are these realistic assumptions? Unfortunately there is very little known about the generation of data in computer systems. In one of the few studies of computer traffic [43] it was observed that the flow of data is reasonably well modeled by a compound Poisson process.

Let us describe the behavior of the buffer of Figure 6.5 when this buffer collects data and forwards it to a host (processor). The buffer might be a *concentrator*, that is, receiving data from many terminals. There are two data flows in the buffer; data enters according to $\mathbf{X}$ and is simultaneously being removed and sent to the processor at the rate of one packet per slot. Let L_j be the number of packets buffered at time $j\Delta - 0$. Then the *buffer storage process* $\mathbf{L} = \{L_j : 0 \leqslant j < \infty\}$ evolves according to

$$L_j = (L_{j-1} - 1)^+ + X_j \qquad (1 \leqslant j < \infty), \tag{6.46}$$

where $a^+ = \max(a, 0)$. Equation (6.46) prescribes that if there are L_{j-1} packets buffered at time $(j-1)\Delta - 0$, then one of these will be removed in the jth slot if $L_{j-1} > 0$ (while none will be removed if $L_{j-1} = 0$) leaving $(L_{j-1} - 1)^+$ packets buffered. These $(L_{j-1} - 1)^+$ packets will be augmented by X_j new packets arriving in the jth slot.

We shall study (6.46). Let

$$h_{j,k} = \Pr\{L_j = k\} \qquad (0 \leqslant j, k < \infty). \tag{6.47}$$

The term with $j = 0$ corresponds to the *start* of operation – the initial condition – in the system and we are free to specify the initial distribution $\{h_{0,k}\}$. Let

$$H_j(z) = E\{z^{L_j}\} = \sum_{0 \leqslant k < \infty} h_{j,k} z^k. \tag{6.48}$$

Since

$$0 \leqslant h_{j,k}, \qquad \sum_{0 \leqslant k < \infty} h_{j,k} = 1,$$

(6.48) converges *at least* for $|z| \leqslant 1$ and is analytic for $|z| < 1$. The evolution equation (6.46) can be translated into an equation relating the probabilities

$$\Pr\{L_j = k\} = \sum_{0 \leqslant i \leqslant k+1} \Pr\{L_{j-1} = i\} \Pr\{X_j = k - (i-1)^+\}$$

$$(0 \leqslant k < \infty, 1 \leqslant j < \infty). \tag{6.49}$$

Equation (6.49) is in turn equivalent to

$$H_j(z) = P(z)[(H_{j-1}(z) - H_{j-1}(0))/z + H_{j-1}(0)] \qquad (1 \leqslant j < \infty), \tag{6.50}$$

where

$$P(z) = E\{z^{X_j}\} = \sum_{0 \leqslant k < \infty} \Pr\{X_j = k\} z^k. \tag{6.51}$$

Starting with an arbitrary choice for $H_0(z)$, we can employ (6.50) to obtain $H_j(z)$ for all $j, 1 \leqslant j < \infty$. To carry out this recursion we may introduce the double generating function

$$H(z, w) = \sum_{0 \leqslant j < \infty} H_j(z) w^j. \tag{6.52}$$

The series (6.52) converges *at least* for $|w| \leqslant 1$ since

$$|H_j(z)| = |E\{z^{L_j}\}| \leqslant E\{|z|^{L_j}\} \leqslant E\{1^{L_j}\} \leqslant 1$$

for $|z| \leqslant 1$. Thus $H(z, w)$ is analytic in the *polydisk* $\{(z, w) : |z|, |w| < 1\}$. The recurrence equation (6.50) now yields

$$H(z, w) = \frac{zH_0(z) + w(z-1)P(z)H(0, w)}{z - wP(z)}. \tag{6.53}$$

The numerator of (6.53) contains the generating function

$$H(0, w) = \sum_{0 \leqslant j < \infty} \Pr\{L_j = 0\} w^j$$

of the probabilities that the buffer is 'empty' at the time $\{j\Delta\}$. These probabilities are to be determined and it appears that (6.50) has yielded an equation in which some information is missing. Note that if we set $z = 0$ in (6.53) we get an identity. We shall see that (6.53) actually contains all the information we need. The value of the 'boundary' term $H(0, w)$ is contained in (6.53). Before proceeding further we make a slight digression.

Consider a gambler who plays a sequence of games of chance. The gambler starts with a capital of L_0 (dollars) and plays a sequence of games. The *entrance* fee for each game is \$1 and the *payoff* on the jth game is X_j (dollars). The payoffs are independent and identically distributed random variables. To conform to the usual Las Vegas policy we continue with our assumption that $E\{X_j\} < 1$. Play continues as long as the gambler has money. The capital of the gambler after the play of the jth game is

$$L_j = L_0 - j + \sum_{1 \leqslant k \leqslant j} X_k. \tag{6.54}$$

The *gambler's ruin* occurs at time T,

$$T = \min \{k : L_k = 0\}. \tag{6.55}$$

Equation (6.55) assigns the value $T = \infty$ if $L_k > 0$ for all k. Unfortunately, in mathematics as in *real life*, the event $\{T = \infty\}$ corresponding to an unlimited number of plays is an event of probability zero. The ruin of the gambler is certain. Let us calculate the time to ruin. Let

$$g_{n,k} = \Pr \left\{ L_n = k \text{ and } \underset{0 \leqslant j \leqslant n}{\text{Min}} L_j > 0 \right\}, \tag{6.56}$$

the probability of

   (i) no ruin before the nth game, and
   (ii) capital at the start of the nth game of k.

We start with the recurrence formula

$$g_{n,k} = \sum_{1 \leqslant j \leqslant k+1} g_{n-1,j} p_{k-j+1} \qquad (1 \leqslant n < \infty, 0 \leqslant k < \infty). \tag{6.57}$$

Equation (6.57) is just a decomposition of the event

   (i) no ruin before the nth game, and
   (ii) capital at the start of the nth game of k

into the $k + 1$ mutually exclusive events $(1 \leqslant j \leqslant k + 1)$

   (i) no ruin before the $(n-1)$th game,

(ii) capital at the start of the $(n-1)$th game of j, and

(iii) gain on the $(n-1)$th game of $k-j+1$.

Introduce the generating functions

$$G_n(z) = \sum_{0 \le k < \infty} g_{n,k} z^k, \tag{6.58}$$

$$G(z, w) = \sum_{0 \le n < \infty} G_n(z) w^n, \tag{6.59}$$

the series converging when $|z|$, $|w| < 1$. In (6.59) $G_0(z)$ is the generating function of the *initial* capital L_0 of the gambler. From (6.57),

$$G_n(z) = P(z)[G_{n-1}(z) - G_{n-1}(0)]/z \qquad (1 \le n < \infty) \tag{6.60}$$

and

$$G(z, w) = \frac{z G_0(z) - w P(z) G(0, w)}{z - w P(z)}. \tag{6.61}$$

Equations (6.53) and (6.61) display the same indeterminacy; they express the solution in terms of an initial condition and a 'boundary' value. To find $G(0, w)$ and hence solve (6.61) we make use of the analyticity of $G(z, w)$. If the denominator of (6.61) vanishes anywhere in the polydisk $\{(z, w): |z|, |w| < 1\}$ then the same must be true of the numerator. We now use Theorem 6.2.7 to conclude that there is a zero $\theta(w)$ of the denominator of (6.61):

$$\theta(w) - w P(\theta(w)) = 0 \qquad (|w|, |\theta(w)| < 1). \tag{6.62}$$

It follows that the numerator of (6.61) must vanish when $z = \theta(w)$:

$$\theta(w) G_0(\theta(w)) - w P(\theta(w)) G(0, w) = 0. \tag{6.63}$$

But $w P(\theta(w)) = \theta(w)$ and hence (6.63) can be written in the form

$$\theta(w)[G_0(\theta(w)) - G(0, w)] = 0. \tag{6.64}$$

For any value of w for which $\theta(w) \neq 0$ we have

$$G(0, w) = G_0(\theta(w)). \tag{6.65}$$

We claim that $\theta(w) \neq 0$ for *every* w, $|w| < 1$; if on the contrary this is not true, then from (6.62) we conclude that $P(0) = \Pr\{X_j = 0\} = 0$ and this contradicts our assumption that $E\{X_j\} < 1$. Equation (6.65) states if the gambler starts with an initial capital of K (dollars), then the ruin time T has generating function $\theta^K(w)$; each additional dollar 'buys' him $\theta(w)$ more 'playing time'. Now let us return to (6.53); $\theta(w)$ is also a root of the denominator of (6.53) and hence the numerator must vanish:

$$\theta(w)H_0(\theta(w)) + w(\theta(w)-1)P(\theta(w))H(0, w), = 0 \qquad (6.66)$$

from which we conclude that

$$H(0, w) = H_0(\theta(w))/[1-\theta(w)]. \qquad (6.67)$$

[handwritten annotations in right margin:]
$$H(0,w) = \dfrac{H_0(\theta(w))}{1-\theta(w)}$$
$$\theta(w) = wP(\theta(w))$$

In principle (6.51) and (6.67) together enable us to determine $H_j(z)$ for all j (and hence $h_{j,k}$ for all j and k). Usually we are interested in only much more modest information. Equation (6.46) defines a Markov chain on the state space $\boldsymbol{S} = \{0, 1, 2, \ldots\}$. The transition function is

$$\Pr\{L_j = k/L_{j-1} = i\} = p_{k-(i-1)^+}.$$

The Markov chain is irreducible – it is possible to go from any one state to any other in *some* number of steps – and hence there exists a stationary distribution.

$$h_k = \lim_{k\to\infty} h_{j,k}, \qquad H(z) = \lim_{j\to\infty} H_j(z).$$

Equation (6.50) implies that $H(z)$ is given by

$$H(z) = \frac{H(0)(z-1)P(z)}{z - P(z)}. \qquad (6.68)$$

Since $H(z)$ is a probability generating function, $H(1) = 1$ and hence the value of $H(0)$ is determined, $H(0) = 1 - \mu$ where $\mu = E\{X_j\} = (d/dz)P(z)|_{z=1}$.

We can also obtain (6.68) via the Tauberian theorem (Theorem 6.2.6); we have

$$H^*(z) = \lim_{N\to\infty} (1/N) \sum_{0\le j\le N} H_j(z) \qquad (6.69)$$

$$= \lim_{w\to 1-} (1-w)H(z, w).$$

From (6.67)

$$\lim_{w\to 1-} (1-w)H(0, w) = \lim_{w\to 1-} (1-w)/(1-\theta(w))$$

$$= 1/[(d/dw)\theta(w)]|_{w=1}$$

while (4.17) provides $(d/dw)\theta(w)|_{w=1} = 1/(1-\mu)$, so that

$$H^*(z) = \frac{(1-\mu)(z-1)P(z)}{z - P(z)}. \qquad (6.70)$$

If $\lim_{j\to\infty} H_j(z)$ exists, it must equal $H^*(z)$.

The 'average' $H^*(z)$ has an important physical interpretation; $H^*(z)$ is the *Cesaro-1* limit of the sequence $\{H_j(z)\}$ and is an average of the generating function of the state variable over time.

From (6.68) we can find the moments of the stationary queue length distribution. If $H(z) = E\{z^L\}$, then

$$E\{L\} = (d/dz)H(z)|_{z=1} = 0.5\sigma^2/[1-\mu] + 0.5\mu,$$

where $\sigma^2 = \text{Var}\{X_i\}$. Next, let us relate the function $\theta(w)$ to the behavior of the buffer model. Let

$$\mathbf{T} = \{T_k : 0 < k < \infty\}$$

denote the *epochs* at which $L_j = 0$ with $j > 0$ and set $\tau_k = T_k - T_{k-1}$ $(1 \leqslant k < \infty)$ with $T_0 = 0$. We have already seen that

$$E\{w^{\tau_1}\} = H_0(\theta(w)). \tag{6.71}$$

We claim that

$$E\{w^{\tau_k}\} = \theta(w) \qquad (1 < k < \infty) \tag{6.72}$$

and that the $\{\tau_k : 1 < k < \infty\}$ are independent. The independence is obvious! When the buffer empties, the influence of the past history is lost. If $\tau_k = 1$, then $X_{T_k} = 1$ and this event has probability $P(0)$. If $\tau_k > 1$, then $X_{T_k} = s$ for some $s > 0$ and hence the waiting time until the next *renewal point* from $T_{k-1} + 1$ has generating function $\theta^s(w)$. Thus

$$\sum_{1 \leqslant j < \infty} \Pr\{\tau_k = j\}w^j = wP(0) + \sum_{1 \leqslant s < \infty} p_s w\theta^s(w) = wP(\theta(w)) = \theta(w).$$

Finally, let us return to equation (6.62) and consider the nature of its solution. Theorem 6.2.8 and equation (6.10) give an explicit solution in terms of the generating function $P(z)$.

Let us consider some examples:

Example 4.1 Poisson process

$$P(z) = \exp \lambda(z - 1),$$

$$\theta(w) = \lambda^{-1} \sum_{0 \leqslant n < \infty} (n+1)^{n-1} w^{n+1} (\lambda e^{-\gamma})^n / n!$$

This is an important result which has interesting connections to the enumeration of trees [150].

Example 4.2 Geometric distribution

$$P(z) = (1 - \rho)/(1 - \rho z),$$

$$\theta(w) = \{1 - [1 - 4w(1 - \rho)]^{0.5}\}/2\rho.$$

Example 4.3 Coin tossing

$$P(z) = 1 - p + pz,$$

$$\theta(w) = w(1 - p)/(1 - pw).$$

Problems

1. Consider a channel with capacity C (packets per slot) removing data from a buffer. If L_j denotes the number of packets in the buffer at the start of the jth slot, then (6.46) is replaced by

   $$L_j = (L_{j-1} - C)^+ + X_j.$$

   Let $H_j(z) = E\{z^{L_j}\}$ and D the operator

   $$D^i : F(z) \rightarrow (d^i/d^i z) F(z)|_{z=0}.$$

   (i) Find the recurrence equation for the $\{H_j(z)\}$.
   (ii) Determine

   $$H(z, w) = \sum_{0 \leqslant j < \infty} H_j(z) w^j.$$

   (iii) Find some expression for the C 'boundary' terms

   $$D^i H(z, w) \qquad (0 \leqslant j < C).$$

   (iv) For what values of C is the Markov chain $\{L_j\}$ recurrent?

6.5 Priority service

In this section we develop the notion of *priority service*. Consider the buffer model of the previous section with two arrival streams (Figure 6.7).

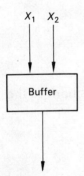

Fig. 6.7

Let

$$\mathbf{X}_i = \{X_{i,j} : 1 \leq j < \infty\} \qquad (i = 1, 2)$$

be independent renewal processes

$$P_i(z) = E\{z^{X_i}\} = \sum_{0 \leq k < \infty} \Pr\{X_{i,j} = k\}z^k;$$

$$\mu_i = E\{X_{i,j}\}, \qquad \sigma_i^2 = \mathrm{Var}\{X_{i,j}\}.$$

We describe the state of the buffer by a (two-dimensional) vector-valued random variable

$$L_j = (L_{1,j}, L_{2,j}),$$

where $L_{i,j}$ is the number of $\mathbf{X}_i$-packets buffered at time $j\Delta - 0$.

The buffer removes data at the rate of one packet per slot. What we must specify is how the two streams interact. We shall assume that $\mathbf{X}_1$-packets are served before $\mathbf{X}_2$-packets; that is, the buffer-manager examines the queue and

(i) if there are $\mathbf{X}_1$-packets waiting chooses one for service,
(ii) if there are no $\mathbf{X}_1$-packets, checks for $\mathbf{X}_2$-packets and if there are any, chooses one for service

In the queueing literature this is referred to as a *non-pre-emptive* priority.

The state equations for the contents of the buffer are

$$L_{1,j} = (L_{1,j-1} - 1)^+ + X_{1,j} \qquad (1 \leq j < \infty), \tag{6.73}$$

$$L_{2,j} = (L_{2,j-1} - \chi_{(L_{1,j-1}=0)})^+ + X_{2,j} \qquad (1 \leq j < \infty). \tag{6.74}$$

Equation (6.73) states that the $(j-1)$th slot is *available* to remove $\mathbf{X}_2$-packets if and only if $L_{1,j-1} = 0$. Note that (6.73) and (6.74) imply

$$L_{1,j} + L_{2,j} = (L_{1,j-1} + L_{2,j-1} - 1)^+ + X_{1,j} + X_{2,j} \qquad (1 \leq j < \infty). \tag{6.75}$$

Let

$$H_{1,j}(z) = E\{z^{L_{1,j}}\} = \sum_{0 \leq k < \infty} h_{1,j,k}z^k, \tag{6.76}$$

$$H_{2,j}(z) = E\{z^{L_{2,j}}\} = \sum_{0 \leq k < \infty} h_{2,j,k}z^k, \tag{6.77}$$

where $h_{i,j,k} = \Pr\{L_{i,j} = k\}$. Equations (6.73) and (6.75) have the form of equation (6.46) and hence the results of Section 6.4 are directly applicable. Equation (6.74) is another matter. When is a slot available to serve the $\mathbf{X}_2$-process? Precisely at those *epochs* at which the buffer contains no $\mathbf{X}_1$-packets. Let

$$\mathbf{T}_1 = \{T_{1,k} : 1 \leqslant k < \infty\} \tag{6.78}$$

denote the epochs $j\Delta > 0$ at which $L_{1,j} = 0$. Then (6.74) can be written

$$L_{2,T_{1,k}} = (L_{2,T_{1,k-1}} - 1)^+ + \sum_{T_{1,k-1} \leqslant j < T_{1,k}} X_{2,j} \qquad (1 < k < \infty). \tag{6.79}$$

If

$$Y_{2,k} = \sum_{T_{1,k-1} \leqslant j < T_{1,k}} X_{2,j},$$

then

$$\mathbf{Y}_2 = \{Y_{2,k} : 1 < k < \infty\}$$

is a renewal process since the *interepoch* times $\tau_{1,k} = T_{1,k} - T_{1,k-1}$ $(1 < k < \infty)$ are independent and identically distributed. What is the generating function of the $\mathbf{Y}_2$-process? If $Z_1, \ldots, Z_n$ are independent random variables with generating functions $Q_1(z), \ldots, Q_n(z)$, then $Z = Z_1 + \cdots + Z_n$ has generating function $Q_1(z) \times \cdots \times Q_n(z)$. Next, let $\{Z_i : 1 \leqslant i < \infty\}$ be independent and identically distributed with generating function $Q(z)$ and suppose N is a positive integer-valued random variable independent of the $\{Z_i\}$ with generating function $R(z)$. Then the random variable $Z_1 + \cdots + Z_N$ which is the sum of a *random* number N of the $\{Z_i\}$ has generating function

$$E\{z^{Z_1 + \cdots + Z_N}\} = \sum_{1 \leqslant k < \infty} \Pr\{N = k\} E\{z^{Z_1 + \cdots + Z_k}\} = R(Q(z)).$$

$Z_1 + \cdots + Z_N$ is a *compound* process. Thus

$$E\{z^{Y_{2,k}}\} = \theta_1(P_2(z)), \tag{6.80}$$

where $\theta_1(w)$ is the solution of

$$\theta_1(w) - wP_1(\theta_1(w)) = 0 \qquad (|w|, |\theta_1(w)| < 1). \tag{6.81}$$

We have

$$E\{\tau_{1,k}\} = (d/dw)\theta_1(w)|_{w=1} = 1/(1 - \mu_1) \qquad (1 < k < \infty)$$

with $\mu_i = E\{X_{i,j}\} = (d/dz)P_i(z)|_{z=1}$. The expectation of $Y_{2,k}$ is thus

$$E\{Y_{2,k}\} = (d/dz)\theta_1(P_2(z))|_{z=1} = \mu_2/(1 - \mu_1). \tag{6.82}$$

Thus the process $\{L_{2,T_k}\}$ is recurrent if and only if $\mu_1/(1-\mu_2)<1$ or equivalently $\mu_1+\mu_2<1$. Of course this was obvious from (6.75).

We can now use the results of Section 6.4 on equation (6.79); if

$$H_2^*(z)=\lim_{k\to\infty} E\{z^{L_{1,T_k}}\}$$

then

$$H_2^*(z)=\frac{1-\mu_1-\mu_2}{1-\mu_1}\frac{(z-1)\theta_1(P_2(z))}{z-\theta_1(P_2(z))}\,. \tag{6.83}$$

We conclude by considering the delay experienced by $\mathbf{X}_i$-packets. There are two terms used in the queueing theory literature; the *queueing time* is the total time spent in the system while the *queueing delay* is the total time spent waiting for service. If a customer enters at time t_{enter}, receives service of duration t_{service} and leaves at time t_{exit}, then

$$\text{Queueing time} = t_{\text{exit}} - t_{\text{enter}},$$

$$\text{Queueing delay} = t_{\text{exit}} - t_{\text{enter}} - t_{\text{service}}.$$

The queueing time and delay differ only by the service time of the customer.

What are the queueing delays of a message of $\mathbf{X}_i$-packets? Suppose a *virtual message* consisting of m $\mathbf{X}_i$-packets were to enter the system at time $(j-1)\Delta-0$, the start of the jth slot. If $i=1$, the virtual message discovers $L_{1,j-1}$ packets in the system and experiences a delay of L_{j-1} slots. Note that the virtual message is delayed only by the $\mathbf{X}_1$-packets already in the system at the time it enters. If $i=2$, the situation is different. The virtual message finds $L_{1,j-1}+L_{2,j-1}$ packets already in the system. It will be delayed by these packets *and* also by any $\mathbf{X}_1$-packets which enter before its last packet begins service. These latter packets pre-empt service from the virtual message. Consider the system of equations

$$L_k = (L_{k-1}-1)^+ + X_{1,k+j} \qquad (1\le k<\infty) \tag{6.84}$$

with

$$L_0 = m-1+L_{1,j-1}+L_{2,j-1}. \tag{6.85}$$

If $L_T=0$ and $L_j\ne0$ for $0\le j<T$, then the last packet of the virtual message will begin service in the Tth slot. Thus

$$t_{\text{enter}} = (j-1)\Delta-0,$$

$$t_{\text{exit}} = (T+j+1)\Delta,$$

so that the queueing time is $(1+T)$ slots. The generating function of T is (*see* (6.71))

$$E\{(\theta_1(w))^{L_0}\},$$

where

$$\theta_1(w) - P_1(\theta_1(w)) = 0.$$

In equilibrium, that is as $j \to \infty$, the generating function of L_0 converges to

$$E(z) = (1 - \mu_1 - \mu_2)\frac{z^{m-1}(z-1)P_1(z)P_2(z)}{z - P_1(z)P_2(z)}. \tag{6.86}$$

Thus $D(z) = z^{1-m}E(\theta_1(z))$ is the generating function of the stationary queueing delay $W(m)$ and we have

$$D(z) = (1 - \mu_1 - \mu_2)\frac{(z^{-1}\theta_1(z))^{m-1}(\theta_1(z)-1)P_2(\theta_1(z))}{z - P_2(\theta_1(z))}. \tag{6.87}$$

The expected value of $W(m)$ is

$$E\{W(m)\} = -(m-1)$$
$$+ \frac{m - 1 + 0.5(\sigma_1^2 + \sigma_2^2)/(1 - \mu_1 - \mu_2) + 0.5(\mu_1 + \mu_2)}{1 - \mu_1}.$$

$$\tag{6.88}$$

Problems

1. Consider the buffer of Section 6.5 with two input arrival processes

$$\mathbf{X}_i = \{X_{i,j} : 1 \leq j < \infty\}.$$

We will *share* the channel by partitioning the set of slots $\mathbf{S} = \{s_j : 1 \leq j < \infty\}$ into two sets $\mathbf{S}_i$ ($i = 1, 2$):

$$\mathbf{S}_i = \{s_{2j+i-2} : 1 \leq j < \infty\} \qquad (i = 1, 2).$$

Find the equation of evolution of the system under this *slot assignment*, the recurrence equation for $\{H_{i,j}(z)\}$, and the stationary distribution.

2. (*Harder problem*) The same as in Problem 1 except that

$$\mathbf{S}_1 = \{s_{3j-2}, s_{3j-1} : 1 \leq j < \infty\},$$
$$\mathbf{S}_2 = \{s_{3j} : 1 \leq j < \infty\}.$$

3. (*Much harder problem*)   Same as in Problem 1 except that we partition the set of slots S into the sets

$$S_1 = \{s_{(m+n)j-k} : n \leqslant k \leqslant m+n-1, 1 \leqslant j < \infty\},$$

$$S_2 = \{s_{(m+n)j-k} : 0 \leqslant k < n, 1 \leqslant j < \infty\}.$$

   The first m of every group of $m+n$ slots to X_1.

6.6   Stars and loops

To understand the models we will construct in this section it is
necessary to review the evolution of the computing system and in
particular the way in which data enters and leaves the system. *In
the beginning* [GENESIS], programs were entered manually using
card or paper-tape readers. A programmer prepared a deck of
cards or a paper tape encoding the series of instructions using
machine language instructions. Output was printed on the system's
printer. As computing systems evolved, it became clear that it
wasn't necessary for programmers actually to be physically present
at the computer and thus was born the notion of remote access
which so characterizes the modern day computing facility. Remote
access was provided by *terminals* with a standard or modified
keyboard. In parallel there was the development of so-called
high-level languages which allowed the user to communicate in a
language close to English. These terminals are linked to the
processor either with *hard-wired connections* or through telephone
lines. In the latter case it is necessary to provide a physical device,
called a *modem* (for modulator–demodulator) to transmit the
digital signals on the analog telephone lines. Each terminal has a
separate telephone or hard-wired connection to the processor. The
problem with this arrangement is one of economics; the rate at
which a user can enter (type) a series of instruction is quite slow
compared with the capacity of the telephone channel to transmit
data. Most of the time the channel from terminal to processor is
not being used. A solution was sought in which many users could
share the same transmission facility. This is in the spirit of the
development of the computer in which it was realized that many
users could simultaneously 'use' a computing system by means of
time sharing. The sharing of the transmission facility is called
multiplexing. In this chapter we consider two network structures

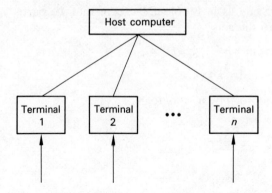

Fig. 6.8 Star network.

for linking terminals to a processor:

(i) the *star* or point-to-point network (Figure 6.8);
(ii) the *loop* network (Figure 6.9).

First some notation. We will denote by

$$\mathbf{X}_i = \{X_{i,j} : 1 \leq j < \infty\} \qquad (1 \leq i \leq n)$$

the arrival process (of packets) at the ith terminal. The $\{\mathbf{X}_i\}$ are

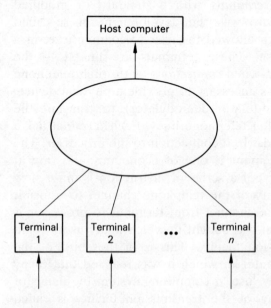

Fig. 6.9 Loop network.

independent renewal processes. We set

$$p_{i,k} = \Pr\{X_{i,j} = k\} \qquad (0 \leq k < \infty,\ 1 \leq i \leq n),$$

$$P_i(z) = \sum_{0 \leq k < \infty} p_{i,k} z^k \qquad (|z| \leq 1,\ 1 \leq i \leq n);$$

$$\mu_i = E\{X_{i,j}\} = (d/dz)P_i(z)|_{z=1}, \qquad \sigma_i^2 = \text{Var}\{X_{i,j}\}.$$

We begin our study with the star network; each terminal is linked to the processor by a dedicated line. We will consider the problem of the flow of data *from* the terminals *to* the processor. The state of the ith terminal will be the variable $L_{i,j}$, which is the number of packets buffered at the ith terminal at the start of the jth slot. Then

$$L_{ij} = (L_{i,j-1} - 1)^+ + X_{i,j} \qquad (1 \leq j < \infty,\ 1 \leq i \leq n). \tag{6.89}$$

Equation (6.89), which has the form of equation (6.46), displays the central characteristic of the star network; namely, the independence of the action of the terminals. Each terminal operates as if it were the only source of data. The processor which receives data from the terminals must share itself among the various users, but the speed of the processor is usually higher than that of the individual terminals and each user feels that he alone commands the use of the processor. The analysis of the star is thus contained in Section 6.4. Each buffer process

$$\mathbf{L}_i = \{L_{i,j} : 0 \leq j < \infty\} \qquad (1 \leq i \leq n)$$

converges in distribution,

$$L_i = \lim_{j \to \infty} L_{ij} \quad \text{(in distribution)},$$

and $H_i(z) = E\{z^{L_i}\}$ is given by

$$H_i(z) = \frac{(1 - \mu_i)(z - 1)P_i(z)}{z - P_i(z)}. \tag{6.90}$$

An important quantity of interest in these models is the queueing delay which we encountered before in Section 6.5. Suppose a *message* of m packets enters at the ith terminal just *before* the start of the jth slot. This message will be delayed by the $L_{i,j-1}$ packets buffered at the ith terminal. Its service will *begin* with slot number $j + L_{i,j-1}$, thus producing a delay of $L_{i,j-1}$ slots. The delay is independent of the length of the message. If $D_{i,j}(z)$ denotes the generating function of the delay, $W_{i,j}$, then

$$D_i(z) = \lim_{j \to \infty} D_{i,j}(z), \qquad W_{i,j} = \lim_{j \to \infty} W_{i,j} \qquad \text{(in distribution)};$$

$$D_i(z) = H_i(z). \tag{6.91}$$

We have

$$E\{L_i\} = E\{W_i\} = 0.5\sigma_i^2/(1 - \mu_i) + 0.5\mu_i. \tag{6.92}$$

Before considering the loop network we digress to consider the question of 'inverting' (6.90) and (6.91); that is, finding the coefficients of the power series given by (6.90) and (6.91). In order to simplify the notation we will suppress the subscript i.

Example 6.1 Poisson process. $P(z) = e^{\lambda(z-1)}$, thus

$$H(z) = \frac{(1 - \lambda)(1 - z)}{1 - z e^{\lambda(1-z)}}, \tag{6.93}$$

which yields

$$H(z) = (1 - \lambda)(1 - z) \sum_{0 \leqslant k < \infty} (z e^{\lambda(1-z)})^k \tag{6.94}$$

which yields

$$\sum_{0 \leqslant i \leqslant j} h_i = (1 - \lambda) \sum_{0 \leqslant k \leqslant j} e^{\lambda k}(-\lambda k)^{j-k}/(j-k)!. \tag{6.95}$$

Example 6.2 Compound Poisson process. $P(z) = \exp \lambda[(1-q)z/(1-qz) - 1]$, thus

$$\sum_{0 \leqslant i \leqslant j} h_i = (1 - \lambda/(1-q)) \left(e^{\lambda j} + \sum_{1 \leqslant k < j} \sum_{1 \leqslant i \leqslant j-k} \right.$$
$$\left. \times C(j-k-1, i-1)q^{j-k-i}e^{\lambda k}(-\lambda k(1-q))^i/i! \right). \tag{6.96}$$

The above formulas clearly show that even with a 'simple' arrival process the computation of the state probabilities may cause problems. Both of the formulas involve the differences between 'large' numerical magnitudes, the bane of numerical analysis. Fortunately there is another approach which is easier to implement and avoids the aforementioned difficulties. From (6.89) we have (suppressing subscripts)

$$h_j = h_0 p_i + \sum_{1 \leqslant k \leqslant j+1} h_k p_{j-k+1}, \tag{6.97}$$

so that we obtain the recurrence formula

$$h_j = p_0^{-1} \left[h_{j-1} - h_0 p_{j-1} - \sum_{1 \leqslant k < j} h_k p_{j-k} \right] \quad (1 \leqslant j < \infty). \tag{6.98}$$

Given the value of h_0, (6.98) provides a recipe for determining the sequence $\{h_j\}$. By taking $h_0 = 1$, we may use (6.98) to find $h_1, \ldots, h_N$ and then scale the magnitudes so that

$$\sum_{0 \leqslant j \leqslant N} h_j = 1.$$

We can even test for the stopping point in the recursion N, by comparing

$$\mu = \sum_{0 \leqslant k < \infty} k p_k$$

with $1 - h_0$.

We now return to the main development and consider the loop network (Figure 6.9). The loop behaves as a 'bus' with one seat which passes the n stations in sequence. The first station with a customer waiting claims the seat. The bus makes repeated tours of the stations. The evolution equations are

$$L_{i,j} = (L_{i,j-1} - \chi_{(L_{1,j-1} = \cdots = L_{i-1,j-1} = 0)})^+ + X_{i,j}$$
$$(1 \leqslant i \leqslant n, 1 \leqslant j < \infty). \tag{6.99}$$

Just as in Section 6.5 (equations (6.74)–(6.76)) we may write

$$L_{1,j} + \cdots + L_{i,j} = (L_{1,j-1} + \cdots + L_{i,j-1} - 1)^+ + X_{1,j} + \cdots + X_{i,j}$$
$$(1 \leqslant i \leqslant n, 1 \leqslant j < \infty). \tag{6.100}$$

Equation (6.100) indicates that a packet will be removed from *one* of the first i terminals provided there is one to remove, while (6.99) indicates that the slot is *available* to the ith terminal if and only if it is not required by one of the first $i-1$ terminals. The analysis of the waiting line at the first terminal is contained in Section 6.4. The first terminal does not feel the presence of any of the other terminals. More generally, the ith terminal does not feel the presence of the jth terminal with $j > i$. The analysis of the waiting line at the second terminal is contained in Section 6.5. A slot is available to the second terminal at the renewal epochs of the first terminal. It is now clear how to proceed. Let us analyze the waiting line at the ith terminal. The jth slot is available for the ith terminal if and only if $L_{1,j} + \cdots + L_{i-1,j} = 0$. Let $T_{i-1,1}, \ldots, T_{i-1,k}, \ldots$ denote the epochs at which

$$\sum_{1 \le j < i} L_{j,T_{i-1,k}} = 0 \qquad (1 \le k < \infty),$$

$$0 = T_{i-1,0} < T_{i-1,1} < \cdots < T_{i-1,k} < \cdots,$$

$$\tau_{i-1,k} = T_{i-1,k} - T_{i-1,k-1} \qquad (1 \le k < \infty).$$

We have

$$\theta_{i-1}(w) = E\{w^{\tau_{i-1,k}}\} \qquad (1 < k < \infty), \tag{6.101}$$

where $\theta_{i-1}(w)$ satisfies

$$\theta_{i-1}(w) - w \prod_{1 \le j < i} P_j(\theta_{i-1}(w)) = 0 \qquad (|w| < 1, |\theta_{i-1}(w)| < 1). \tag{6.102}$$

The *embedded process* $\{L_{i,T_{i-1,k}}\}$ satisfies the equation

$$L_{i,T_{i-1,k}} = (L_{i,T_{i-1,k}} - 1)^+ + \sum_{T_{i-1,k-1} < j \le T_{i-1,k}} X_{i,j} \qquad (1 \le k < \infty) \tag{6.103}$$

and converges in distribution:

$$L_i^* = \lim_{k \to \infty} L_{i,T_{i-1,k}},$$

$$H_i^*(z) = \lim_{k \to \infty} E\{z^{L_{T_{i-1,k}}}\}.$$

The arrival process to the ith terminal between service epochs,

$$Y_{i,k} = \sum_{T_{i-1,k-1} < j \le T_{i-1,k}} X_{i,j} \qquad (1 < k < \infty),$$

is a renewal process with generating function $\theta_{i-1}(P_i(z))$ having expectation

$$\mu_i / (1 - \mu_1 - \cdots - \mu_{i-1}),$$

so that

$$H_i^*(z) = \frac{1 - \mu_1 - \cdots - \mu_i}{1 - \mu_1 - \cdots - \mu_{i-1}} \frac{(z-1)\theta_{i-1}(P_i(z))}{z - \theta_{i-1}(P_i(z))} \tag{6.104}$$

provided $\mu_1 + \cdots + \mu_i < 1$. From (6.92) and (6.104) we may find the expectation of L_i^*. First some notation. If $F(z)$ is a probability generating function, define

$$M_1\{F\} = (d/dz)F(z)_{z=1},$$

$$M_2\{F\} = (d^2/dz^2)F(z)_{z=1} + (d/dz)F(z)_{z=1} - [(d/dz)F(z)_{z=1}]^2.$$

If F is the probability generating function of the random variable X, then

$$M_1\{F\} = E\{X\}, \qquad M_2\{F\} = \text{Var}\{X\}.$$

If F and G are probability generating functions, then $H(z) = F(G(z))$ is a probability generating function. A simple computation shows

$$M_1\{H\} = M_1\{F\}M_1\{G\}, \tag{6.105}$$

$$M_2\{H\} = M_2\{F\}M_2^2\{G\} + M_1\{F\}M_2\{G\}. \tag{6.106}$$

We have

$$M_1\{\theta_{i-1}\} = 1/(1 - \mu_1 - \cdots - \mu_{i-1}), \tag{6.107}$$

$$M_2\{\theta_{i-1}\} = \sum_{i \leq j < i} \sigma_j^2 \Big/ (1 - \mu_1 - \cdots - \mu_{i-1})^3. \tag{6.108}$$

Equations (6.105)–(6.108) provide expressions for the mean and variance of $\{Y_{i,k}\}$. Using (6.92) we then obtain the expectation of L_i^*.

Finally we consider the queueing delay. Suppose a virtual message of m packets enters the ith terminal just before the start of the jth slot. This message will be delayed by

(i)   all packets already in the network at terminals $1, 2, \ldots, i$ at time $(j-1)\Delta - 0$;
(ii) all packets which enter the network at terminals $1, 2, \ldots, i - 1$ before the last packet of the message enters service.

To find the queueing delay we consider the system

$$L_k = (L_{k-1} - 1)^+ + X_k \tag{6.109}$$

with

$$L_0 = m - 1 + L_{1,j-1} + \cdots + L_{i,j-1} \tag{6.110}$$

and

$$X_k = X_{1,k+j} + \cdots + X_{i-1,j+k}. \tag{6.111}$$

If $L_T = 0$ and $L_j \neq 0$, $0 \leq j < T$, then at the start of the $(T+j)$th slot the last packet of the virtual message will enter service. The queueing time of the virtual message is thus $T+1$. But

$$E\{w^T\} = F_{i,j}(\theta_{i-1}(w)), \tag{6.112}$$

where $F_{i,j}(z) = E\{z^{L_0}\}$. In equilibrium

$$F_i(z) = \lim_{j \to \infty} F_{i,j}(z)$$

$$= (1 - \mu_1 - \cdots - \mu_i) \frac{z^{m-1}(z-1)P_1(z) \times \cdots \times P_i(z)}{z - P_1(z) \times \cdots \times P_i(z)}. \tag{6.113}$$

If $W_i(m)$ is the (equilibrium) queueing delay with generating function $D_i(m)(z)$, then

$$D_i(m)(z) = (1 - \mu_1 - \cdots - \mu_i)$$

$$\times \frac{(w^{-1}\theta_{i-1}(w))^{m-1}(\theta_{i-1}(w) - 1)P_i(\theta_{i-1}(w))}{w - P_i(\theta_{i-1}(w))}. \tag{6.114}$$

The expected value of $W_i(m)$ is

$$E\{W_i(m)\} = -(m-1)$$

$$+ \frac{m - 1 + 0.5(\sigma_1^2 + \cdots + \sigma_i^2)/(1 - \mu_1 - \cdots - \mu_i) + 0.5(\mu_1 + \cdots + \mu_i)}{1 - \mu_1 - \cdots - \mu_{i-1}}. \tag{6.115}$$

From (6.115) we observe that $E\{W_i(m)\}$ is nondecreasing in i and m. Thus the terminals at the 'end' of the loop experience greater delays. We will consider ways of alleviating this in the next two sections.

6.7 Loops with priority

In this section we examine two related networks and show how the methods of the previous section can be extended. The quality of service in a loop network, as measured by queueing delay, depends upon position. If the users of the system have widely different rates $\{\mu_i\}$ of sending data, then this effect becomes even more pronounced. Of course we could run the 'bus' backwards if the terminals at the end were the big users, but this doesn't help terminals in the 'middle'. We will give a possible solution to the mismatch of position and service demanded by introducing priorities and the possibility of *exchange*. In the loop (Figure 6.9) a slot once claimed by a terminal was not relinquished. If we admit the possibility of relinquishing slots the situation is altered.

Let $\pi = (\pi_1, \pi_2, \ldots, \pi_n)$ be a permutation of the integers $1, 2, \ldots, n$. π will define priority of service in the loop in the sense that π_i-packets have priority over π_j-packets if $i < j$ and we will write

$$\mathbf{X}_{\pi_i} > \mathbf{X}_{\pi_j} \qquad (i < j).$$

If the tth slot upon reaching the kth terminal contains a π_j-packet and finds π_i-packets waiting for service an *exchange* is made; the π_j-packet 'gets off' and the slot is taken by the π_i-packet. Thus at the kth terminal there will be waiting packets from the $\mathbf{X}_{\pi_r}$-process for r such that $\pi_r^{-1} \geq \pi_i^{-1}$. We take as state variables $L_j[k \mid r]$, which are the number of $\mathbf{X}_r$-packets at the kth terminal at the start of the jth slot:

$$L_j[A \mid B] = \sum_{k \in A, r \in B} L_j[k \mid r].$$

We start as before with the equation of evolution:

$$
\begin{aligned}
L_j[i \mid \pi_1, \ldots, \pi_r] &= (L_{j-1}[i \mid \pi_1, \ldots, \pi_r] \\
&\quad - \chi_{(L_{j-1}[1, \ldots, i-1 \mid \pi_1, \ldots, \pi_r]=0)})^+ \\
&\quad + X_{i,j}\chi_{i \in \{\pi_1, \ldots, \pi_r\}}.
\end{aligned} \tag{6.116}
$$

To prove (6.116) let us observe that the number of $\{\mathbf{X}_{\pi_j} : 1 \leq j \leq r\}$ waiting at the ith terminal will be reduced by one (if there are any waiting) if and only if there are no such packets waiting at any of the first $i - 1$ terminals:

$$L_{j-1}[1, \ldots, i-1 \mid \pi_1, \ldots, \pi_r] = 0.$$

During the jth slot this number will be increased by $X_{i,j}$ arriving packets provided that $i \in \{\pi_1, \ldots, \pi_r\}$. This proves (6.116). On the other hand,

$$
L_j[1, \ldots, i \mid \pi_1, \ldots, \pi_r] = (L_{j-1}[1, \ldots, i \mid \pi_1, \ldots, \pi_r] - 1)^+
$$
$$
+ \sum_{s, 1 \leq s \leq i, s \in \{\pi_1, \ldots, \pi_r\}} X_{s,j} \tag{6.117}
$$

since once again the jth slot will carry away from the first i

terminals a packet of highest priority. Setting $i = n$ we have

$$L_i[1, \ldots, n \mid \pi_1, \ldots, \pi_r] = (L_{j-1}[1, \ldots, n \mid \pi_1, \ldots, \pi_r] - 1)^+$$

$$+ \sum_{1 \leqslant s \leqslant r} X_{i, \pi_s}. \tag{6.118}$$

Once again we have the equations for the loop network. In particular a slot will be available to remove $\{X_{\pi_s} : 1 \leqslant s \leqslant r\}$-packets from the ith terminal only at the renewal epochs of the $\{L_i[1, \ldots, i-1 \mid \pi_1, \ldots, \pi_r]\}$-process:

$$L_i[1, \ldots, i-1 \mid \pi_1, \ldots, \pi_r] = 0.$$

This provides us with formulas for the queueing delay. These renewal epochs have an *interepoch time* with generating function $\theta(w) = \theta_{i-1 \mid \pi_1, \ldots, \pi_r}(w)$ which satisfies

$$\theta(w) - w \sum_{s, 1 \leqslant s \leqslant i-1, s \in \{\pi_1, \ldots, \pi_r\}} P_s(\theta(w)) = 0. \tag{6.119}$$

To find the queueing delay we suppose that a virtual message of m X_{π_r}-packets enter the π_rth terminal at the start of the jth slot. There are

$$L_i[1, \ldots, n \mid \pi_1, \ldots, \pi_r]$$

packets already in the network the service of which will precede that of the virtual message. The virtual message will also be delayed by packets from the $\{X_{\pi_s} : 1 \leqslant s < r\}$-processes which enter before the last packet of the virtual message enters service. Consider the system

$$L_k = (L_{k-1} - 1)^+ + X_k \qquad (1 \leqslant k < \infty) \tag{6.120}$$

with

$$L_0 = m - 1 + L_{j-1}[1, 2, \ldots, n \mid \pi_1, \ldots, \pi_r], \tag{6.121}$$

$$X_k = \sum_{1 \leqslant s < r} X_{\pi_s, k+j} \qquad (1 \leqslant k < \infty). \tag{6.122}$$

The queueing time of the virtual message is $T + 1$ (slots), where $L_T = 0$ and $L_j \neq 0$, $0 \leqslant j < T$. In equilibrium, as $j \to \infty$, $E\{z^{L_0}\} \to H_r^*(z)$,

$$H_r^*(z) = (1 - \mu_1 - \cdots - \mu_r) \frac{z^{m-1}(z-1)P_{\pi_1}(z) \times \cdots \times P_{\pi_r}(z)}{z - P_{\pi_1}(z) \times \cdots \times P_{\pi_r}(z)},$$

$$\tag{6.123}$$

so that the equilibrium queueing delay $W_r(m)$ has generating function

$$D_r(z) = (1 - \mu_1 - \cdots - \mu_r)$$
$$\times \frac{(z^{-1}\theta_{\pi_1, \ldots, \pi_{r-1}}(z))^{m-1}(\theta_{\pi_1, \ldots, \pi_{r-1}}(z) - 1)P_{\pi_r}(\theta_{\pi_1, \ldots, \pi_{r-1}}(z))}{z - P_{\pi_r}(\theta_{\pi_1, \ldots, \pi_{r-1}}(z))}.$$

$$(6.124)$$

If we denote by $d_r(\pi)$ the expected value of $W_r(m)$, then

$$d_{\pi_r} = -(m-1)$$
$$+ \frac{m - 1 + 0.5(\sigma_{\pi_1}^2 + \cdots + \sigma_{\pi_r}^2)/(1 - \mu_{\pi_1} - \cdots - \mu_{\pi_r}) + 0.5(\mu_{\pi_1} + \cdots + \mu_{\pi_r})}{1 - \mu_{\pi_1} - \cdots - \mu_{\pi_{r-1}}}.$$

$$(6.125)$$

Consider the problem of choosing a priority structure π to 'minimize' the *delays*. There is no entirely satisfactory *objective* function to minimize. Two possibilities are

$$D_1(\pi) = \sum_{1 \leqslant r \leqslant n} d_r(\pi),$$

$$D_\infty(\pi) = \underset{1 \leqslant r \leqslant n}{\text{Max}}\, d_r(\pi).$$

We will prove

Theorem 6.7.1 *If* $\mu = (\mu_1, \ldots, \mu_n)$ *and* $\sigma^2 = (\sigma_1^2, \ldots, \sigma_n^2)$ *satisfy the* montonicity *condition* $\mu_i \leqslant \mu_j$ *if and only if* $\sigma_i^2 \leqslant \sigma_j^2$ *then* v *minimizes* $D_1(\pi)$ *if and only if*

$$\mu_{v_1} \leqslant \cdots \leqslant \mu_{v_n} \qquad (6.126)$$

with

$$\sigma_{v_i}^2 \leqslant \sigma_{v_{i+1}}^2 \quad if \quad \mu_{v_i} = \mu_{v_{i+1}}. \qquad (6.127)$$

Proof Given π and i, $1 \leqslant i \leqslant n$, define ζ by

$$\zeta_k = \begin{cases} \pi_k & \text{if } 1 \leqslant k \leqslant n, \quad k \neq i, i+1, \\ \pi_{i+1} & \text{if } k = i, \\ \pi_i & \text{if } k = i+1. \end{cases}$$

Let

$$A = \sum_{1 \leqslant k < i} \mu_{\pi_k}, \qquad B = \sum_{1 \leqslant k < i} \sigma_{\pi_k}^2.$$

Then

$$D_1(\pi) - D_1(\zeta) = 0.5(1-A)^{-1}\{(B+\sigma_i^2)(1-A-\mu_i)^{-1}$$
$$- (B+\sigma_{\pi_{i+1}}^2)(1-A-\mu_{\pi_{i+1}})^{-1} + \mu_{\pi_i} - \mu_{\pi_{i+1}}\}$$
$$+ \frac{\{m + 0.5(B+\sigma_{\pi_i}^2 + \sigma_{\pi_{i+1}}^2)(1-A-\mu_{\pi_i}-\mu_{\pi_{i+1}})^{-1}}{(1-A-\mu_{\pi_i})(1-A-\mu_{\pi_{i+1}})}.$$

$$(6.128)$$

There are two cases to be examined.

Case 1: $\mu_{\pi_i} \leqslant \mu_{\pi_{i+1}}$. The second term in (6.128) is nonpositive while for the first we have the upper bound

$$(\mu_{\pi_i} - \mu_{\pi_{i+1}})\{1 + (B+\sigma_{\pi_{i+1}}^2)(1-A-\mu_{\pi_i})^{-1}(1-A-\mu_{\pi_{i+1}})^{-1}\},$$

which is nonpositive. Thus $D_1(\pi) \leqslant D_1(\zeta)$.

We leave the proof of the second case to the reader. ∎

If the arrival processes $\{X_j\}$ are compound Poisson with generating function

$$P_j(z) = \exp \lambda_j[((1-q_j)z/(1-q_j z)) - 1]$$

then

$$\mu_j = \lambda_j/(1-q_j), \qquad \sigma_j^2 = \lambda_j(1+q_j)/(1-q_j)^2;$$

then they satisfy the monotonicity condition if $q_i = q$ independent of j.

The analysis given for the loop system allowing *exchanges* can be applied to a related problem. Consider the *cascade network* shown in Figure 6.10. This is an example of a *store-and-forward*

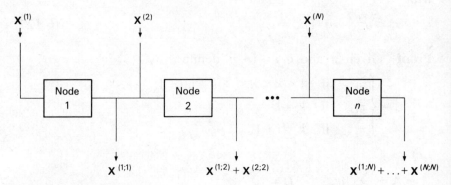

Fig. 6.10 Cascade network.

network. Think of the nodes as 'cities': node 1 is New York, node 2 is Chicago and node n is Los Angeles. A message from Chicago to Los Angeles enters node 2 and makes its way to Los Angeles passing through nodes $2, 3, \ldots, n$. The service operation is transmission. The mode of operation of the store-and-forward network is called *packet-switching.* A message is *packetized* – broken into equal size blocks called *packets* – which are individually sent through the network and assembled together at the final destination. The ARPA network is much more complicated than the one in Figure 6.10, admitting alternate routes to reach the destination.

The arrival process

$$\mathbf{X}_{(i;j)} = \{X_{(i;j),k} : 1 \leq k < \infty\},$$

$$\mu_{(i;j)} = E\{X_{(i;j),k}\},$$

$$\sigma_{(i;j)^2} = \mathrm{Var}\{X_{(i;j),k}\},$$

$$P_{(i;j)}(z) = E\{z^{X_{(i;j),k}}\}$$

describes the packets with *origin i* and *destination j.* We assume independence of the arrival processes. The network allows the possibility of exchanges. It remains to define the *queue discipline.* Consider a permutation of the indices $\{(i;j)\}$ defining an ordering

$$(i_1; j_1) > \cdots > (i_m; j_m) \qquad (m = n(n-1)/2). \tag{6.129}$$

We will say that $(i_a; j_a)$-packets *have priority over* $(i_b; j_b)$-packets if $a < b$. When a slot reaches a node, it is claimed by the packet of highest priority either currently using the slot or waiting at the node. We introduce the state variables $L_t[k \mid (i; j)]$, which are the number of $(i; j)$-packets waiting at node k at the start of the tth slot:

$$L_t[A \mid B] = \sum_{k \in A, (i_s; j_s) \in B} L_t[k \mid (i_s; j_s)].$$

The processes $\{\mathbf{X}_{(i;j)}\}$ do not entirely interfere with one another. For example, the $(1; 1)$-process does not interfere with the $(2; 2)$-processes because the former packets have left the network before the latter packets enter. Let

$$P_{[k \mid (i;j)]} = \{(i_a; j_a) : (i_a; j_a) > (i; j) \text{ and } i_a \leq k \leq j_a\} \qquad (i \leq k \leq j);$$

$P_{[k \mid (i;j)]}$ is the set of processes which can interfere with $\mathbf{X}_{(i;j)}$ at node k.

We will only analyze one of the orderings (6.129):

$$(1; n) > (2; n) > \cdots > (n; n) > (1; n-1)$$
$$> (2, n-1) > \cdots > (n-1; n-1) > \cdots > (1; 1). \qquad (6.130)$$

We have

$$P_{[k \mid (i;j)]} = \{(s; t) : t > j, 1 \leq s \leq k\}$$
$$\cup \{(s; j) : 1 \leq s \leq i\} \qquad (i \leq k \leq j).$$

Lemma 6.7.2 *Under* (6.130) *an* $(i; j)$-*packet will leave the sub-network of nodes* $1, 2, \ldots, k$ *in the tth slot if and only if there are no* $P_{[i \mid (i;j)]}$-*packets in this subnetwork waiting for service at time* $(t - 1)\Delta - 0$.

Proof Of course what we are asserting is that

$$L_t[1, \ldots, k \mid (i; j)] = (L_t[1, \ldots, k \mid (i; j)] - \chi_{L_t[1, \ldots, n \mid P[k \mid (i;j)]] = 0})^+$$
$$+ X_{(i;j),t}, \qquad (6.131)$$

$$L_t[1, \ldots, k \mid (i; j) \cup P_{[k \mid (i;j)]}] = (L_t[1, \ldots, k \mid (i;j) \cup P_{[k \mid (i;j)]} - 1)^+$$
$$+ \sum_{1 \leq r < i, s > j} X_{(r;s),k}$$
$$+ \sum_{1 \leq r \leq k} X_{(r;j),t}, \qquad (6.132)$$

which we recognize as the equations for the loop system.

Among the $P_{[k \mid (i;j)]} \cup (i; j)$-packets in the subnetwork, let $(r; s)$ have the highest priority. Then the tth slot will come to some node in the subnetwork containing an $(r; s)$-packet and such a packet will leave the subnetwork. This proves (6.131), (6.132), and the lemma. ∎

The queueing delay for $(i; j)$-packets may now be obtained by considering the renewal epochs of the $\{L_t[1, \ldots, j \mid P_{[j \mid (i;j)]}]\}$-process, the interepoch interval having generating function $\theta_{(i;j)}(w)$:

$$\theta_{(i;j)}(w) - w \prod_{1 \leq r \leq j, s > j} P_{(r;s)}(\theta_{(i;j)}(w)) \prod_{1 \leq r < i} P_{(r;j)}(\theta_{(i,j)}(w)) = 0.$$

Two concluding remarks:

(i) The ordering (6.130) may be replaced by

$$(i_1; j_1) > \cdots > (i_m; j_m), \qquad j_r \geq j_s \quad \text{if} \quad r \leq s$$

and the conclusion of Lemma 6.7.2 remains true.

(ii) In a loop network we may model the flow of data *from* the processor *to* the terminals by representing this latter flow by a 0th terminal and imposing a priority structure on service.

6.8 Polling

To remove the effect of position in a loop system on service, a generalization of the round-robin discipline, usually referred to as *polling*, has been proposed and implemented. Figure 6.11 represents a *multi-drop* network.

The terminals are polled (in the order $1, 2, \ldots, n$) and asked if they have data to send to the processor. When the ith terminal is polled and responds affirmatively, it holds the channel until all packets have been removed. The host then polls the $(i+1)$th terminal and the process continues. A poll of each of the n terminals is a *cycle*. Let $L_{i,j}$ be the number of packets at ith terminal at start of jth slot, U_j be the state of the jth slot:

$$U_j = \begin{cases} i & \text{if the } j\text{th slot is available to the } i\text{th terminal,} \\ 0 & \text{otherwise.} \end{cases}$$

Then

$$L_{i,j} = (L_{i,j-1} - \chi_{(U_{j-1}=i)})^+ + X_{i,j}. \tag{6.133}$$

Between the *end* of the transmission from the ith terminal to the *start* of the transmission of the $(i+1)$th terminal, the terminals are kept waiting due to system *overhead*. We refer to it as a *reply time*; it corresponds to the state $U_j = 0$. As in previous sections we

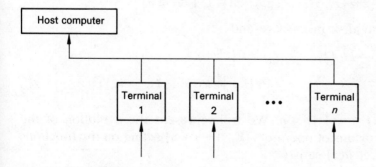

Fig. 6.11 Multi-drop network.

assume that the arrival processes

$$\mathbf{X}_i = \{X_{i,j} : 1 \leq j < \infty\}$$

are independent renewal processes. We will give an analysis only for the case of identically distributed processes.

$$P(z) = E\{z^{X_{i,j}}\},$$

$$\mu = E\{X_{i,j}\},$$

$$\sigma^2 = \mathrm{Var}\,\{X_{i,j}\}.$$

The random process (6.133)

$$\mathbf{L} = \{L_j = (L_{1,j}, L_{2,j}, \ldots, L_{n,j})\}$$

has natural renewal epochs

$$0 = \tau_{1,1} < \tau_{1,2} < \cdots < \tau_{1,n} < \tau_{2,1} < \cdots,$$

where $\tau_{i,j}$ is the time in the ith cycle at which the channel is made available to the jth terminal. Let $\nu_{i,j}$ be the time in the poll of the jth terminal in the ith cycle at which the buffer is first empty. Thus

$$\tau_{i,j} < \nu_{i,j} < \tau_{i,j+1}.$$

We assume that the reply times

$$\{\tau_{i,j+1} - \nu_{i,j}\}$$

are independent and identically distributed with generating function

$$R(z) = E\{z^{\tau_{i,j+1} - \nu_{i,j}}\}.$$

The random process $\mathbf{L}$ itself is *not* a Markov chain, but when we observe it at the renewal epochs $\{\tau_{i,j}\}$ it is Markovian. Let

$$D^n = \{z = (z_1, z_2, \ldots, z_n) : |z_i| \leq 1, 1 \leq i \leq n\}$$

be the (poly)disk in n-space and

$$H_{i,j}(z) = H_{i,j}(z_1, \ldots, z_n) = E\{z^{L_{i,j}}\} =$$

$$\sum_{0 \leq k_1 < \infty, \ldots, 0 \leq k_n < \infty} \Pr\{L_{\tau_{1,j}} = k_1, \ldots, L_{\tau_{n,j}} = k_n\} z_1^{k_1} \times \cdots \times z_n^{k_n},$$

where $1 \leq i < \infty$, $1 \leq j \leq n$. We will represent the evolution of the system by means of operators $\{\mathbf{E}_j : 1 \leq j \leq n\}$ acting on the functions $\{H_{i,j}(z)\}$. Let $\theta(z)$ satisfy

$$\theta(z) - zP(\theta(z)) = 0 \qquad (6.134)$$

and define the operator $\mathbf{E}_j$ by

$$\mathbf{E}_j : H(z_1, \ldots, z_n) \rightarrow$$

$$R\left(\prod_{1 \leq k \leq n} P(z_k) H\left(z_1, \ldots, z_{j-1}, \theta\left(\prod_{1 \leq k \leq n, k \neq j} P(z_k) \right), z_{j+1}, \ldots, z_n \right) \right).$$

$$(6.135)$$

Lemma 6.8.1

$$(\mathbf{E}_j H_{i,j})(z) = \begin{cases} H_{i,j+1}(z) & if \quad 1 \leq j < n, \\ H_{i+1,1}(z) & if \quad j = n. \end{cases}$$

Proof From time $\tau_{i,j}$ to $\nu_{i,j}$ data is being removed from the ith terminal (at the rate of one packet per slot) until (at time $\nu_{i,j}$) the buffer is empty. The length of the interval $\nu_{i,j} - \tau_{i,j}$ is distributed as the time to the first renewal epoch of the buffer studied in Section 6.4 (equation (6.71)). Thus

$$H_{i,j}(z_1, \ldots, z_{j-1}, \theta(w), z_{j+1}, \ldots, z_n)$$

is the generating function of

(i) the number of packets buffered all terminals excluding the jth terminal at time $\tau_{i,j}$, and
(ii) the length of the interval $\nu_{i,j} - \tau_{i,j}$.

While packets are being removed from the jth terminal, packets are also arriving at the remaining $n-1$ terminals. In an interval of m slots,

$$\prod_{1 \leq k \leq n, k \neq j} P^m(z_k)$$

is the generating function of the number of entering packets, so that

$$\theta\left(\prod_{1 \leq k \leq n, k \neq j} P(z_k) \right)$$

is the generating function for the compound process of the number of entering packets over the interval $\nu_{i,j} - \tau_{i,j}$. Thus

$$H_{i,j}\left(z_1, \ldots, z_{j-1}, \theta\left(\prod_{1 \leq k \leq n, k \neq j} P(z_k) \right), z_{j+1}, \ldots, z_n \right)$$

is the generating function at time $\nu_{i,j}$. Since $\tau_{i,j+1} - \nu_{i,j}$ has generating function $R(z)$,

$$R\left(\prod_{1 \leqslant k \leqslant n} P(z_k)\right)$$

is the generating function of the number of arrivals in the reply interval. ∎

Remarks The *embedded* process $\{L_{\tau_{i,j}}\}$ is a Markov chain with nonstationary transition function; that is, the transition matrix

$$Q_j : L_{\tau_{i,j}} \to L_{\tau_{i+1,j}}$$

depends on j. The usual way of studying Markov chains is to consider iterates of the transition operator (matrix) and their effect on a state probability vector. It is convenient in this analysis to associate a generating function with the state probability and to represent the action of the transition matrix on the state probability by an operator on the generating function. Thus $\mathbf{E}_j$ corresponds to the transition matrix Q_j.

While $\{L_{\tau_{i,j}}\}$ is not stationary, $\{L_{\tau_{i,1}}\}$ is stationary with transition matrix

$$Q = Q_n \times \cdots \times Q_1$$

and operator

$$\mathbf{E} = \mathbf{E}_n \times \cdots \times \mathbf{E}_1.$$

$\mathbf{E}$ is the *cycle* operator. We will prove

(i) $(\mathbf{E}^n H_{1,1})(z) \to H_1^*(z)$ as $n \to \infty$ *independent* of the initial state $H_{1,1}(z)$;
(ii) $(\mathbf{E}H_1^*)(z) = H_1^*(z)$.

Theorem 6.8.2 *If* $E\{R\} = r < \infty$ *and* $n\mu < 1$, *then* $(\mathbf{E}H_1^*)(z) = H_1^*(z)$ *has a unique solution*

$$H_1^*(z) = \prod_{0 \leqslant j < \infty} R\left(\prod_{1 \leqslant k \leqslant n} P(V_{1+j-k}(z))\right) \qquad (6.136)$$

where

$$
V_{(k)}(z_1, \ldots, z_n) = \begin{cases} z_{1-k} & \text{if} \quad -(n-1) \leqslant k \leqslant 0, \\ \theta \left(\prod_{1 \leqslant i < n} P(z_i) \right) & \text{if} \quad k = 1, \\ \theta \left(\prod_{1 \leqslant i < n} P(V_{(k-i)}(z)) \right) & \text{if} \quad 1 < k < \infty. \end{cases}
$$

$$(6.137)$$

Proof   We begin by proving

Lemma 6.8.3

$$V_{(k+j-1)}(z) = V_{(j)}(V_{(k-1)}(z), V_{(k-2)}(z), \ldots, V_{(k-n)}(z))$$
$$(1 \leqslant k < \infty, \ -(n-1) \leqslant j < \infty). \tag{6.138}$$

Proof of Lemma 6.8.3   For $-(n-1) \leqslant j \leqslant 0$, (6.138) follows from the definition (6.137) of the functions $\{V_{(k)}\}$. For $0 < j < \infty$ the proof is by induction on j. If (6.138) holds for $j < s$, then for $j = s$ the right-hand side of (6.138) is by (6.137) equal to

$$\theta \left(\prod_{1 \leqslant i < n} P(V_{(s-i)}(z), V_{(k-1)}(z), V_{(k-2)}(z), \ldots, V_{(k-n)}(z)) \right),$$

$$(6.139)$$

to which we may apply the induction hypothesis, obtaining

$$\theta \left(\prod_{1 \leqslant i < n} P(V_{(s+k-1-i)}(z)) \right). \tag{6.140}$$

Using (6.53) we recognize that (6.140) is $V_{(s+k-1)}(z)$, which completes the induction proof.   ∎

We now make use of the hypothesis that the $\{X_i\}$ have the same distribution. If $H_1^*(z)$ is invariant under $\mathbf{E}$, then

$$(\mathbf{E}_1 H_1^*)(z_1, z_2, \ldots, z_n) = H_1^*(z_2, z_3, \ldots, z_n, z_1). \tag{6.141}$$

There are two ways of proving (6.141):

(i) The statistical indistinguishability of the terminals implies that the system loses track of the 'name' of the terminal. Thus, in equilibrium, after the first terminal is served, the $(i+1)$th terminal must 'look like' the ith terminal in the sense of distribution.

(ii) If $\varphi : (H(z_1, \ldots, z_n) \rightarrow H(z_2, \ldots, z_n, z_1)$, then

$$\mathbf{E}_j = \varphi^{(j-1)} \mathbf{E}_1 \varphi^{-(j-1)},$$

so that

$$\mathbf{E} = (\varphi^{-1} \mathbf{E}_1)^n.$$

The equality

$$F^{(*}(z) = (\mathbf{E} F^{(*}(z))$$

implies

$$H_1^*(z) = (\varphi^{-1} \mathbf{E}_1 H_1^*)(z).$$

We may write (6.141) as

$$H_1^*(z_1, \ldots, z_n)$$
$$= R\left(\prod_{1 \leqslant k \leqslant n} P(z_k) \right) H_1^* \left(\theta\left(\prod_{1 \leqslant k < n} P(z_k) \right), z_1, \ldots, z_{n-1} \right), \qquad (6.142)$$

which may be expressed as

$$H_1^*(V_{(0)}, V_{(-1)}, \ldots, V_{(-n+1)})$$
$$= R\left(\prod_{1 \leqslant k \leqslant n} P(V_{(1-k)}) \right) H_1^*(V_{(1)}, V_{(0)}, \ldots, V_{(2-n)}). \qquad (6.143)$$

By an induction argument (which we leave to the reader)

$$H_1^*(V_{(j)}, V_{(j-1)}, \ldots, V_{(1+j-n)})$$
$$= R\left(\prod_{1 \leqslant k \leqslant n} P(V_{(1+j-k)}) \right) H_1^*(V_{(j+1)}, V_{(j)}, \ldots, V_{(2+j-n)}), \qquad (6.144)$$

where $0 \leqslant j < \infty$. Setting aside the question of convergence, equation (6.144) provides the formula of (6.136). Thus it remains for us to establish the convergence of (6.136).

Let $\boldsymbol{F}^n$ denote the class of generating function of n-dimensional (nonnegative integer-valued) random variables. If $K \in \boldsymbol{F}^n$ has bounded partial derivatives in the open unit (poly)disk

$$\{(z_1, \ldots, z_n) : |z_1| < 1, \ldots, |z_n| < 1\}$$

then

$$|1 - K(z_1, \ldots, z_n)| \leqslant \sum_{1 \leqslant i \leqslant n} |z_i - 1| \, |(\partial/\partial z_i)K|_{z_i = 1 (1 \leqslant j \leqslant n)}.$$

Each term of (6.136) is a probability generating function to which we may apply the estimate so that (6.136) converges provided

$$\sum_{0\leq j<\infty} \left| 1 - R\left(\prod_{1\leq k\leq n} P(V_{(1+j-k)}(z_1, \ldots, z_n)) \right) \right| < \infty \qquad (6.145)$$

and (6.145) is satisfied if

$$\sum_{0\leq j<\infty} \sum_{1\leq i<n} (\partial/\partial z_i) R\left(\prod_{1\leq k\leq n} P(V_{(1+j-k)}(z_1, \ldots, z_n)) \right) \Bigg|_{z_j=1(1\leq j<n)} \qquad (6.146)$$

Let

$$a_{j,i} = (\partial/\partial z_i) V_{(j)}(z_1, \ldots, z_n)|_{z_j=1(1\leq j\leq n)}. \qquad (6.147)$$

Then we must verify that

$$\sum_{1\leq i<\infty} \sum_{0\leq j\leq n} \sum_{1\leq k\leq n} r\mu a_{1+j-k,i} < \infty. \qquad (6.148)$$

The double sequence $\{a_{j,i}\}$ satisfies the recurrence

$$a_{j,i} = \begin{cases} 0 & \text{if} \quad -(n-1)\leq j\leq 0, \quad j\neq i, \\ 1 & \text{if} \quad j=1-i, \\ \mu/(1-\mu) & \text{if} \quad j=1, \quad i\neq n, \\ 0 & \text{if} \quad j=1, \quad i=n, \end{cases} \qquad (6.149)$$

and

$$a_{j,i} = [\mu/(1-\mu)] \sum_{1\leq s<n} a_{j-s,i} \quad (1\leq i\leq n, 1\leq j<\infty). \qquad (6.150)$$

To solve (6.149) and (6.150) we introduce the generating functions

$$A_i(z) = \sum_{1\leq j<\infty} a_{j,i} z^j \quad (1\leq i\leq n, |z|<1) \qquad (6.151)$$

Then from (6.149) and (6.150) we have

$$A_i(z) = \frac{z\mu(1-z^{n-i})/(1-\mu)(1-z)}{1-\mu(z-z^n)/(1-\mu)(1-z)}. \qquad (6.152)$$

We now see that our formal operations are valid – the $\{A_i(z)\}$ have a positive radius of convergence. The singularities of $A_i(z)$ are the points at which

$$0 = 1 - \frac{\mu(z-z^n)}{(1-\mu)(1-z)}. \qquad (6.153)$$

If

$$1 > \frac{(n-1)\mu}{1-\mu}$$

or equivalently $n\mu < 1$, then

$$1 > \left| \frac{\mu(z-z^n)}{(1-\mu)(1-z)} \right|$$

on $|z| = 1$, so that by Rouché's theorem the denominator of (6.152) is free of zeros in the unit disk $\{z : |z| \leqslant 1\}$. Thus the functions $\{A_i(z)\}$ are analytic in $\{z : |z| < \rho\}$ for some $\rho > 1$. Finally

$$A_i(1) = \frac{(n-i)\mu}{(1-n\mu)}. \tag{6.154}$$

This completes the proof of Theorem 6.8.2. ∎

Observation If the infinite product (6.136) converges, this necessitates

$$1 = \lim_{j \to \infty} R\left(\prod_{1 \leqslant k \leqslant n} P(V_{(1+j-k)}(z)) \right).$$

The proof of convergence of the product (6.136) provides us with the value of

$$\lim_{i \to \infty} E\{L_{\tau_{i,1}}\}.$$

We have

$$H_1^*(z_1, 1, 1, \ldots, 1) = \prod_{0 \leqslant j < \infty} R\left(\prod_{1 \leqslant k \leqslant n} P(V_{(1+j-k)}(z_1, 1, 1, \ldots, 1)) \right). \tag{6.155}$$

Using the notation $M_i\{\cdot\}$ $(i = 1, 2)$ introduced in Section 6.6 and equations (6.105) and (6.106),

$$M_1\{H_1^*\} = \sum_{0 \leqslant j < \infty} M_1\{R\} \left(M_1\{P\} \prod_{i \leqslant k \leqslant n} M_1\{Y_{(1+j-k)}\} \right), \tag{6.156}$$

where

$$Y_{(j)}(z_1) = V_j(z_1, 1, 1, \ldots, 1)$$

and

$$\underline{H}_1^*(z) = H_1^*(z, 1, 1, \ldots, 1).$$

But

$$M_1\{\underline{Y}_{(j)}\} = a_{j,1}, \tag{6.157}$$

so that

$$M_1\{\underline{H}_1^*\} = r\mu\left[1 + \sum_{1 \leqslant j < \infty} \sum_{1 \leqslant k \leqslant n} a_{1+j-k,1}\right] = nr\mu(1-\mu)/(1-n\mu). \tag{6.158}$$

We shall need an expression for $M_2\{\underline{H}_1^*\}$ and we now turn to its computation. We start with (6.136).

$$M_2\{\underline{H}_1^*\} = M_2\{R(P)\} + \sum_{1 \leqslant j < \infty} M_2\left\{R\left(\prod_{1 \leqslant k < n} P(\underline{Y}_{(1+j-k)})\right)\right\}. \tag{6.159}$$

But

$$M_2\left\{R\left(\prod_{1 \leqslant k \leqslant n} P(\underline{Y}_{(1-j-k)})\right)\right\} = \delta^2\left\{\sum_{1 \leqslant k \leqslant n} a_{1+j-k,1}\mu\right\}^2$$
$$+ r \sum_{1 \leqslant k \leqslant n} \sigma^2 a_{1+j-k,1}^2 + \mu M_2\{\underline{Y}_{(1+j-k)}\}, \tag{6.160}$$

where

$$r = M_1\{R\}, \qquad \delta^2 = M_2\{R\}.$$

But from (6.150)

$$\sum_{1 \leqslant k \leqslant n} a_{1+j-k,1}\mu = \mu\left\{a_{j,1} + \sum_{2 \leqslant k \leqslant n} a_{1+j-k,1}\right\}$$
$$= \mu a_{j,1} + (1-\mu)a_{j,1} = a_{j,1}.$$

If we introduce the variable

$$\nu_j = \mu M_2\{\underline{Y}_{(j)}\} + \sigma^2 a_{j,1}^2 - \mu a_{j,1}$$

then we may write (6.159)

$$M_2\{\underline{H}_1^*\} = \delta^2\left\{\mu^2 + \sum_{1 \leqslant j < \infty} a_{j,1}^2\right\} + r\left\{\sigma^2 + \sum_{1 \leqslant j \leqslant n}\left\{\nu_j + a_{j,1} + \sum_{1 \leqslant k < n} \nu_{j-k}\right\}\right\}. \tag{6.161}$$

From (6.137),

$$M_2\{\underline{V}_j\} = [\sigma^2/(1-\mu)^3]\left\{\sum_{1\leqslant k<n} \mu a_{j-k,1}\right\}^2 + (1-\mu)^{-1}\sum_{1\leqslant k<n} \sigma^2 a_{j-k,1}^2$$
$$+ \mu M_2\{\underline{V}_{(j-k)}\},$$

which provides the recurrence relation

$$v_j = [\sigma^2/(1-\mu)]a_{j,1}^2 + [\mu/(1-\mu)]\sum_{1\leqslant k<n} v_{j-k} \qquad (1\leqslant j<\infty). \tag{6.162}$$

Introduce the generating functions

$$V(z) = \sum_{1\leqslant j<\infty} v_j z^j, \qquad B(z) = \sum_{1\leqslant j<\infty} a_{j,1}^2 z^j.$$

We deduce from (6.162) that

$$V(z)\left[1 - \frac{\mu}{1-\mu}\frac{z-z^{n-1}}{1-z}\right] = B(z)\frac{\mu}{1-\mu} + (\sigma^2-\mu)\frac{\mu}{1-\mu}\frac{z-z^{n-1}}{1-z}, \tag{6.163}$$

which gives

$$V(1) = \frac{(\sigma^2-\mu)\mu(n-1)+\sigma^2 B(1)}{(1-n\mu)}. \tag{6.164}$$

Equations (6.161)–(6.163) give the result

$$M_2\{H_1^*\} = \frac{nr\sigma^2}{1-n\mu}[(1-\mu)+B(1)] + \delta^2(\mu^2+B(1)), \tag{6.165}$$

so that it remains to calculate $B(1)$. We have

$$A_1(z) = \frac{z\mu(1-z^{n-1})/(1-\mu)(1-z)}{1-\mu(z-z^n)/(1-\mu)(1-z)}, \tag{6.166}$$

so that by Parseval's theorem

$$B(1) = (1/2\pi)\int_0^\pi A_1(e^{i\theta})A_1(e^{-i\theta})\,d\theta.$$

We will evaluate this integral by Cauchy's theorem as the contour integral

$$B(1) = (1/2\pi i)\oint_\Gamma z^{-1}A_1(z)A_1(1/z)\,dz,$$

the contour being the unit circle $\Gamma = \{z : |z| = 1\}$. Let

$$\xi = \frac{\mu}{1-\mu}, \tag{6.167}$$

$$\omega(z) = \xi z^n - (1+\xi)z + 1, \tag{6.168}$$

$$\psi(z) = z^n \omega(1/z) = \xi - (1+\xi)z^{n-1} + z^n. \tag{6.169}$$

Then

$$z^{-1} A_1(z) A_1(1/z) = -\frac{\xi^2 (1-z^{n-1})^2}{\omega(z)\xi(z)}. \tag{6.170}$$

Note that (6.170), which is the integrand of the contour integral, is analytic at $z = 1$; while $\omega(1) = \psi(1) = 0$ we have

$$(d/dz)\psi(z)|_{z=1} = -(d/dz)\omega|_{z=1} = (1 - n\mu)/(1 - \mu) > 0.$$

We assert that $\psi(z)$ has $n - 1$ simple zeros in the unit disk. To prove this, write

$$\psi(z)/(1-z) = -z^{n-1} + \xi(1 - z^{n-1})/(1-z).$$

On $|z| = 1$ we have

$$|\xi(1-z^{n-1})/(1-z)| \leq (n-1)\xi < 1 = |z^{n-1}|,$$

so that by Rouché's theorem $\psi(z)$ and z^{n-1} have the same number of zeros. To prove that they are simple we suppose on the contrary that

$$\psi(y) = (d/dz)\psi(z)|_{z=y} = 0.$$

Then

$$\xi - (1+\xi)y^{n-1} + y^n = 0,$$

$$-(n-1)(1+\xi)y^{n-2} + ny^{n-1} = 0,$$

from which we conclude that y is real, $0 < y < 1$, and

$$y = (n-1)(1+\xi)/n = (n-1)/(n-n\mu).$$

But $\psi(1) = 0$ so that by Rolle's theorem $(d/dz)\psi(z)$ must vanish somewhere on the interval $y < z < 1$. But

$$(d/dz)\psi(z) = z^{n-2}[nz + (n-1)(1+\xi)],$$

which provides a contradiction.

Let $\{z_i : 1 \leqslant i < n\}$ denote the $n-1$ simple zeros of $\psi(z)$. The integral

$$B(1) = (1/2\pi i) \oint z^{-1} A_1(z) A_1(1/z) \, dz$$

can then be evaluated as the sum

$$B(1) = -\xi^2 \sum_{1 \leqslant j < n} \frac{(1 - z_j^{n-1})^2}{\psi'(z_j)\omega(z_j)}. \tag{6.171}$$

Next

$$\psi(z_j) = 0 = z_j^n - (1+\xi)z_j^{n-1} + \xi,$$
$$\psi'(z_j) = -z_j^{n-2}[(n-1)(1+\xi) - nz_j],$$
$$\omega(z_j) = \xi z_j^n - (1+\xi)z_j + 1,$$

so that

$$-\frac{\xi^2(1 - z_j^{n-1})^2}{\psi'(z_j)\omega(z_j)} = \frac{\xi z_j}{(1+\xi)[(n-1)(1+\xi) - Nz_j)]},$$

which gives

$$B(1) = \frac{\xi}{1+\xi} \sum_{1 \leqslant j < n} \frac{z_j}{(n-1)(1+\xi) - nz_j}. \tag{6.172}$$

Finally we write $\psi(z) = (z - z_1)(z - z_2) \times \cdots \times (z - z_{n-1})$ and evaluate the logarithmic derivative of $\psi(z)$ at $z = n^{-1}(n-1)(1+\xi)$,

$$(d/dz) \log \psi(z)|_{z=n^{-1}(n-1)(1+\xi)} = 0 = \frac{n}{(n-1)\xi - 1}$$

$$+ \sum_{1 \leqslant j \leqslant n} \frac{n}{(n-1)(1+\xi) - nz_j},$$

so that

$$B(1) = \frac{(n-1)\mu^2}{1 - n\mu}. \tag{6.173}$$

We have thus proved

Theorem 6.8.4 *If $n\mu < 1$ and*

$$\underline{H_1^*}(z) = H_1^*(z, 1, 1, \ldots, 1)$$

with $H_1^*(z_1, z_2, \ldots, z_n)$ given by (6.136), then

$$M_1\{H_1^*\} = nr\mu(1-\mu)/(1-n\mu), \tag{6.174}$$

$$M_2\{H_1^*\} = \delta^2\mu^2 n(1-\mu)/(1-n\mu) + [nr\sigma^2/(1-n\mu)][1-(n+1)\mu$$
$$+ (2n-1)\mu^2]. \tag{6.175}$$

Now we return to the question of the existence of the limit

$$\lim_{i\to\infty} H_{i,j}(z_1, z_2, \ldots, z_n).$$

A straightforward (but laborious) computation shows that

$$(\mathbf{E}H_{1,1})(z) = \prod_{1\leqslant j\leqslant n} R\left(\prod_{1\leqslant k\leqslant n} P(V_{(j-k)}(z))\right)$$
$$\times H_{1,1}(V_{(n)}(z), V_{(n-1)}(z), \ldots, V_{(1)}(z)). \tag{6.176}$$

Applying Lemma 6.8.3 we have

$$(\mathbf{E}^s H_{1,1})(z) = \prod_{1\leqslant j\leqslant sn} R\left(\prod_{1\leqslant k\leqslant n} P(V_{(j-k)}(z))\right)$$
$$\times H_{1,1}(V_{(sn)}(z), V_{(sn-1)}(z), \ldots, V_{((s-1)n+1)}(z)).$$
$$\tag{6.177}$$

But the convergence of the infinite product (6.136), as we have already noted, implies that the nth term converges to one. Thus

Theorem 6.8.5 *If $n\mu < 1$, $M_1\{R\} < \infty$, then $(\mathbf{E}_1^s H_{1,1})(z)$ converges to $H_1^*(z)$ (6.136) as $s \to \infty$.*

The analysis given for the limiting behavior of $H_{i,1}(z)$ is also valid for the limiting behavior of $H_{i,j}(z)$. If we set

$$H_j^*(z_1, \ldots, z_n) = \lim_{i\to\infty} H_{i,j}(z_1, \ldots, z_n)$$

then

Theorem 6.8.6 *If $n\mu < 1$, $r < \infty$, then*

$$\lim_{i\to\infty} H_{i,j}(z) = H_j^*(z) \tag{6.178}$$

exists, and with

$$H_j^*(z_1, \ldots, z_n) = H_1^*(z_j, \ldots, z_n, z_1, \ldots, z_{j-1}). \tag{6.179}$$

We have been studying an embedded process of the random process $\{L_j\}$. We understand how the contents of the buffers fluctuate, but only at the points at which service starts. If we ask the question, 'What is the expected contents of the buffer?' we are faced with a problem. First, $L_{i,j}$ – the contents of the ith buffer at the start of the jth slot – probably does not converge in distribution. I say 'probably' because the random process $\{L_j\}$ is not Markovian and we do not have a way to determine if a stationary law exists. On the other hand the ratio

$$AV_N\{L_{1,j}\} = (1/N) \sum_{0 \leq j < N} L_{1,j} \tag{6.180}$$

is an average of $L_{1,j}$ over the first N slots. We can write

$$AV_N\{L_{1,j}\} = (1/\{\tau_{M,1} + N - \tau_{M,1}\}) \left\{ \sum_{1 \leq k \leq M} \sum_{\tau_{k-1,1} \leq j < \tau_{k,1}} L_{1,j} \right.$$

$$\left. + \sum_{\tau_{k,1} \leq j < N} L_{1,j} \right\}. \tag{6.181}$$

In (6.181) M is the (random) number of cycles in the first N slots. As $N \to \infty$, we must have $M \to \infty$ (with probability one) so that the ratio N/M converges to the expected length of a cycle. The sum

$$\sum_{\tau_{k-1,1} \leq j < \tau_{k,1}} L_{1,j}$$

is over the $(k-1)$th cycle. Since the state at the *start* of a cycle converges in distribution, we will show that the average *over* a cycle converges in distribution. The final term in (6.181) will converge to zero as $N \to \infty$. The lemma we need is

Lemma 6.8.7 *If*

$$L_j = (L_{j-1} - 1)^+ + X_j$$

and

$$T = \min \{j : L_j = 0\}$$

then

$$E\left\{ \sum_{0 \leq n < T} w^n z^{L_n} \right\} = z \frac{H_0(z) - H_0(\theta(w))}{z - wP(z)}, \tag{6.182}$$

where $H_0(z) = E\{z^{L_0}\}$.

Proof

$$E\left\{\sum_{0\leqslant n<T} w^n z^{L_n}\right\} = \sum_{0\leqslant j<\infty}\sum_{0\leqslant n<j}\sum_{1\leqslant k<\infty} z^k w^n \Pr\{L_n = k, T = j\}$$

$$= \sum_{0\leqslant n<\infty}\sum_{1\leqslant k<\infty} z^k w^n \Pr\{L_n = k, T>n\}. \quad (6.183)$$

But $g_{n,k} = \Pr\{L_n = k, T>n\}$ are the probabilities discussed in Section 6.4 in relation to the problem of *gambler's ruin*, at which time we proved that

$$G(z, w) = \sum_{0\leqslant n<\infty}\sum_{0\leqslant k<\infty} g_{n,k} w^n z^k = \frac{zH_0(z) - wP(z)H_0(\theta(w))}{z - wP(z)}.$$

$$(6.184)$$

The right-hand side of (6.183) is clearly $G(z, w) - G(0, w)$, which gives (6.182). ∎

To find the expected length of a cycle (in equilibrium) we argue as follows. At the start of a cycle the expected length of the queue (at the first terminal) is $nr\mu/(1 - n\mu)$. The interval of time until the buffer at this terminal is empty has length $nr/(1 - \mu)$, so that the expected length of the interval until control is passed to the second terminal is

$$r + nr/(1 - \mu) = nr/(1 - \mu).$$

Since the input processes are identically distributed we have

Lemma 6.8.8 *If $n\mu < 1$ and $r < \infty$, then*

$$\lim_{m\to\infty} E\{\tau_{m,1} - \tau_{m-1,1}\} = nr/(1 - n\mu). \quad (6.185)$$

Let

$$A_{i,j}(z_1, \ldots, z_n) = E\left\{\sum_{\tau_{i,j}\leqslant k<\tau_{i,j+1}} z_1^{L_{k,1}} \times \cdots \times z_n^{L_{k,2}}\right\}. \quad (6.186)$$

Setting

$$z = z_j, \qquad w = \prod_{1\leqslant k\leqslant n,\, k\neq j} P(z_k)$$

in Lemma 6.8.7, we obtain

$$
E\left\{ \sum_{\tau_{i,j} \leq k < \nu_{i,j+1}} z_1^{L_{k,1}} \times \cdots \times z_n^{L_{k,n}} \right\}
$$

$$
= z_j \left(H_{i,j}(z_1, \ldots, z_n) - H_{i,j}\left(z_1, \ldots, z_{j-1}, \theta\left(\prod_{1 \leq k \leq n,\, k \neq j} P(z_k)\right),\right.\right.
$$

$$
\left.\left. \times z_{j+1}, \ldots, z_n\right)\right) \Big/ \left(z_j - \prod_{1 \leq k \leq n} P(z_k)\right).
$$

Note next that the generating function at time $\nu_{i,j}$ is

$$
H_{i,j}\left(z_1, \ldots, z_{j-1}, \theta\left(\prod_{1 \leq k \leq n,\, k \neq j} P(z_k)\right), z_{j+1}, \ldots, z_n\right)
$$

so that

$$
E\left\{ \sum_{\nu_{i,j} \leq k < \tau_{i,j+1}} z_1^{L_{k,1}} \times \cdots \times z_n^{L_{k,n}} \right\}
$$

$$
= H_{i,j}\left(z_1, \ldots, z_{j-1}, \theta\left(\prod_{1 \leq k \leq n,\, k \neq j} P(z_k)\right), z_{j+1}, \ldots, z_n\right)
$$

$$
\times \left(1 - R\left(\prod_{1 \leq k \leq n} P(z_k)\right)\right) \Big/ \left(1 - \prod_{1 \leq k \leq n} P(z_k)\right) \tag{6.187}
$$

Combining (6.187) and Lemma 6.8.8 we have proved.

Theorem 6.8.9 *If $n\mu < 1$, $r < \infty$, then*

$$
\lim_{m \to \infty} E\left\{ \tau_{m,1}^{-1} \sum_{0 \leq k < \tau_{m,1}} z_1^{L_{k,1}} \times \cdots \times z_n^{L_{k,n}} \right\} = H_1(z_1, \ldots, z_n)
$$

$$
= \frac{1 - n\mu}{nr} \frac{\sum_{1 \leq j \leq n} z_j \{ H_j^*(z_1, \ldots, z_n) - H_j^*(z_1, \ldots, z_{j-1}, \theta(\prod_{1 \leq k \leq n, k \neq j} P(z_k)), z_{j+1}, \ldots, z_n) \}}{z_j - \prod_{1 \leq k \leq n} P(z_k)}
$$

$$
+ \frac{1 - n\mu}{nr}\left(1 - R\left(\prod_{1 \leq k \leq n} P(z_k)\right)\right)
$$

$$
\times \frac{\sum_{1 \leq j \leq n} F_j^*(z_1, \ldots, z_{j-1}, \theta(\prod_{1 \leq k \leq n, k \neq j} P(z_k)), z_{j+1}, \ldots, z_n)}{1 - \prod_{1 \leq k \leq n} P(z_k)},
$$

$$
\tag{6.188}
$$

$$
H_1(z, 1, 1, \ldots, 1) = \frac{1 - n\mu}{nr}\left[\frac{H_1^*(z) - 1}{z - P(z)} + \frac{1 - H_1^*(z)}{1 - P(z)}\right]. \tag{6.189}
$$

We may now obtain the stationary expected queue length at a terminal by differentiating (6.189) at $z = 1$, obtaining

Theorem 6.8.10 *If $n\mu < 1$, $r < \infty$, then*

$$\lim_{N \to \infty} N^{-1}E\left\{\sum_{0 \leqslant k < N} L_{k,j}\right\} = 0.5\delta^2/2r + 0.5\sigma^2/(1 - n\mu)$$

$$+ 0.5nr\mu(1 - \mu)/(1 - n\mu). \qquad (6.190)$$

We will not discuss the question of queueing delay; details can be found in [92]. There are many unsolved problems related to polling:

(i)   What is the behavior of a system with arrival processes $\mathbf{X}_i = \{X_{i,j}\}$ which are *not* identically distributed?

(ii)   Is there some advantage to polling in a different order? Let us call

$$\{\pi_1, \ldots, \pi_m\}, \qquad \pi_i \in \{1, 2, \ldots, n\} \qquad (1 \leqslant i \leqslant m)$$

a *generalized polling sequence* (repetitions allowed) meaning that we intend to poll the terminals in the order terminal π_1 polled first, terminal π_2 polled second, . . . , terminal π_m polled mth. What generalized polling sequence is *best*?

(iii) Suppose we modify polling to allow only the transfer of a *maximum* of N packets on each poll. How does this system behave?

There is very little known concerning these problems. The second problem has been considered in [35] and the third in [94].

References

1   Abramson, N. The ALOHA system, in *Computer Communication Networks* (N. Abramson and F. F. Kuo, eds), Prentice Hall, Englewood Cliffs, N.J., 1973, pp. 501–517.

2   Abramson, N. and Kuo, F. F. (eds) *Computer Communication Networks*, Prentice-Hall, Englewood Cliffs, N.J., 1973.

3   Ahlfors, L. V. *Complex Analysis*, McGraw-Hill, New York, 1953.

4   Anderson, R. R. *et al.*, Simulation performance of ring-switched data network, *IEEE Trans. Comm.* **COM-20**, 576–591, 1972.

5   Avi-Itzhak, B. Heavy traffic characteristics of a circular data network, *Bell System Tech. J.*, **50**, 2521–2549, 1971.

6   Baskett, F., Chandy, K. M., Muntz, R. R., and Palacios, F. G. Open, closed and mixed networks of queues with different classes of customers, *JACM*, **22,** 248–260, 1975.

7   Bhat, U. N. Sixty years of queueing theory, *Management Sci.*, **15,** B280–B294, 1969.

8   Burke, P. J. The Output of a Queueing System, *Oper. Res.*, **4,** 699–704, 1956.

9   Burke, P. J. Output processes and tandem queues, in *Proceedings of the 22nd International Symposium on Computer Communication Networks and Teletraffic*, pp. 419–428, April 1972.

10 Buzen, J. P. Computational algorithms for closed queueing networks with exponential servers, *Comm. ACM*, **16,** 527–531, 1973.

11 Carleial, A. B. and Hellman, M. E. Bistable behavior of ALOHA-type systems, *IEEE Trans. Comm.*, **COM-23,** 401–410, 1975.

12 Chandy, K. M. The analysis and solutions for general queueing networks, in *Proceedings of the 6th Princeton Conference on Information Science and Systems*, pp. 224–228, 1972.

13 Chandy, K. M., Herzog, U., and Woo, L. Parametric analysis of queueing networks, *IBM J. Res. Dev.*, **19,** 36–42, 1975.

14 Chandy K. M., Herzog, U., and Woo, L. Approximate analysis of general queueing networks, *IBM J. Res. Dev.*, **19,** 43–49, 1975.

15 Chang, J. H. Terminal response times in data communication systems, *IBM J. Res. Dev.*, **19,** 43, 1975.

16 Chang, W. Sequential server queues for computer communication system analysis, *IBM J. Res. Dev.*, **19,** 272–282, 1975.

17 Cherry, W. P. and Disney, R. L. Some topics in queueing network theory, in *Mathematical Methods in Queueing Theory* (A. B. Clarke, ed.), Springer-Verlag, Berlin, 1974, pp. 23–44.

18 Chow, W.-M. Central server model for multiprogrammed computer system with different classes of jobs, *IBM J. Res. Dev.*, **19,** 314–320, 1975.

19 Chu, W. W. Buffer behavior for batch Poisson arrivals and single constant output, *IEEE Trans. Comm.*, **COM-18,** 613–618, 1970.

20 Chu, W. W. (ed) *Advances in Computer Communications*, Artech House, Dedham, Mass., 1974.

21 Chu, W. W. Demultiplexing considerations for statistical multiplexors, *IEEE Trans. Comm.*, **COM-20,** 603–609, 1972.

22 Chu, W. W. Asynchronous time-division multiplexing, in *Computer Communication Networks* (N. Abramson and F. F. Kuo, eds), Prentice Hall, Englewood Cliffs, N.J., 1973, pp. 237–268.

23 Chu, W. W. and Konheim, A. G. On the analysis and modeling of a class of computer communication systems, *IEEE Trans. Comm.*, **COM-20,** 645–660, 1972.

24 Chu, W. W. and Liang, L. C. Buffer behavior for mixed input traffic

and single control output rate, *IEEE Trans. Comm.*, **COM-20,** 230–235, 1972.

25 Closs, F. Packet arrival and buffer statistics in a packet switching node, in *Proceedings of the Third Data Communication Symposium,* St. Petersburg, Fla., pp. 12–17, November 1973.

26 Cohen, J. W. *The Single Server Queue,* North-Holland, Amsterdam, 1969.

27 Cooper, R. B. and Murray, G. Queues served in cyclic order, *Bell System Tech. J.,* **48,** 375–390, 1969.

28 Cooper, R. B. *Introduction to Queueing Theory,* Macmillan, London and New York, 1972.

29 Cox, D. R. *Renewal Theory,* Methuen, London, 1962.

30 Cox, D. R. A use of complex probabilities in theory of stochastic processes, *Proc. Cambridge Phil. Soc.,* **51,** 313–319, 1955.

31 Cox, D. R. and Smith, W. L. *Queues,* Methuen, London, 1958.

32 Daley, D. J. Note on queueing output processes, in *Mathematical Methods in Queueing Theory* (A. B. Clarke, ed.), Springer-Verlag, Berlin, 1974, pp. 23–44.

33 Davies, D. W. and Barber, D. L. A. *Communication Networks for Computers,* John Wiley, New York, 1973.

34 Doob, J. L. *Stochastic Processes,* John Wiley, New York, 1953.

35 Eisenberg, M. Queues with periodic service and changeover times, *Oper. Res.,* **2,** 440–451, 1972.

36 Farber, D. J. A ring network, *Datamation,* pp. 44–46, February 1975.

37 Farber, D. J. and Larson, K. The structure of a distributed computer system – the communication system, in *Proceedings of the 22nd International Symposium on Computer Communications, Networks and Teletraffic,* Brooklyn Polytechnic Institute, 1972.

38 Farmer, W. D. and Newhall, E. E. An experimental distributed switching system to handle bursty computer traffic, in *Proceedings of an ACM Symposium on Problems on the Optimization of Data Communication Systems,* Pine Mountain, Georgia, pp. 1–33, October 1969.

39 Feller, W. *An Introduction to Probability Theory and its Applications,* Vol. II, John Wiley, New York, 1966.

40 Foster, F. G. On stochastic matrices associated with certain queueing processes, *Ann. Math. Stat.,* **24,** 355–360, 1953.

41 Fraser, A. G. Spider – an experimental data communications system, *IEEE International Conference on Communications,* Minneapolis, pp. 21F-1–21F-10, June 1974.

42 Fraser, A. G. On the interface between computers and data communications systems, *Comm. ACM,* **15,** 566–573, 1972.

43 Fuchs, E. and Jackson, P. E. Estimates of distributions of random

variables for certain computer communications traffic models, in *Proceedings of an ACM Symposium on Problems on the Optimization of Data Communications Systems*, Pine Mountain, Georgia, pp. 202–225, October 1969.

44 Gall, D. A. and Müller, H. R. Waiting-time distribution and buffer overflow in priority queues systems, *IEEE Trans. Comm.*, **COM-20,** 865–877, 1972.

45 Gaver, D. P., Jr and Lewis, P. A. W. Probability models for buffer storage allocation problems, *JACM*, **18,** 186–198, 1971.

46 Gaver, D. P. and Shedler, G. S. Processor utilization in multiprogramming systems via diffusion approximations, *Oper. Res.*, **21,** 569–576, 1973.

47 Gavish, B. and Konheim, A. G. Computer communication via satellites – a queueing model, *IEEE Trans. Comm.*, **COM-25,** 140–147, 1975.

48 Gnedenko, B. V. and Kovalenko, I. N. *Introduction to Queueing Theory*, Israel Program for Scientific Translations, Jerusalem, 1968.

49 Gopinath, B., Mitra, D., and Sondhi, M. M. Formulas on queues in burst processes – I, *Bell System Tech. J.*, **52,** 9–33, 1973.

50 Gopinath, B. and Mitra, D. Buffering of data interrupted by a source with priority, in *Proceedings of the Fourth Asilomar Conference on Circuits and Systems*, 1970.

51 Gordon, W. J. and Newell, G. F. Closed queueing systems with exponential servers, *Oper. Res.*, **15,** 254–265, 1967.

52 Green, P. E., Jr and Lucky, R. W. (eds) *Computer Communications*, IEEE Press, New York, 1974.

53 Green, P. E., Jr. and Tang, D. T. Some recent developments in teleprocessing system optimization, *IEEE Intercon.*, **1,** 1–7, 1973.

54 Greenberg, I. Distribution-free analysis of M/G/1 and G/M/1 queues, *Oper. Res.*, **21,** 629–635, 1973.

55 Grimsdale, R. L. and Kuo, F. F. (eds), *Computer Communication Networks*, NATO Advanced Study Institute Series, Noordhoff, Leyden, The Netherlands, 1975.

56 Hashida, O. Gating multiqueues served in cyclic order, *Syst. Com. Contr.*, **1,** 1–8, 1970.

57 Hashida, O. Analysis of multiqueue, *Rev. Elec. Commun. Lab. Japan*, **20,** 189–199, 1972.

58 Hayes, J. F. and Sherman, D. N. Traffic analysis of a ring switched data transmission system, *Bell System Tech. J.*, **50,** 2947–2978, 1971.

59 Hayes, J. F. and Sherman, D. N. A study of data multiplexing techniques and delay performance, *Bell System Tech. J.*, **51,** 1983–2011, 1972.

60 Hayes, J. F. Performance models of an experimental computer communication system, *Bell System Tech. J.*, **53,** 225–259, 1974.

61 Heiman, D. and Neuts, M. F. The single server queue in discrete

numerical analysis IV, *Nav. Res. Log. Quart.*, **20,** 753–766, 1973.

62 Herzog, V. Optimal scheduling strategies for real-time computers, *IBM J. Res. Dev.*, **19,** 494–504, 1975.

63 Hsu, J. A general queueing model for buffer storage problems, *IEEE Trans. Comm.*, **COM-20,** 744–747, 1973.

64 Hsu, J. Buffer behavior with Poisson arrivals and geometric output process, *IEEE Trans. Comm.*, **COM-22,** 1940–1941, 1974.

65 Jackson, J. R. Two shop-like queueing systems, *Management Sci.*, **10,** 131–142, 1963.

66 Katz, S. and Konheim, A. G. Priority disciplines in a loop system, *JACM*, **21,** 340–349, 1974.

67 Kaye, A. R. Analysis of a distributed central loop for data transmission, in *Proceedings of the 22nd International Symposium on Computer-Communication Networks and Teletraffic*, Polytechnic Institute of Brooklyn, pp. 47–58, April 1972.

68 Keilson, J. *Green's Function Methods in Probability Theory*, Hafner Publishing Company, New York, 1965, pp. 147–172.

69 Kendall, D. G. Stochastic processes occurring in the theory of queues and their analysis by the method of imbedded Markov chain, *Ann. Math. Stat.*, **24,** 338–354, 1953.

70 Khintchine, A. Y. *Mathematical Methods in Queueing Theory*, Griffen, London, 1960.

71 Kingman, J. F. C. The heavy traffic approximation in the theory of queues, in *Proceedings of the Symposium on Congestion Theory* (W. Smith and W. Wilkinson, eds), University of North Carolina Press, Chapel Hill, 1965, pp. 137–159.

72 Kingman, J. F. C. A martingale inequality in the theory of queues, *Proc. Cambridge Phil. Soc.*, **59,** 359–361, 1963.

73 Kingman, J. F. C. Inequalities in the theory of queues, *R. Stat. Soc. J.*, **32,** 102–110, 1970.

74 Kleinrock, L. *Communication Nets*, McGraw-Hill, New York, 1964.

75 Kleinrock, R. A conservation law for a wide class of queueing disciplines, *Naval Res. Log. Quart.*, **12,** 181–192, 1965.

76 Kleinrock, R. Time-shared systems: a theoretical treatment, *JACM*, **14,** 242–261, 1967.

77 Kleinrock, R. Analytic and simulation methods in computer network design, in *Proceedings of the 1970 Spring Joint Computer Conference*, pp. 569–579, 1970.

78 Kleinrock, R. Scheduling, queueing and delays in time-shared systems and computer networks, in *Computer Communication Networks* (N. Abramson and F. F. Kuo, eds), Prentice-Hall, Englewood Cliffs, N.J., 1973, pp. 95–141.

79 Kleinrock, R. *Queueing Systems*, Vol. 1: *Theory*, John Wiley, New York, 1975.

80 Kleinrock, R. Performance models and measurements of the

ARPA computer network, in *Computer Communication Networks* (R. L. Grimsdale and F. F. Kuo, eds), Noordhoff, Leyden, 1975, pp. 63–88.

81 Kleinrock, L. and Lam, S. S. Packet switching in a multiaccess broadcast channel: performance evaluation, *IEEE Trans. Comm.*, **COM-23,** 410–423, 1975.

82 Kobayashi, H. Application of diffusion approximation to queueing networks, Part I, *JACM*, **21,** 316–328, 1974.

83 Kobayashi, H. Application of diffusion approximation to queueing networks, Part II, *JACM*, **21,** 459–469, 1974.

84 Kobayashi, H. Bounds for the waiting time in queueing systems, in *Computer Architecture and Networks* (E. Gelenbe and R. Mahl, eds), North-Holland/American Elsevier, New York, 1974.

85 Kobayashi, H. On discrete-time processes in a packetized communication system, *ALOHA System Technical Report B75-28*, University of Hawaii, February 1975.

86 Kobayashi, H. System design and performance analysis using analytic models, in *Software Modelling and Its Impact on Performance* (K. M. Chandy and R. T. Yeh, eds), Prentice-Hall, Englewood Cliffs, N.J., 1976. (Also *IBM Research Report RA75*.)

87 Kobayashi, H., Onozato, Y., and Huynh, D. An approximate method for design and analysis of an ALOHA system, *ALOHA System Technical Report*, University of Hawaii, March 1976.

88 Kobayashi, H. and Reiser, M. On generalization of job routing behavior in a queueing network model, *IBM Research Report RC-5252*, February 1975.

89 Konheim, A. G. and Meister, B. Service in a loop system, *JACM*, **19,** 92–108, 1972.

90 Konheim, A. G. and Meister, B. Two-way traffic in loop service systems, *Networks*, **1,** 291–301, 1972.

91 Konheim, A. G. and Meister, B. Distributions of queue lengths and waiting times in a loop with two-way traffic, *J. Comput. Syst. Sci.*, **7,** 506–521, 1973.

92 Konheim, A. G. and Meister, B. Waiting lines and times in a system with polling, *JACM*, **21,** 470–490, 1974.

93 Konheim, A. G. Service epochs in a loop system, in *Proceedings of the 22nd International Symposium on Computer-Communication Networks and Teletraffic*, pp. 125–143, April 1972.

94 Konheim, A. G. Chaining in a loop system, *IEEE Trans. Comm.*, **COM-24,** 203–209, 1976.

95 Konheim, A. G. An elementary solution of the queueing system G/G/1, *SIAM J. Comput.*, **4,** 540–545, 1975.

96 Konheim, A. G. and Reiser, M. A queueing model with finite waiting room and blocking, *JACM*, **23,** 328–341, 1976.

97   Kropfl, W. J. An experimental data block switching system, *Bell System Tech. J.*, **51**, 1147–1165, 1972.

98   Kuczma, A. The interrupted Poisson process as an overflow process, *Bell System Tech. J.*, **52**, 437–447, 1973.

99   Kuo, F. F. and Binder, R. D. Computer-communications by radio and satellite: the ALOHA system, in *Computer Communication Networks* (R. L. Grimsdalc and F. F. Kuo, eds), Noordhoff, Leyden, 1975, pp. 397–408.

100 Lewis, P. A. W. and Yue, P. C. Statistical analysis of series of events in computer systems, in *Statistical Computer Performance Evaluation* (W. Freiberger, ed.), Academic Press, New York and London, 1972, pp. 265–280.

101 Lindley, D. V. The theory of queues with a single server, *Proc. Cambridge Phil. Soc.*, **48**, 277–289, 1952.

102 Loéve, M. *Probability Theory*, D. Van Nostrand, Princeton, 1960.

103 Marks, B. I. State probabilities of M/M/1 priority queues, *Oper. Res.*, **21**, 974–987, 1974.

104 Marshall, K. T. Some inequalities in queueing, *Oper. Res.*, **16**, 651–665, 1968.

105 Martin, J. *System Analysis for Data Transmission*, Prentice-Hall, New York, 1967.

106 McDonald M. and Rudin, H., Jr Note on inherent and imposed priorities in packet switching, *IEEE Trans. Comm.*, **COM-22**, 1678–1681, 1974.

107 Meisling, T. Discrete-time queueing theory, *J. Oper. Res.*, **6**, 96–105, 1958.

108 Mirasol, N. M. The output of a M/G/∞ queueing system is Poisson, *Oper. Res.*, **11**, 282–284, 1963.

109 Muntz, R. R. Poisson departure processes and queueing networks, in *Proceedings of the Seventh Annual Princeton Conference on Information Science and Systems*, pp. 435–440, March 1973.

110 Neuts, M. F. Two queues in series with a finite intermediate waiting room, *J. Appl. Prob.*, **5**, 123–142, 1968.

111 Neuts, M. F. The single server queue in discrete numerical analysis I, *Nav. Res. Log. Quart.*, **20**, 297–304, 1973.

112 Neuts, M. F. and Klimko, E. The single server queue in discrete numerical analysis III, *Nav. Res. Log. Quart.*, **20**, 557–567, 1973.

113 Newell, G. F. *Applications of Queueing Theory*, Chapman and Hall, London, 1971.

114 Newell, G. F. Graphical representation of queues evolution for multiple-server systems, in *Mathematical Methods in Queueing Theory* (A. B. Clarke, ed.), Springer-Verlag, Berlin, 1974, pp. 63–80.

115 Newhall, E. E. and Venetsanopoulos, A. N. Computer-

communications – representative systems, in *Proceedings of IFIP 1971*, North-Holland, Amsterdam, 1971, pp. 545–552.

116 O'Donovan, T. M. Direct solution of M/G/1 processor-sharing models, *Oper. Res.*, **22,** 1234–1235, 1974.

117 Pack, C. D. The effects of multiplexing on a computer-communication system, *Comm. ACM*, **16,** 161–168, 1973.

118 Pack, C. D. The optimum design of a random computer buffer in a remote data collection, *IEEE Trans. Comm.*, **COM-22,** 1501–1504, 1974.

119 Pawlikowski, K. Queue length distribution in some loop computer network, *Bull. Acad. Pol. Sci. Ser. Sci. Tech.*, **XXII** (6), 55–62, 1974.

120 Pawlikowski, K. Virtual delay distributions in some loop computer networks, *Bull. Acad. Pol. Sci. Ser. Sci. Tech.*, **XXII** (7), 63–69, 1974.

121 Pedersen, R. D. and Shah, J. C. Multiserver queue storage requirements with unpacked messages, *IEEE Trans. Comm.*, **COM-20,** 462–465, 1972.

122 Pierce, J. R. Network for block switching of data, *Bell System Tech. J.*, **51,** 1133–1145, 1972.

123 Pierce, J. R. How far can data loops go?, *IEEE Trans. Comm.*, **20,** 527–530, 1972.

124 Pollaczek, F. Fonctions caractéristiques de certain es répartitions définies au moyen de la notion d'orde. Application à la théorie des attentes, *C.R. Acad. Sci. Paris*, **234,** 2334–2336, 1952.

125 Reich, E. Waiting times when queues are in tandem, *Ann. Math. Stat.*, **28,** 768–773, 1957.

126 Reich, E. Departure processes, in *Congestion Theory* (W. L. Smith and W. E. Wilkinson, eds), University of North Carolina Press, Chapel Hill, 1965, pp. 439–457.

127 Reiser M. and Kobayashi, H. Queueing networks with multiple closed chains: theory and computational algorithms, *IBM J. Res. Dev.*, **19,** 282–294, 1975.

128 Reiser, M. and Kobayashi, H. Horner's rule for the evaluation of general closed queueing networks, *Comm. ACM*, **18,** 592–593, 1975.

129 Riordan, J. *Stochastic Service Systems*, John Wiley, New York, 1962.

130 Robilland, P. N. An analysis of a loop switching system with multirank buffers based on the Markov process, *IEEE Trans. Comm.*, **22,** 1772–1778, 1974.

131 Ross, S. M. Bounds on the delay distribution in GI/G/1 queues, Report ORC 73-1, Department of Industrial Engineering and Operations Research, University of California, Berkely, January 1973.

132   Rubin, I. Communication networks: message path delays, *IEEE Trans. Information Theory*, November 1974.

133   Rubin, I. Message path delays in packet-switching communication networks, *IEEE Trans. Comm.*, **COM-23,** 186–192, 1975.

134   Rudin, H., Jr Performance of simple multiplexor-concentrators for data communication, *IEEE Trans. Comm.*, **COM-19,** 178–187, 1971.

135   Schmookler, M. S. Limited capacity discrete time queues with single or bulk arrival, *IBM Technical Report*, TR 00.2048, IBM Poughkeepsie Laboratory, 1970.

136   Schultz, G. D. A stochastic model for message-assembly buffering with a comparison of block assignment strategies, *JACM*, **19,** 483–495, 1972.

137   Schwartz, M., Boorstyn, R. R., and Pickholtz, R. L. Terminal-oriented computer-communication networks, *Proc. IEEE*, **60,** 1408–1422, 1972.

138   Smith, W. L. Renewal theory and its ramifications, *J. R. Stat. Soc.*, **20,** 243–302, 1958.

139   Spragins, J. D. Loop transmission systems – mean value analysis, *IEEE Trans. Comm.*, **COM-20,** 592–602, 1972.

140   Spragins, J. D. Loops used for data collection, presented at the 22nd International Symposium on Computer-Communication Networks and Teletraffic, Polytechnic Institute of Brooklyn, April 1972.

141   Spitzer, F. The Wiener–Hopf equation whose kernel is a probability density, *Duke Math. J.*, **24,** 327–343, 1957.

142   Steward, E. H. A loop transmission system, *Proceedings of the 1970 IEEE International Conference on Communications*, San Francisco, Vol. 2, pp. 36.1–36.9, June 1970.

143   Syski, R. *Introduction to Congestion Theory in Telephone Systems*, Oliver and Boyd, Edinburgh, 1960.

144   Wallace, V. L. Algebraic techniques for the numerical solution of queueing networks, in *Mathematical Methods in Queueing Theory* (A. B. Clarke, ed.), Springer-Verlag, Berlin, 1974, pp. 295–305.

145   Welman, E. A fixed optimum cell-size for records of various lengths, *JACM*, **12,** 53–70, 1965.

146   Whitaker, B. A. Analysis and optimal design of a multiserver multiqueue system with finite waiting space in each queue, *Bell System Tech. J.*, **54,** 595–623, 1975.

147   Whitt, W. Heavy traffic limit theorems for queues: a survey, in *Mathematical Methods in Queueing Theory* (A. B. Clarke, ed.), Springer-Verlag, Berlin, 1974.

148   Whittaker, E. T. and Watson, G. N. *A Course of Modern Analysis*, Cambridge University Press, Cambridge, 1952.

149 Wolff, R. W. Work-conserving priorities, *J. Appl. Prob.* **7,** 327–337, 1970.

150 Wright, E. M. Solution of the equation $ze^z = a$, *Bull. Amer. Math. Soc.*, **65,** 89–93, 1959.

151 Wu, R. M. and Chen, Y.-B. Analysis of a loop transmission system with round-robin scheduling of services, *IBM Systems Development Division Internal Report, TR* 21.560, August 1974.

152 Wyner, A. D. On the probability of buffer overflow under an arbitrary bounded input-output distribution, *SIAM J. Appl. Math.*, **27,** 544–570, 1974.

153 Yuen, M. L. T. and Black, E. E. Traffic flow in a distributed loop switching system, in *Proceedings of the 22nd International Symposium on Computer-Communications, Networks and Teletraffic*, Polytechnic Institute of Brooklyn, pp. 29–46, April 1972.

154 Zafiropulo, P. Reliability optimization in multi-loop communication networks, *IEEE Trans. Comm.*, **COM-21,** 898, 1973.

7 Operating system security verification

JONATHAN K MILLEN *The MITRE Corporation*

7.1 Introduction

7.1.1 Security problems in computers

The confinement problem, so named by B. Lampson [9], is how to constrain untrusted computer programs in such a way that information made available to them is not passed along to unauthorized individuals. Protecting information from unauthorized disclosure is only one of the three categories usually recognized for information security problems in computers:

unauthorized disclosure (leakage, compromise),
unauthorized modification (loss and spoofing),
denial of service.

'Compromise' has a slightly different meaning from unauthorized disclosure, since it refers to circumstances implying a possible exposure of information, when it may not be known whether unauthorized individuals actually took advantage of it. An example would be a document that had been left in a rubbish barrel. 'Unauthorized modification' includes both information loss and spoofing; 'spoofing' is the act of introducing new information that masquerades as legitimate. Denial of service includes anything from system 'crashes' to intolerable delays in normal processing.

7.1.2 Security technology areas

By investigating constraints to computer programs, i.e. software security, we are putting aside the other areas commonly listed within computer security:

physical,
personnel,
electromagnetic,
communications.

Physical protection prevents forced access to the computer; personnel protection prevents unauthorized individuals from entering via the front door; shielding prevents eavesdropping by radio; and encryption defeats eavesdropping when two parts of a computer system are connected by radio or cable transmissions.

7.1.3 The confinement problem

The confinement problem exists only in computers that have inputs and outputs in two or more different categories of authorization. The problem occurs when information is conveyed from an input in one category to an output in another category. A computer program could conceivably accomplish this by reading input from, say, the terminal keyboard of one user, storing it internally, and later (or immediately) printing it out on the terminal printer or display screen of another user.

7.1.4 Access control

The most widespread remedy for this problem, for large computer systems, is access control. Computer programs are viewed in the same light as people trying to get access to documents; someone or something must be there to refuse and prevent access to unauthorized requestors. In a computer security context, the programs are on the inside, trying to get access to input and output devices, and also to files in the computer containing information that may be shared by several programs. In a computer system large enough to have several users, access to files and to device input and output areas is normally requested from a program called, variously, a supervisor, monitor, executive, or operating system. The supervisor is a natural candidate to take on the job of access control.

7.1.5 Indirect channels

It was pointed out by Lampson that leakage of information can occur in spite of perfect access controls. This is possible because, in order to handle access requests by all other programs, the supervisor must communicate with all of them. It follows that the supervisor has the power to collect and distribute information in an unauthorized fashion. The only protection we have from leakage via the supervisor is our ability to analyze it for leakage channels, and redesign it to eliminate them.

An opportunity for unauthorized disclosure of information is characterized either as a *direct* channel, arising from defective access controls, or an *indirect* channel, arising from leakage through the supervisor. The techniques for detecting direct and indirect channels from a supervisor design are different but related, having some parts in common.

We will see later on that it really does take some systematic analysis to be sure that the supervisor does not harbor indirect channels even when it has been designed with the best of intentions. It is vulnerable because the programs that request supervisor services may (we assume) be acting without regard to security, or even maliciously attempting to defeat it.

It may seem surprising that a user would ever expose private data to a program he does not trust. But the most useful computer services for text or tabular data, such as editing, bookkeeping, report generation, update/retrieval, etc., are large, complex programs. More often than not, they have been obtained from outside sources, and they could also have been modified surreptitiously after delivery. Guaranteed trustworthy? Hardly. But designing and analyzing a supervisory program for security purposes can be much less work than analyzing or rewriting all applications software.

7.1.6 Theory (a brief survey)

The theoretical foundations of computer security are very young, with the exception of cryptographic approaches, because multiple-user computer systems are not very old themselves. Conscious attention to access control as a security issue began around 1969 (Weissman [16]). At first it was hard to separate security problems from basic operating system design issues (Lampson [8], Graham and Denning [6]), but computer security attained a separate theoretical existence when Harrison, Ruzzo, and Ullman [7] proved an undecidability result about a simple abstract model of a class of access control systems.

There are presently several theoretical approaches that address problems in the area of software-related computer security. From DeMillo *et al.* [3], there seem to be at least the following:

statistical data bases,
encryption,
access control,
information flow.

Statistical data base problems arise when a data base consisting of private entries exists, and various types of summary information – averages, counts, medians – are extracted from it and made public upon request. Surprisingly little summary information can permit the requestor to deduce an entire entry, especially if he already has some public information that is reflected in the data base. Encryption needs no introduction, except to call attention to the recent activity concerning public key systems – in which one can encrypt a message using one, publicly known, key, but the receiver must decrypt it using a different, secret key – and signature schemes [15].

The last two topics fall under the common heading of 'operating system security', and are the main topics of these notes. We will not be concerned with questions about the decidability of access control mechanisms, but only with techniques for verifying that a particular supervisory program design enforces a given access policy. Information flow approaches give rise to techniques for analyzing a program for information leakage, either application programs (indicating a need for access control) or supervisory programs (detecting indirect channels).

7.1.7 Preview

The material to be covered will be presented in a fashion that roughly parallels the historical development of the subject. We begin by looking at how a supervisory program uses the features built into a computer to enforce access control. While there is no end to the possibilities for computer architectures that will support access controls, a particular architecture will be introduced below as the basis for a case study of access control analysis. The computer in the case study will be imaginary, but it does bear a resemblance to the DEC PDP-11 series of computers. There will be a digression on a notational scheme used to specify the design of a system in a way that is precise enough for security analysis, but that relieves us from writing out the actual computer program for the supervisor or the processor handbook for the hardware.

A plausible design for a supervisory program will be given as an object for study. The design will be motivated briefly by a discussion of the 'process' concept as it applies to computer security, but our main purpose is to use the design as an example to illustrate how an access control policy is verified.

The concept of information flow analysis will be presented, and its application to detecting indirect channels explained. When using it on the case study, we will find some channels. We will also find some apparent channels that (it turns out) are not real. The pessimism of the technique given for information flow analysis is easily explained, but not so easily cured.

By returning to a careful re-examination of information flow as a form of deduction that can take place in any discrete-time system, we can show the beginnings of a new formulation of information leakage problems that is suitable for an understanding of the successes and deficiencies of the analysis techniques presented earlier.

7.2 A computer architecture

7.2.1 System overview

A certain imaginary computer has the block diagram shown in Figure 7.1.

The CPU, or central processing unit, contains registers for computational and control purposes. The MMU is the memory management unit, containing additional registers which participate in access control. A number of input/output control units (I/O CU) are attached directly to fixed areas in main memory. They handle data transfers to and from devices, such as display/keyboard terminals.

7.2.2 Registers and memory locations

We are interested in the registers and memory locations that hold data, and in the possible transfers of information among them. The registers and memory locations will be named as shown in Figure 7.2.

The process registers in the CPU form an array $R(i)$, where i

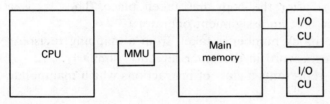

Fig. 7.1

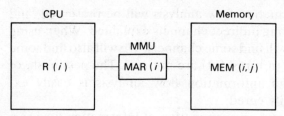

Fig. 7.2

ranges from 0 to, say, 7. Each register $R(i)$ can hold an integer in a finite range determined by the machine's word size. (In a PDP-11, the word size is 16 bits, giving a range $[-32768, 32767]$.)

The MMU contains two mapping registers of the same size, MAR (0) and MAR (1). Main memory is a two-dimensional array MEM (i, j) of locations of the same word size. The first coordinate is called the *block number*, and the second coordinate is called the *displacement*. These coordinates must both be nonnegative; their upper bound is, again, determined by the word size.

7.2.3 The instruction set

The possible transfers of information between registers depend on which *mode* the machine is in. It has two modes: *unprivileged*, or *user* mode, and *privileged*, or *supervisor* mode. In each mode, transfers of information are caused by executing instructions in the corresponding instruction set.

Rather than list the entire unprivileged instruction set, we can get by with the following summary:

FETCH (i, j, k): $R'(i) = \text{MEM (MAR } (j), k)$
STORE (i, j, k): $\text{MEM}' (\text{MAR } (j), k) = R(i)$
COMPUTE$_k$ (i): $R'(i) = f_k (R(0), \ldots, R(7))$
TRAP: enter privileged mode

A FETCH copies a word from memory into a process register. (The prime (′) after the R indicates that we are referring to the new contents of $R(i)$ after the copy has taken place. The '=' is a genuine equality, not an assignment operator.)

Note that the block number is taken from a mapping register.

STORE copies a word in the other direction similarly.

COMPUTE$_k$ represents a class of instructions which manipulate process registers.

TRAP causes the processor to enter supervisor mode, in which a different instruction set is employed, and other changes also take place to be described below.

7.2.4 The microprogram

There is a quite rigorous sense in which the four instruction types listed above exhaust the information transfers possible in unprivileged mode. When executing an instruction, the computer actually goes through a number of steps, each of which is one of the types listed.

A typical instruction, as stored in main memory, has the format

instruction code	source operand addr	destination addr

If the instruction were

add	20	21

the computer might add the contents of main memory location 20 to the contents of a predetermined register and store the result in location 21, and then go on to the next instruction in memory. The sequence of steps needed to execute one instruction of this type has the general form

1. FETCH instruction code.
2. FETCH source operand address.
3. FETCH source operand.
4. COMPUTE with operand and some register.
5. FETCH destination address.
6. STORE result in destination.
7. COMPUTE to increment the register used to remember the next instruction address.

The steps above are just one possible path through a fixed, hardware-defined program called the *microprogram*, which is used to interpret programs stored in main memory. The four instruction types FETCH, STORE, COMPUTE, and TRAP are actually *microinstructions*. The instruction set at the user level has not, and, for our purposes, need not, be defined.

7.2.5 Privileged mode

It is not possible, in this machine, to modify mapping registers with unprivileged instructions. That fact is central to the supervisor's ability to control access of programs to files. We will identify 'files' with 'memory blocks', and make sure that applications programs run in unprivileged mode. This is possible because the privileged mode can be entered only via a TRAP instruction, which causes the following changes:

> A separate set of processor registers and mapping registers is employed in the microinstructions given above.
> New microinstructions are available which permit access to user process registers and mapping registers, and permit a return to unprivileged mode.

7.2.6 Conclusions

The main thing to keep in mind about the switch to privileged mode is that, because a separate instruction address register comes into play, control is transferred to a different program – the supervisor. It should be plausible at this point that the supervisor is able to control the access of application programs to memory blocks, including those memory blocks containing the supervisory program itself. A great deal more could be said at this level, but let us move on to the design of the supervisory program.

Before presenting the supervisory program design, it will be necessary to take a more thorough look at the notation we have already used to specify the microinstructions, and which will be used to specify the supervisory software as well.

7.3 Nonprocedural transition specifications

7.3.1 Transition rules

A discrete-time system consists of variables and transition rules. Transition rules are specified most simply with 'next-state equations', for example

$$X' = X + 1.$$

X is a system variable. The transition rule above defines a system the behavior of which can be expressed in tabular form this way:

Time	0	1	2	3	$\cdots$
X	3	4	5	6	$\cdots$

A table like this is called a *simulation*. The initial value of 3 for X was chosen arbitrarily.

7.3.2 Inputs

Some variables in a system may be unconstrained; they are called *inputs*. Their values are presumed to be either random, or perhaps set externally by a system user. Consider a system with variables X and Y, and the transition rule

$$X' = Y$$

Here Y is an input. A possible simulation is

Time	0	1	2	3	$\cdots$
X	3	5	2	7	$\cdots$
Y	5	2	7	6	$\cdots$

7.3.3 Conditional expressions

Next-state equations may be conditionally chosen. For example,

$$\text{if} \quad Y = 0 \quad \text{then} \quad X' = X - 1$$
$$\text{else} \quad X' = X + 1$$

defines a system with the simulation

Time	0	1	2	3	4	$\cdots$
X	2	3	4	3	4	$\cdots$
Y	3	2	0	4	5	$\cdots$

Conditional expressions may also be used to define values. The transition rule above can also be represented by

$$X' = (\text{if} \ Y = 0 \ \text{then} \ X - 1 \ \text{else} \ X + 1).$$

7.3.4 Operations

The previous example could also be expressed as a pair of 'operations':

$$\text{INCREMENT:} \quad X' = X + 1,$$
$$\text{DECREMENT:} \quad X' = X - 1.$$

The input variable Y is not shown explicitly; but it is understood that some input variable is present to choose between the two operations.

7.3.5 Parameters

Operations can be parameterized:

$$\text{ADD}(i): \quad X' = X + i.$$

The dummy variable i is a parameter, not a system variable. It is understood, however, that there is an implicit input variable, say Z, to hold the parameter, so that the full transition rule is really

$$X' = X + Z.$$

Note that inputs can be eliminated from specifications by introducing operations and parameters.

7.3.6 Indices

Variables can be indexed. In fact, all the variables in the computer described in the previous section are indexed. FETCH, STORE, and COMPUTE are examples of operations that deal with indexed variables.

7.3.7 Terminology

Specifications of this type are called *nonprocedural* to differentiate them from algorithmic representations of the operations. The best example of the difference between the two is the EXCHANGE operation:

(nonprocedural)	(algorithmic)
EXCHANGE: $Y' = X$	EXCHANGE: $T \leftarrow X$
$X' = Y$	$X \leftarrow Y$
	$Y \leftarrow T$

The two equations in the nonprocedural version are true simultaneously; the three statements in the algorithmic version are supposed to be executed in the indicated sequence.

The idea that nonprocedural specifications could be used in a practical way for software system development was first pursued seriously by Parnas [14].

Transition specifications are those that show the relationship between the states of the system at any two consecutive points in time. There is a more general type called *algebraic* specifications, which is still in early stages of development.

7.3.8 Parnas convention

Under the Parnas convention, transitions of the form $X' = X$, indicating that a variable does not change, are never shown explicitly. Consider the system

> if $Y = 0$ then $X' = X + 1$
>
> else $X' = X$.

Using the Parnas convention, this would be written

> if $Y = 0$ then $X' = X + 1$.

The Parnas convention makes specifications easier to read. Translating back from a specification in which the Parnas convention has been used to a fully explicit specification, by supplying the missing no-change rules, can be difficult.

Problem

Write a nonprocedural transition specification for an elevator. It should have input variables representing buttons, indexed by floor:

> $ELB\,(f)$, $WBU\,(f)$, $WBD\,(f)$.

Buttons are either 'in' or 'out'. (It would be permissible to use other pairs of values, like 'true' and 'false' or 1 and 0, of course.) ELB buttons are inside the elevator. WBU and WBD are the up- and down-wall buttons on each floor. There should be three more variables indicating the state of the elevator:

> FLOOR,   DOOR,   and   DIR.

The use of FLOOR is obvious. The number of floors is arbitrary. DOOR is either 'open' or 'closed', and DIR is 'up', 'down', or 'off'.

The passage of time is the hardest aspect of this problem. Several choices are possible, but the following is recommended: let the state of FLOOR and DOOR mark points in time. This means that there will be transition rules like

> $FLOOR' = FLOOR + 1$,
>
> if $DOOR = $ 'closed'   then $DOOR' = $ 'open'.

Changes in DIR occur only when FLOOR or DOOR is changing.

Buttons can go in at any time, but they are inspected only at the times when the other variables are being recomputed. A real elevator pops out certain buttons when it arrives at a floor, but in this problem you may as well regard buttons are pure inputs, since a person could come along and push a button in again immediately anyway. With this approach, the elevator specification will be one large conditional operation. You may use the Parnas convention.

Do not forget to return the elevator to the first floor when all buttons are out.

The solution of this problem is given in the Appendix.

7.4 A supervisory program design

7.4.1 Processes

A supervisor supports the 'process' abstraction. A process is the computer's internal analog of a person at work. A process has the following attributes:

> a sequence of instructions or service requests,
> process-local storage,
> access to shareable storage,
> authorization attributes,
> status: awake or asleep.

The instruction sequence is derived from a stored program in shareable storage to which the process currently has access. The process executes both unprivileged instructions and traps; the purpose of a trap is to request a supervisor service.

7.4.2 Supervisor services

Typical supervisor services are these:

> Memory management
> > reallocate shareable storage
> > get or release access to shareable storage
> Process control
> > process swap
> > create or cancel process
> > interprocess communication
> Input/output
> Interrupt handling

In our example computer, memory blocks are treated as shareable storage. This means that different processes may execute instructions that fetch or store to the same memory block. Memory blocks will have authorization attributes which limit the degree of sharing that can take place. Reallocation of a memory block means that it is erased and may be given a new authorization attribute.

CPU registers are process-local storage. While the same physical registers are used by all processes, only one process is 'awake' and using the registers at a given time. Upon request from the process that is currently awake, the supervisor will save the contents of its registers, putting the process to 'sleep', and load the process

---

Supervisor Variables

CP	current process
PAL (p)	authorization level of process p
SR (p, i)	save area for registers of process p
SMAR (p, i)	save area for mapping registers of process p
BAL (b)	authorization level of block b
BAP (b)	block status: active (**true**) or purged (**false**)
BAC (b)	block access count
BDF (b)	device flag: is block b a buffer permanently attached to a device (true/false)?

Operations

PURGE (b): if BAC $(b) = 0$ and not BDF (b)
        then BAL$'(b) = $ syshi
           not BAP$'(b)$
           $(\forall i)$ MEM$'(b, i) = 0$

RAISE (b): if not BAP (b)
       then BAL$'(b) = $ PAL (CP)
          BAP$'(b)$

GET (b, n): if BAP (b) and
          BAC $(b) = 0$ and
          BAL $(b) = $ PAL (CP)
       then BAC$'(b) = 1$
          BAC$'$ (MAR $(n)) = 0$
          MAR$'(n) = b$

SWAP: CP$' = $ CP $+ 1$ (mod P)
      $(\forall i)$ R$'(i) = $ SR (CP$'$, i)
      $(\forall i)$ SR$'$ (CP, i) $= $ R (i)
      $(\forall i)$ SMAR$'$ (CP, i) $= $ MAR (i)
      $(\forall i)$ MAR$'(i) = $ SMAR (CP$'$, i)

Fig. 7.3 Nonprocedural transition specification for a supervisor.

registers with the saved register contents for some sleeping process, thus awakening it. This is a process swap.

The supervisor to be introduced below for case study will not provide any of the remaining services. We will have a fixed set of processes. Input and output will be handled by the application programs; they just have to get access to the memory blocks used for communicating with the desired device control units. Inter-process communication can be accomplished (inconveniently) through shared memory blocks. Interrupts are not implemented in our example computer.

A nonprocedural transition specification for the supervisor is given in Figure 7.3. Computer variables are mixed in with super-visor variables in the operations, simply because manipulating hardware registers is an essential part of the supervisor's job.

7.4.3 Discussion of supervisor design

Of the eight supervisor variables, four refer to processes and four refer to memory blocks. The current process variable, CP, indi-cates which process is awake; the others are asleep. The set of possible values for CP is the set of process indices, which are integers in the range $[0, P-1]$. The specification is not complete without giving the range of each variable, but details of that sort have been suppressed in this example. It is implicitly assumed that indices are kept within the range for which the indexed variable is defined. This can be a significant concern for the correctness of software and hardware implementations of the supervisor, but it need not worry us at this level.

Each process has an 'authorization level' PAL (p). The only assumption that we are presently making about authorization levels is that there is a particular level 'syshi' which is not equal to PAL (p) for any p. Note that PAL (p) is constant, since no opera-tion changes it.

A process swap involves saving the contents of the processor and mapping registers while a process is asleep. Indexed variables SR (p, i) and SMAR (p, i) provide storage for this purpose.

Blocks have authorization levels, too; block b has authorization level BAL (b). The access policy for this system will require a process to match any block it accesses in authorization.

In a system with a finite number of blocks, storage can be used more efficiently if it is possible to change the authorization level of a block. That way, transitory surges of storage demands at any level can be accommodated. Changes in block levels cannot be left uncontrolled, however, since information will be compromised if it is in a block the level of which is changed. Consequently, a change in block level can be accomplished only by supervisor request, and the supervisor erases the block at the time the change is made.

In the example system it takes two requests to change the block level: one to 'purge' the block, erasing it and making it available for other use, and one to 'raise' it again and give it the level of the current process.

A block cannot be accessed while it is in the purged state, otherwise it could receive information which would be compromised when it is raised later. The supervisor variable $BAP(b)$ indicates the current state (active or purged) of each memory block.

The variable $BAC(b)$ is the access count: the number of processes having access to the block b. This will be either 1 or 0.

The purpose of GET is to give a process access to a block by putting the block number into a mapping register. Note that GET also causes the block previously addressed by that mapping register to be released; its access count, BAC, becomes 0.

There is a variable $BDF(b)$ that indicates which blocks are supposed to be connected to input/output device control units. This variable plays no role in the forthcoming verification, but it is essential to security. It ensures a match between the authorization level of users of the system, sitting at terminals, and the authorization levels assigned to the blocks containing data that is communicated to and from them. We are assuming here that the authorization levels of the terminal devices are fixed, and the terminals are protected physically against unauthorized use. Hence the blocks connected to them must also be fixed in level, and there is a test on BDF in PURGE to make sure that device blocks are never purged. The match between the block level and the associated device levels must be set up when the system is started.

7.5 Access control verification

7.5.1 Access control policy

In an access control verification, it is our job to determine whether the events sketched in Figure 7.4 can occur.

Fig. 7.4 Direct channel: $a \neq b$.

A simulation showing the information transfers in detail is given in Figure 7.5.

Some process is active at the time the FETCH is executed. At that time, there is a mapping register, say MAR (0), containing the block number i. It seems appropriate to say that the process has access to block i under those conditions. Similarly, when the STORE to block j is executed, the current process is considered to have access to block j. If the supervisor imposes a rule, called an 'access control policy', that a process can have access to a block only when their authorization levels are equal, it will prevent the direct channel we are considering.

Let us restate the definition of access and the access control policy more formally:

> A process p has *access* to a block b if
> $p = CP$ and $(\exists i)\, MAR\,(i) = b$.

> *Access control policy:* if process p has access to block b then $PAL\,(p) = BAL\,(b)$.

The above policy can be stated more briefly as

$$(\forall i)\, PAL\,(CP) = BAL\,(MAR\,(i)). \tag{R1}$$

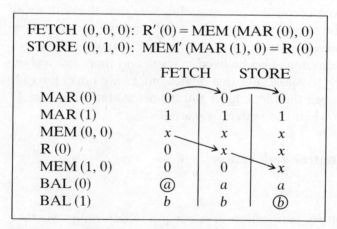

Fig. 7.5 Simulation illustrating a direct channel.

This policy was motivated by the fact that a compromise via a direct channel can occur in its absence. Hence the policy (R1) is necessary. In other systems, a condition as strong as (R1) might not be necessary. More sophisticated systems distinguish 'read' from 'write' access, and order the authorization levels so that information may be allowed to flow from level b to level a, say, but not the other way. The access control policy could acknowledge those differences.

The policy (R1) is not sufficient for security against unauthorized disclosure, because of indirect channels which may exist. It is still worthwhile to verify that the policy is enforced, because statements like (R1) play a part in the information flow analysis. In some environments, where indirect channels are unlikely or unimportant because the user software is trusted to some degree, and other measures are taken to identify suspicious program behavior, access control verification may be considered sufficient for practical purposes.

7.5.2 Invariants

The policy (R1) is an *invariant* because it is required to be true at all times. We verify it inductively. If it is true at time t, then to prove it is true at time $t+1$, we must show that it is preserved by every operation. Let R be an invariant, and let T be the transition rule of an operation. Let R′ be the result of priming every variable in R, so that it refers to the state following execution of T. We must show that

(R and T) implies R′.

If this is true for every operation T, and if R is true at a particular time t_0, then R will be true at any time after t_0.

When transition rules are written in a conditional next-state-equation form, using the Parnas convention, the following sequence of steps is convenient in checking that an invariant is preserved by an operation.

1. Identify the assumptions and cases in which some variable in the invariant is affected by the operation. (If no variable in the invariant is affected by the operation, the invariant is preserved trivially: R′ = R.)
2. Prime each variable in the invariant; call the result the 'transformed invariant'. (This is R′.)

3. In the transformed invariant, delete the primes from those variables unaffected by the operation in this case.

4. Find expressions for the next-state values of the variables affected by the operation (the ones still primed), and then substitute them into the transformed invariant.

5. Prove the transformed invariant, using the original form of the invariant if necessary.

7.5.3 Proof example

The proof that the access policy is preserved by GET is illustrated here.

We will state the access policy in the form

$$PAL\,(CP) = BAL\,(MAR\,(i)). \tag{R1}$$

The quantifier '$(\forall i)$' has been dropped; we will just remember that i is a free dummy variable.

The operation GET (b, n) affects BAC (b), BAC $(MAR\,(n))$, and MAR (n), when its hypothesis is true. Since MAR (i) occurs in (R1), we conclude that

1. GET (b, n) affects (R1) only when

   $i = n$ and
   BAP (b) and
   BAC $(b) = 0$ and
   BAL $(b) = PAL\,(CP)$.

We assume the conditions stated in step 1 and continue. First, prime the variables in (R1).

2. The transformed invariant is

   $$PAL'\,(CP') = BAL'\,(MAR'\,(i)).$$

Since GET leaves unchanged the variables PAL, CP, and BAL, we can delete their primes, so the transformed invariant becomes

3. $PAL\,(CP) = BAL\,(MAR'\,(i))$.

The next-state expression for MAR$'(i)$ is found from the operation. Since $i = n$, we have from the transition rule for GET that

   $$MAR'\,(i) = MAR'\,(n) = b.$$

After substitution, the transformed invariant is now

4. $PAL\,(CP) = BAL\,(b)$.

Now, we just have to prove the statement

5. PAL (CP) = BAL (b).

But one of the assumptions in step 1 was the conclusion above, so we are done.

7.5.4 New invariants

When we test whether the access policy is preserved by SWAP, the need for an additional invariant will become apparent. Perform the five steps as before.

1. SWAP affects MAR (i) and CP, in all cases; no assumption is needed.

2. The transformed invariant is, as before,

PAL' (CP') = BAL' (MAR' (i)).

3. This time, we can delete the primes only from PAL and BAL, giving

PAL (CP') = BAL (MAR' (i)).

From SWAP we find that

CP' = CP + 1 (mod P)

and

MAR' (i) = SMAR (CP', i).

After substitution, the transformed invariant is

PAL (CP + 1 (mod P)) = BAL (SMAR (CP + 1 (mod P), i)).

5. We have to show that

PAL (CP + 1 (mod P)) = BAL (SMAR (CP + 1 (mod P), i)).

There appears to be no way to prove the statement in step 5.

The old-state form of the invariant does not help. Furthermore, no assumptions were made in step 1. What can we do?

Let us take a look at the statement to be proved in a slightly more general form:

PAL (p) = BAL (SMAR (p, i)),

where $p \neq$ CP.† This says that the access level of a sleeping process

† CP + 1(mod P) $\neq$ CP, except when $P = 1$, and we will assume $P \neq 1$.

is equal to the access level of a block the number of which *was* in a mapping register, but was saved in SMAR (p, i) when p was swapped out. In other words, process p had access to block SMAR (p, i) when p was last awake. At that time, the access policy would have guaranteed equality of access levels, and the equality should still be true. This argument leads us to *postulate* a new invariant:

$$(\forall p) \text{ if } p \neq \text{CP} \quad \text{then} \quad (\forall i)(\text{PAL } (p) = \text{BAL } (\text{SMAR } (p, i))).$$

$$\text{(R2)}$$

This new invariant, (R2), is sufficient to allow us to complete the proof of step 5 above. It is quite legitimate to use all postulated invariants in the proof of the transformed invariant in step 5, since we may imagine that all of the invariants are being proved simultaneously, as a conjunction. In fact, we must not forget that we now have the new burden of proving (R2) inductively, just as we are doing for (R1).

The rest of the proof that the access policy (R1) holds for the case study supervisor is left to the reader. A total of ten invariants are needed, including (R1). One of the later invariants encountered is

$$(\forall p)(\forall q) \text{ if } p \neq \text{CP} \neq q \neq p$$

$$\text{then } (\forall i)(\forall j) \text{ SMAR } (p, i) \neq \text{SMAR } (q, j).$$

It is one of four invariants that say, essentially, that a block number appears in at most one mapping register, whether saved or actual.

Do not forget that the unprivileged operations, FETCH, STORE, and COMPUTE, must also preserve the invariants. It is typical of access control invariants, however, that their variables are not affected by the unprivileged operations (else there would be a serious problem!).

7.6 Information flow analysis

7.6.1 Insufficiency of access control

A supervisor can enforce an access policy and thus prevent direct channels, and yet permit information leakage. This will be shown true for the case study supervisor, but a simpler example will be given first.

Consider the following two operations, which might have been included in the supervisor:

READ (i): $X' = R(i)$
WRITE (i): $R'(i) = X.$

Here, X is a new supervisor variable. These operations do not affect any of the variables in the access control policy or any of the other invariants needed to prove it. Consequently the access policy is still enforced, with these operations present.

Data can be compromised with the sequence of operations below:

$$\text{MEM (MAR } (j),\, k) \xrightarrow{\text{FETCH } (i,\, j,\, k)} R(i) \xrightarrow{\text{READ } (i)} X \xrightarrow{\text{SWAP}}$$

$$\rightarrow X \xrightarrow{\text{WRITE}(i)} R(i) \xrightarrow{\text{STORE}(i,j,k)} \text{MEM (MAR } (j),\, k)$$

If this happens, MEM (MAR (j), k) at time 5 has the same value as MEM (MAR (j), k) at time 0. This is a compromise because SWAP changed the mapping registers, so that MAR (j) at times 0 and 5 represent (in general) two different blocks, which may have different authorization levels. The details can be checked in the simulation in Figure 7.6.

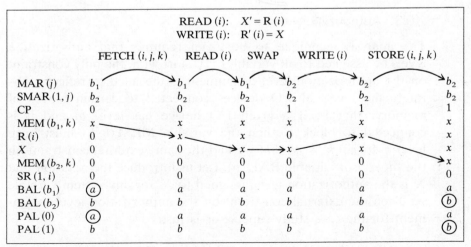

		READ (i): $X' = R(i)$ WRITE (i): $R'(i) = X$				
		FETCH (i, j, k)	READ (i)	SWAP	WRITE (i)	STORE (i, j, k)
MAR (j)	b_1		b_1	b_1	b_2	b_2	b_2
SMAR $(1, j)$	b_2		b_2	b_2	b_2	b_2	b_2
CP	0		0	0	1	1	1
MEM (b_1, k)	x		x	x	x	x	x
R (i)	0		x	x	0	x	x
X	0		0	x	x	x	x
MEM (b_2, k)	0		0	0	0	0	x
SR $(1, i)$	0		0	0	0	0	0
BAL (b_1)	a		a	a	a	a	a
BAL (b_2)	b		b	b	b	b	b
PAL (0)	a		a	a	a	a	a
PAL (1)	b		b	b	b	b	b

Fig. 7.6 Simulation illustrating indirect channel. (Note that the access policy is satisfied.)

This type of channel for compromise is called *indirect* because data passes through a supervisor internal variable, in this case X. The access control policy fails to prevent it because supervisor internal variables are not considered shared storage to which a process must request access. While the notion of 'access' could be extended to remedy the deficiency, it seems more straightforward to focus attention on system variables and the information transfers between them.

7.6.2 Information flow concepts

An information flow approach for detecting channels for compromise involves

flow rules,
authorization levels for all variables,
flow policy.

Each of these will be discussed briefly before embarking on the detailed development of the technique.

Flow rules identify statements in transition rules that cause information flow from one variable to another. The most obvious flow rule, and the only one needed to detect the channel given as an example above, is that a next-state equation of the form $X' = Y$ causes a flow from Y to X. This is true for any two variables X and Y, indexed or not.

7.6.3 Authorization levels

The analysis technique to be given requires that authorization levels be assigned to all variables. To start with, the only constraint on the authorization level assignment is the need to reflect accurately the levels of I/O devices connected to certain blocks of memory; that is, if a given I/O device has level a, and it is connected to block b, then the variable $\text{MEM}(b, k)$ must have level a, for all k. Note that we had the same external constraint on the supervisor variable $\text{BAL}(b)$. Let us introduce the notation that $\underline{X}$ is the authorization level assigned to X, for any system variable X. Then the external constraint on the authorization level assignment for the case study supervisor is just:

$$(\forall b, k) \text{ if } \text{BDF}(b) \text{ then } \underline{\text{MEM}(b, k)} = \underline{\text{BAL}}(b).$$

Other authorization levels are not specified, but we will see after discussing the flow policy what should be done about them.

In general, the authorization level of a variable is not constant, but, rather, depends on other variables; i.e. it depends on the current state of the system.

7.6.4 Flow policy

Like an access policy, a flow policy requires that authorization levels be properly matched when information can be transferred from one object to another. There are supervisor variables containing information that is not private, but which can be transferred to memory blocks. Constants, like $BDF(b)$, fall into this category. There is no reason why any user should not have its value, since the information was not introduced by any other user. Hence we have to relax the access policy to allow flow from a variable of level 'public' to any other. For this and other reasons, it is convenient to assume a *partial ordering* on the set of authorization levels, and to permit flow from a variable to any other variable whose level is higher or equal in the ordering.

For our case study, it is enough to assign incomparable levels $a_0, a_1, \ldots$ to the user terminals and their associated memory blocks, and provide a minimum level 'public' and a maximum level 'syshi'. The partial ordering is indicated by the directed graph below, where $a \geqslant b$ if there is a path from a to b. (Graphs like this, in which arcs are always implicitly directed downward, are called Hasse diagrams.)

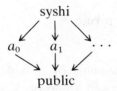

The flow policy is this: information flow from X to Y is permitted only when $\underline{X} \leqslant \underline{Y}$. The level $\underline{X}$ is evaluated in the state before the transition(s) causing the flow, and the level $\underline{Y}$ is evaluated in the state after the transition(s) causing the flow. This flow policy applies to all systems; only the authorization level assignments and partial orderings have to be tailored to individual systems.

7.6.5 Prevention of storage channels

By enforcing the flow policy for each transition rule, we can prevent direct and indirect channels resulting from a chain of information transfers like

$$Y \rightarrow Z_1 \rightarrow Z_2 \rightarrow \cdots \rightarrow Z_n \rightarrow X.$$

Such a chain cannot result in a compromise, because

$$\underline{Y} \leqslant \underline{Z_1} \leqslant \cdots \leqslant \underline{Z_n} \leqslant \underline{X},$$

from which it follows that $\underline{Y} \leqslant \underline{X}$, so that the transfer of information would be considered permissible.

It is important to notice that this result holds without any assumptions on the authorization level assignment (other than the flow policy itself). In other words, *if there exists* an authorization level assignment which respects external constraints and for which the flow policy holds, then all direct and indirect channels for compromise are prevented. Incidentally, channels resulting from a chain of flows between system variables are referred to as *storage* channels. This is a more general category including both direct and indirect channels.

7.6.6 Explicit flow

So far, we have given only one flow rule, saying that

$$X' = Y$$

causes a flow

$$Y \rightarrow X.$$

Now, let us consider whether the transition rule

$$X' = Y + Z$$

causes a flow $Y \rightarrow X$. Knowing that the new value of X is 4, for example, does not generally tell us what the old value of Y was. However, it does convey some information. For example, suppose that Y and Z have possible values 0, 1, 2, 3. If X becomes 4, we know that Y must have been one of 1, 2, 3. The exclusion of even one possible value for Y is information about Y, and we will count that situation as implying a flow from Y to X.

Consequently, we postulate the more general flow rule:

$$X' = f(\ldots, Y, \ldots)$$

causes the flow

$$Y \rightarrow X.$$

This is called *explicit flow*.

7.6.7 Conditional flow

A conditional statement like

if $Y = 0$ then $X' = Z$

causes an explicit flow $Z \rightarrow X$, but only when $Y = 0$.

We can generalize this observation to any transition rule of the form

if a then $T(X \rightarrow Y)$,

where $T(X \rightarrow Y)$ is any transition rule for which $X \rightarrow Y$. Such a rule causes a *conditional* flow

$$a \Rightarrow X \rightarrow Y.$$

If the Parnas convention is being used, the transition rule above might really mean

if $Y = 0$ then $X' = Z$ else $X' = X$,

which may be written as a pair of rules:

if $Y = 0$ then $X' = Z$;

if $Y \neq 0$ then $X' = X$.

The second rule causes an additional conditional flow:

$$Y \neq 0 \Rightarrow X \rightarrow X.$$

The no-change transitions $X' = X$ eliminated by the Parnas convention have to be recreated if the associated flows are to be found by this technique.

7.6.8 Implicit flow

A conditional statement like

if $Y = 0$ then $X' = 0$

also causes some information flow from Y to X. To take an extreme example, suppose that both Y and X are binary; they have the possible values 0, 1. Consider the simulations

$$\begin{array}{c|cc} X & 1 & \nearrow 0 \\ Y & 0 & 0 \end{array} \quad \text{and} \quad \begin{array}{c|cc} X & 1 & \nearrow 1 \\ Y & 1 & 1 \end{array}$$

and notice the apparent copying of data from Y to X. This flow does not occur if X has the value 0 to start with, but we choose to take a pessimistic approach (from the point of view of security) and say, as a rule, that there is a flow $Y \rightarrow X$.

We now generalize to any transition rule of the form

$$\text{if } f(Y, \ldots) \text{ then } X' = a,$$

where $f(Y, \ldots)$ is any expression involving a variable Y, indexed or not, and a is any expression with no primed variables. In this situation there is an *implicit* flow $Y \rightarrow X$.

Conditional transition rules can be nested, like

$$\text{if } Y = 0 \quad \text{then} \quad (\text{if } Z = 0 \text{ then } X' = 0).$$

The implicit flow $Z \rightarrow X$ is evidently conditional on $Y = 0$; that is,

$$Y = 0 \Rightarrow Z \rightarrow X.$$

To determine the flow from Y, the transition rule can be turned around in the equivalent form

$$\text{if } Z = 0 \quad \text{then} \quad (\text{if } Y = 0 \text{ then } X' = 0),$$

in which it is evident that

$$Z = 0 \Rightarrow Y \rightarrow X.$$

Both forms are equivalent to

$$\text{if } (Y = 0 \text{ and } Z = 0) \quad \text{then} \quad X' = 0,$$

which seems to imply unconditional implicit flows $Y \rightarrow X$ and $Z \rightarrow X$.

This points up one of the difficulties with this information flow analysis technique: it is syntactic. Two equivalent but different-looking flow rules can yield different flow analyses. The results sometimes indicate a possible information flow in cases when there is none, but the opposite mistake is never made: where there is information flow, this technique will detect it regardless of which form the transition rule takes.

7.6.9 Indices

Where a variable like X or Y occurs in the rules given above, an indexed variable for which the index is a constant may be substituted. Thus, the transition rule

$$X'(1) = Y(2)$$

causes the explicit flow

$$Y(2) \rightarrow X(1).$$

When variables occur in indices, however, as in

$$X' = Y(Z),$$

we might wonder whether $Z \rightarrow X$. Questions of this sort can be answered by reducing the transition rule to a form with constant indices. This is done by introducing dummy variables for all indices. For example, the transition rule above is equivalent to

$$(\forall i) \text{ if } Z = i \quad \text{then} \quad X' = Y(i).$$

In this form we can recognize the implicit flow $Z \rightarrow X$, as well as the conditional flows

$$(\forall i) \ Z = i \Rightarrow Y(i) \rightarrow X,$$

which can be rewritten equivalently and unconditionally as

$$Y(Z) \rightarrow X$$

as expected.

The flow from an index is particularly startling when $Y(i)$ happens to have the value i, for all i; then $X' = Y(Z)$ becomes equivalent to $X' = Z$.

In general, variables occurring in indices are sources of information.

A variable index for a primed variable gives a perhaps surprising result. The transition rule

$$X'(Y) = 1$$

causes not only a flow $Y \rightarrow X'(Y)$ but also a flow $Y \rightarrow X'(i)$ for all i. This becomes clearer when dummy indices are introduced, viz.

$$(\forall i) \text{ if } Y = i \quad \text{then} \quad X'(i) = 1,$$

giving the implicit flows $(\forall i) \ Y \rightarrow X(i)$.

To give a concrete example, suppose it happens that $X(i) = 0$ for all i; then, after the transition, one can learn something about Y by looking at any of the new values of $X(i)$. For, if $X'(i) = 1$, we can conclude that $Y = i$. But, even if $X'(i) = 0$, we know at least that $Y \neq i$.

Problems

1. Show that $X'(A, B) = 0$ causes flows

$$(\forall i)\ A \rightarrow X(i, B),$$
$$(\forall j)\ B \rightarrow X(A, j).$$

2. Show that the transition rule

$$\text{if}\quad Y(Z, U(W))\quad \text{then}\quad X'(A, B) = C(D)$$

causes the flows

$$Y(Z, U(W)) \Rightarrow C(D) \rightarrow X(A, B),$$
$$Y(Z, U(W)) \Rightarrow \quad D \rightarrow X(A, B),$$
$$Y(Z, U(W)) \Rightarrow \quad A \rightarrow X(i, B)\quad \text{for all } i,$$
$$Y(Z, U(W)) \Rightarrow \quad B \rightarrow X(A, i)\quad \text{for all } i,$$
$$Y(Z, U(W)) \rightarrow X(A, B),$$
$$Z \rightarrow X(A, B),$$
$$U(W) \rightarrow X(A, B),$$
$$W \rightarrow X(A, B).$$

7.7 Flow analysis in practice

7.7.1 Objectives

The rules for information flow analysis introduced in the previous section are to be applied to the supervisor design and the imaginary computer discussed earlier. We wish to see if the information policy is satisfied, and if not, what indirect channels exist. It should not be surprising that the flow policy is applied to the computer operations as well as the supervisor, since FETCH and STORE play a prominent role in the examples of compromises we have seen.

7.7.2 Effects of specification conventions

Two notational conventions were used in writing the transition specification of the computer and the supervisor, primarily in order to make them easier to read: parameterized operations and the Parnas convention.

There are several operations, and most of them have parameters, so there are some input variables that have not been explicitly indicated. We have to put them back in before looking for flows. We should also put all no-change transition statements $X' = X$ back in, so that the new value of every variable (for every value of each index) will be determined unambiguously by the specification, as intended. Note that the example given earlier of an indirect channel, using new operations READ and WRITE, hinges on the flow $X \rightarrow X$ implied by a SWAP operation. This channel would not, in general, be detected unless the no-change transition rule $X' = X$ is added to the specification.

7.7.3 Operations and parameters: the computer

There are four microinstructions, most parameterized. Where do the parameter values and choice of operation come from? The sequence of microinstruction requests is controlled by the microprogram, which has its own local storage. This local storage is not an input, because its contents are determined from the contents of the processor registers and its own prior contents. Let us assume a set of four microregisters MI (i) which determine, respectively, the microinstruction and the parameters i, j, k that appear in the microinstruction specifications. Then there are transition rules

$$MI' (i) = m_i (MI (0), \ldots, MI (3), R (0), \ldots, R (7)),$$

where the function m_i is defined by the microprogram built into the computer. In fact, a CPU is little more than the implementation of a microprogram.

The FETCH operation, in terms of the microregisters, becomes

if MI $(0) =$ FETCH

then $R' (MI (1)) = MEM (MAR (MI (2)), MI (3))$,

for STORE we get

if MI $(0) =$ STORE

then $MEM' (MAR (MI (2)), MI (3)) = R (MI (1))$,

for $COMPUTE_k$ we get

   if $MI (0) = COMPUTE$

   then $R' (MI (1)) = f_{MI(3)}(R (0), \ldots, R (7))$,

and for TRAP we get

   if $MI (0) = TRAP$

   then ...,

where the ellipsis depends on the choice of supervisor operation and its parameters.

7.7.4 Operations and parameters: the supervisor

When a TRAP instruction is executed, some supervisor operation causes supervisor internal variables and, often, also some computer registers to be updated. Supervisor internal variables are actually implemented by words within a particular block of memory used by the supervisor. When the supervisor is implemented, care should be taken that supervisor memory is never available for use by a process. How this protection is accomplished depends on the particular supervisor and computer. In our case, it would be enough to set $BAL (b) = $ syshi and $BDF (b) = TRUE$ for a supervisor block b.

   The choice of the supervisor operation and its parameters is communicated to the supervisor by placing them in locations decided upon in advance; for example, the first few words in the memory block accessible with mapping register 0. Thus, the operation and two parameters can be found in $MEM (MAR (0), k)$ for $k = 0, 1, 2$. We will not bother to rewrite the supervisor specification using these variables explicitly, but the flow analysis will have to take them into account.

7.7.5 Standard form of supervisor operations

The supervisor operations all have the following form:

   $OP (b, n)$: if a_0 and $\cdots$ and a_n

         then $X'_0(f_0) = g_0$,

            $X'_1(f_1) = g_1$,

               $\vdots$

where the a_i, f_i, and g_i are expressions without primed variables, except for a few occurrences of CP′ on the right in SWAP, which could be removed easily.

Let us abbreviate the memory locations used to store the operation choice and parameters by F, B, and N, respectively. Then each operation can be written as a set of rules of the form

> if $F = \text{OP}$ and $B = b$ and $N = n$ and a_0 and $\cdots$ and a_n
>
> then $X_i'(f_i) = g_i$.

The parameter conditions $B = b$ and $N = n$ can be left out of those operations that do not need them.

Applying the rules for information flow derived in the last section results in the 'universal analysis' below:

> $B = b$ and $N = n$ and a_0 and $\cdots a_n \Rightarrow F \to X_i(f_i)$,
>
> $F = \text{OP}$ and $N = n$ and a_0 and $\cdots a_n \Rightarrow B \to X_i(f_i)$,
>
> $F = \text{OP}$ and $B = b$ and a_0 and $\cdots a_n \Rightarrow N \to X_i(f_i)$,
>
> $F = \text{OP}$ and $B = b$ and $N = n$ and a_0 and $\cdots$ and a_{j-1}
>
> and a_{j+1} and $\cdots$ and $a_n \Rightarrow \bar{a}_j \to X_i(f_i)$ for each j,
>
> $F = \text{OP}$ and $N = n$ and $B = b$ and a_0 and $\cdots$ and a_n
> $\Rightarrow \bar{g}_i \to X_i(f_i)$,
>
> $F = \text{OP}$ and $N = n$ and $B = b$ and a_0 and $\cdots$ and a_n
> $\Rightarrow \bar{f}_i \to X_i(k)$ for all k,

where if a is an expression without primed variables, $\bar{a}$ is the collection of variables that occur in a. For example,

$$\overline{Y(Z(W))} = \{Y(Z(W)), Z(W), W\}.$$

This list of flows is not quite universal because X_i could be doubly indexed, or its index could be indexed, and the last flow would have to be modified accordingly.

7.7.6 Mechanization

It takes a great deal of labor to expand even as small a specification as we have been working with into standard form, add the omitted no-change transition rules, and generate all of the resulting flows. There are currently some efforts to automate the process with software tools.

7.7.7 Origins

Information flow analysis was introduced for programs by D. Denning [1, 2] under the assumption that authorization levels are constant. An early attempt to perform a similar type of analysis on formal specifications was described by Millen [11]. These techniques are conceptually related to data flow analysis, as used in program optimization techniques. Data flow analysis concentrates on explicit flow and conditional flow (viewed as 'control flow' in that context), but implicit flow is a new idea that arose from security considerations.

7.7.8 Constant authorization levels

It should be remarked that flow analysis is a great deal easier when authorization levels are constant. In particular, conditional flows may be turned into unconditional flows without affecting the results, since knowledge about the current state is irrelevant to determining authorization levels.

There is a trick to turn any specification into one with constant authorization levels. If X is a variable with varying authorization level, replace it with the indexed variable $X(i)$, where i ranges over authorization levels, and choose a reasonable level for an index value in each rule where X appears. Then assign the level i to $X(i)$. This idea is due to SRI [13].

There is a price to be paid for doing this: one must eventually prove that the software or hardware that implemented the first specification still correctly implements the new one. In effect, the extra work involved is that necessary to show that the original specification implements the new one. The net advantage of doing this is that the job of showing correct implementation may be preferred to some of the complexities of flow analysis.

7.8 Case study results

This section includes an authorization level assignment for the supervisor and computer variables, and the flow analysis of a few transition rules that illustrate some problems and conclusions that are typical for this technique.

7.8.1 Authorization level assignment

The assignments in Table 7.1 were produced by a combination of experience, guesswork, and trial-and-error activity. Keep in mind

Table 7.1 Authorization level assignments

Variable	Level
CP	Public
PAL (*p*)	Public
SR (*p*, *i*)	PAL (*p*)
SMAR (*p*, *i*)	PAL (*p*)
BAL (*b*)	BAL (*b*)
BDF (*b*)	Public
BAC (*b*)	BAL (*b*)
BAP (*b*)	BAL (*b*)
R (*i*)	PAL (CP)
MAR (*i*)	PAL (CP)
MEM (*b*, *i*)	BAL (*b*)

that the assignment is arbitrary except for the need to satisfy external constraints – on the levels of device blocks – and the desire to satisfy the flow policy. Most of the assignments are intuitively plausible: all constants (and unchanging variables like PAL and BDF) are 'public'; all other variables associated with a memory block *b* are given the level BAL (*b*); variables associated with a process *p* are given the level PAL (*p*); and registers have the current process level PAL (CP). Most of the assignments were forced by the flow policy, but there are some violations anyway.

7.8.2 Use of access policy

Flow analysis supersedes an access control approach because flow analysis of FETCH and STORE operations automatically generates an access policy – the same one postulated earlier on more intuitive grounds.

The transition rule for FETCH generates, among others, the flow

$$MI (0) = FETCH \Rightarrow MEM (MAR (MI (2)), MI (3))$$
$$\rightarrow R (MI (1)).$$

Using the authorization level assignments in Table 7.1, the flow policy requires that

$$BAL (MAR (MI (2))) \leqslant PAL (CP).$$

The access policy (R1) takes care of this requirement. Note that STORE requires the opposite inequality, since it implies a flow

$$MI\ (0) = STORE \Rightarrow R\ (MI\ (1))$$
$$\rightarrow MEM\ (MAR\ (MI\ (2)),\ MI\ (3))$$

for which the flow policy requires

$$PAL\ (CP) \leqslant BAL\ (MAR\ (MI\ (2))).$$

The access policy (R1) covers this as well. In this context, of course, we do not regard (R1) as a 'policy'; we are working with the flow policy. However, (R1) is still an invariant, and such invariants are often needed to show that the flow policy is satisfied.

7.8.3 Flow from operation choice variable

Using the abbreviations F, B, and N, as before, for the memory locations chosen to transmit the parameters of a supervisor request, we find that RAISE includes the following transition rule:

if $F = RAISE$ and $B = b$ and not $BAP\ (b)$ then $BAP'\ (b)$.

This rule will serve to illustrate some of the more difficult aspects of flow analysis in practice. We have the flow

$$B = b \quad \text{and not } BAP\ (p) \Rightarrow F \rightarrow BAP\ (b).$$

To check the flow policy, we have to find the authorization levels of F and $BAP\ (b)$. Recall that F is an abbreviation for $MEM\ (MAR\ (0),\ 0)$. Its level is $BAL\ (MAR\ (0))$.

The level of $BAP\ (b)$ is $BAL\ (b)$, but we shall write it as $BAL'\ (b)$ as a reminder that it is to be evaluated in the new state after the transition. The value of $BAL'\ (b)$ depends on which operation was chosen. The rule that we are working on came from RAISE, but the condition for the flow was only '$B = b$ and not $BAP\ (b)$'. We cannot assume any particular value for F when we are analyzing flow from F. We have to investigate all possibilities.

There are only two places in the specification where $BAL\ (b)$ is changed: (1) in PURGE, where it may become syshi, and (2) in RAISE, where it may become $PAL\ (CP)$. Otherwise (3) it remains unchanged.

The flow policy requires that

$$BAL\ (MAR\ (0)) \leqslant BAL'(b)$$

for the above flow.

In case 1, $BAL'(b) = syshi$ and the inequality is automatically satisfied.

In case 2, we need

$$BAL(MAR(0)) \leqslant PAL(CP);$$

this follows from the invariant (R1).

In case 3, we need

$$BAL(MAR(0)) \leqslant BAL(b).$$

We can assume the flow condition '$B = b$ and not $BAP(b)$'. If $BAP(b)$ is false, block b has been purged; since PURGE sets $BAL(b)$ to syshi, we would expect to have an invariant:

$$(\forall b) \text{ if not } BAP(b) \text{ then } BAL(b) = syshi \tag{RN}$$

This new invariant, which must be checked inductively in the usual way, is sufficient to ensure that the flow policy is satisfied in case 3.

7.8.4 A formal flow violation

The flow to be investigated next results in a violation of flow policy, but it will be possible to rewrite the offending transition rule into an equivalent form that satisfies the policy. The violation found at first is called 'formal' because it arises from the form of the specification, and not from a channel.

GET includes the rule

> if $F = GET$ and $B = b$ and $N = n$
> and $BAP(b)$ and $BAC(b) = 0$ and $BAL(b) = PAL(CP)$
> then $BAC'(MAR(n)) = 0$.

Under the condition given, there is a flow

$$MAR(n) \rightarrow BAC(i)$$

for all i. The flow policy requires that

$$PAL(CP) \leqslant BAL'(i) = BAL(i)$$

since BAL is not changed in GET, and we have the condition $F = GET$. As it stands, there is no reason to believe that the flow policy is satisfied. However, the flow really exists only for those values of i that could be values of $MAR(n)$, and that fact can be used as follows.

Rewrite the transition rule this way:

($\forall i$) if $F = \text{GET}$ and $B = b$ and $N = n$
  and $\text{BAP}(b)$ and $\text{BAC}(b) = 0$ and $\text{BAL}(b) = \text{PAL}(\text{CP})$
  and $\text{BAL}(i) = \text{PAL}(\text{CP})$
  and $i = \text{MAR}(n)$
then $\text{BAC}'(i) = 0$.

This rule is equivalent to the original one because the new condition $\text{BAL}(i) = \text{PAL}(\text{CP})$ is redundant; it is implied by the invariant (R1) under the condition $i = \text{MAR}(n)$.

The troublesome flow becomes

($\forall i$)$F = \text{GET}$ and $\cdots$
  and $\cdots$
  and $\text{BAL}(i) = \text{PAL}(\text{CP})$
  $= \text{MAR}(n) \rightarrow \text{BAC}(i)$,

and this time the flow policy requirement

$\text{PAL}(\text{CP}) \leqslant \text{BAL}(i)$

is immediate from the new condition in the flow.

7.8.5 A real flow violation

In RAISE, we have the transition rule

If $F = \text{RAISE}$ and $B = b$ and not $\text{BAP}(b)$
then $\text{BAP}'(b)$.

One of the flows resulting from this rule is

$F = \text{RAISE}$ and $B = b \Rightarrow \text{BAP}(b) \rightarrow \text{BAP}(b)$.

The flow policy requires that

$\text{BAL}(b) \leqslant \text{BAL}'(b)$.

Let us consider two cases. If $\text{BAP}(b)$ is true, then RAISE has no effect and $\text{BAL}'(b) = \text{BAL}(b)$, and we are done. However, if $\text{BAP}(b)$ is false, then we know that $\text{BAL}(b) = \text{syshi}$, from the new invariant (RN), and also that $\text{BAL}'(b) = \text{PAL}(\text{CP})$, from the effect of RAISE. The flow policy then requires that

$\text{syshi} \leqslant \text{PAL}(\text{CP})$,

which cannot be true (unless all processes are syshi, yielding a degenerate system).

The first appropriate response to a flow violation is to see if it is formal, i.e. if it can be removed by rewriting the function in an equivalent form. If no suitable equivalent form is apparent, as is the case here, the next step is to try a perturbation of the authorization level assignment. In this case we might try a different assignment for the level of BAP (b). In this system, no other assignment for BAP (b) works, essentially because the process that purges a block and the process that activates it could be any two processes at any two levels. No technique other than exhaustive trial and error is presently known to come to this conclusion, although systematic techniques could probably be worked out. When a negative conclusion is suspected, the third type of positive action that can be attempted is to demonstrate a compromise by means of a simulation or an equivalent argument. A compromise will be demonstrated below.

The compromise follows the indirect channel sketched below:

$$B = \text{MEM (MAR (0), 1)} \xrightarrow{\text{PURGE}} \text{BAP} (B) \xrightarrow{\text{SWAP}}$$

$$\text{BAP} (B) \xrightarrow{\text{RAISE}}$$

$$\rightarrow \text{BAP} (B) \xrightarrow{\text{GET}} \text{MAR} (N) \xrightarrow{\text{STORE}} \text{MEM (MAR} (j), k).$$

The complexity of the compromise scenario makes it difficult to give a complete story, but the following sequence of events is roughly sufficient to exploit the compromise.

1. Process 0 requests that some block, say b_0, be purged. Note that the parameter b_0 is taken from MEM (MAR (0), 1), the authorization level of which is PAL (0). The PURGE rule causes BAP (b_0) to be made false (assume BAC $(b_0) = 0$).
2. Process 0 requests SWAP; now process 1 is the current process (CP = 1).
3. Process 1 requests RAISE (b_1). Now, b_1 may or may not be equal to b_0. We may assume that b_1 is chosen from among the same set of possibilities as b_0, and that all of the blocks in that set are active but not accessed, and they all have level PAL (0), before step 1.

   If $b_1 = b_0$, RAISE causes BAP (b_1) to become true.

   If $b_1 \neq b_0$, RAISE has no effect on BAP (b_1) (b_1 assumed active).

4. Process 1 requests GET (b_1, j).

If $b_1 = b_0$, GET causes MAR (j) to become b_1.

If $b_1 \neq b_0$, GET has no effect because BAL $(b_1) =$ PAL $(0) \neq$ PAL (1).

5. Process 1 requests STORE (i, j, k).

If $b_1 = b_0$, STORE causes MEM (b_1, k) to become equal to R (i).

If $b_1 \neq b_0$, STORE causes MEM (MAR $(j), k)$ to become equal to R (i).

We can assume that the original value of MAR (j) was b_2, a block number not in the set of possibilities for b_1. At the conclusion of the above sequence, MEM (b_2, k) has been changed to the value of R (i) if $b_1 \neq b_0$, but it has not been changed if $b_1 = b_0$. Thus, by looking at MEM (b_2, k), one can deduce whether $b_1 = b_0$ or not. But b_0 was the value of MEM (MAR $(0), 1)$, at level PAL (0), while MEM (b_2, k) has the level PAL (1) (since it was accessible to process 1 via MAR (j)). This is a compromise.

A number of details have been left out; in particular, some STORE's are necessary to set the parameters and operations for supervisor calls. It is hoped that the general idea has been conveyed well enough to point the way for, say, a system penetrator.

7.9 Constraints

7.9.1 Drawbacks of information flow analysis

Information flow analysis, as described in the previous sections, is sensitive to the form of a transition rule. A transition rule that apparently causes a flow from one variable to another can sometimes be rewritten into an equivalent form in which no such flow may be deduced, or perhaps it appears only under certain conditions that were not recognized at first.

Information flow analysis is also unable to deal with the nontransitivity of information flow; that is, if information flows from A to B, and then from B to C, it is not always the case that C has received information from A. Information can be lost on the way, as in the following example. Consider the transition rules

$$X' = Y - Z,$$

$$Y' = W,$$

$$Z' = W.$$

There is explicit flow from W to Y and from Y to X. But the simulation below illustrates that X never receives any information from W; in fact, X becomes, and remains, zero after two transitions.

X	x	$y - z$	0	0	$\cdots$
Y	y	w	w_1	w_2	$\cdots$
Z	z	w	w_1	w_2	$\cdots$
W	w	w_1	w_2	w_3	$\cdots$

The fact that information can be lost means that the flow policy, which is based on transition-by-transition flow, may be too pessimistic at times.

The rationale for each information flow rule was that if $X \rightarrow Y$ under whatever conditions were indicated, one could *sometimes* exclude at least one possible value for X prior to the transition, by using knowledge of the value of Y after the transition. This view of the meaning of information flow will be retained, but it is now to be applied exactly.

7.9.2 Deduction and compromise

Information can be compromised if a user with access to some system inputs and outputs can deduce something about an *input* that he is not authorized to observe. Let us assume that the input–output relation of the system, i.e. its design, is public knowledge. The information to be protected is that entered by any user into the inputs authorized to him.

A deduction may require observations over a period of time. A typical deduction is illustrated below:

Time	0	1	2
Observations	$Y = 0$		$Z = 1, Y = 2$
Deduction		$X \neq 1$	

Here three observations, of variables Y and Z, over three times, are assumed to exclude the value 1 for X at a particular time relative to the observations. If X is an input at an authorization level greater than or incomparable to the levels of Y and Z, a deduction like this would be a compromise.

The statement that a variable has a particular value, like '$X = 1$', is called a *condition*. The deduction above can be collapsed into a single line, called a *constraint*:

$$(Y = 0), \quad (X = 1), \quad (Z = 1, Y = 2),$$

where the succession of conditions listed are mutually exclusive in the given system. Thus, any deduction gives rise to a constraint.

A constraint is *prime* if the removal of any condition results in a nonconstraint. If a constraint is prime, it can be used to make a deduction about any of the variables in it at whatever relative times they are mentioned. For, if any condition, like $Z = 1$ above, is removed, the remaining conditions can occur; and when they do, they give rise to the deduction $Z \neq 1$.

We have already seen that any deduction gives rise to a constraint. In fact, a deduction about a variable gives rise to a prime constraint containing that variable. For, we can start with the constraint derived from the deduction, and strike out conditions from it as long as the result is still a constraint. This procedure leaves us with a prime constraint. The condition for the variable about which the deduction is made cannot be removed, because the deduction is possible only when the remaining conditions are all observable, i.e. form a nonconstraint.

7.9.3 More general deductions

Sometimes a combination of inputs may be regarded as a single input. At a logic design level, for example, an input with four possible values $0, 1, 2, 3$, might be represented as a pair of binary variables, using a code like $0 = (0, 0)$, $1 = (0, 1)$, $2 = (1, 0)$, and $3 = (1, 1)$. Under the circumstances, we are interested in deductions about sets of variables.

In some systems, the authorization level of an input can change from state to state. This does not affect our notion of what a deduction is, but it does complicate the determination of which possible deductions are to be considered compromises.

In the example given above, an observation of $X = 1$ followed by $Z = 1$ tells us that $Y = 0$ in the previous state cannot be followed by $Y = 2$ two states later. This does not exclude any one value for

Y in either state, but it excludes a certain pattern of values, and may, in some circumstances, be considered a compromise of Y.

For the present, it is desired only to note that these concerns exist, and that the prime constraints of a system provide the information necessary to address them. The focus on deductions, rather than compromise, was suggested by Furtek [4].

7.9.4   Definitions

To see how the prime constraints of a system may be found, it is first necessary to have a clear idea of what a system is. A system has a finite set of variables, where each variable has its own finite value set; and it has a set of transitions. To display a system concisely, we say that a *system* is a pair

$$(V, T)$$

where V is a *value-set function* and T is the set of *transitions*. The set of *variables* is just the domain of V. For each variable X, the value set of X is $V(X)$.† Let A be the set of variables.

A *state* is a function q on A assigning values to variables. Thus, for each variable X, we have $q(X) \in V(X)$. Let Q be the set of states.

The transition set T is a set of state pairs. Thus,

$$T \subseteq Q \times Q.$$

A *simulation* is a state sequence $(q_1, \ldots, q_n)$ of length at least 2, such that each successive pair of states is a transition: for $i = 1, \ldots, n-1$, $(q_i, q_{i+1}) \in T$.

A constraint was characterized informally above as a sequence of conjunctions of conditions that was not satisfied by any simulation. In what follows, we will be working with state sequences, and it will be convenient to regard a condition as a set of states.

Let X be a variable and i a possible value for X. Then the *condition X_i* is defined by

$$X_i = \{q \in Q \mid q(X) = i\}.$$

A *term* is a nonempty intersection of conditions. We will want to know that the individual conditions can be reconstructed from a term. To check if there was a condition on X, just look at the values assigned to X by the states in the term. If they all assign the same value i to X, the condition X_i participated in the intersection.

† We assume that $V(X)$ has at least two elements.

Otherwise, no condition on X participated in the intersection and all values of X will appear. More formally:

Theorem *Let C be a set of conditions such that $\bigcap C \neq \emptyset$. Then*

$$C = \{X_i \mid \bigcap C \subseteq X_i\}.$$

Proof It is immediate that $C \subseteq \{X_i \mid \bigcap C \subseteq X_i\}$, since C is a set of conditions.

Now, suppose that $\bigcap C \subseteq X_i$. We wish to show that $X_i \in C$. If $X_i \notin C$, either $X_j \in C$ for some $j \neq i$, or no condition on X appears in C. We will arrive at a contradiction in both cases.

If $X_j \in C$ for $j \neq i$, produce $q \in \bigcap C$ and note that $q \in X_j$, so $q(X) = j \neq i$ and $q \notin X_i$. Consequently $\bigcap C \not\subseteq X_i$, contradiction.

If no condition on X appears in C, again choose $q \in \bigcap C$ and let

$$q'(Y) = \begin{cases} j \neq i & \text{if} \quad Y = X, \\ q(Y) & \text{if} \quad Y \neq X. \end{cases}$$

For each condition $Y_k \in C$, $q'(Y) = q(Y) = k$, so $q' \in \bigcap C$. But $q'(X) = j \neq i$, so $q' \notin X_i$ and $\bigcap C \not\subseteq X_i$, contradiction. This completes the proof. ∎

With the previous theorem in hand, it makes sense to define $\bar{t}$ for a term t as the set of conditions such that $\bigcap \bar{t} = t$.

A *constraint* is a Cartesian product of terms that contains no simulations. A constraint is *prime* if it is maximal. We should check that this definition of primeness is the same as the informal one given earlier; that is, if t is any term of a prime constraint p, then the result of replacing it by $\bigcap t'$, where t' is a proper subset of $\bar{t}$, should be a nonconstraint. But this is easy to show, because, if $t' \subset \bar{t}$, then $t = \bigcap \bar{t} \subset \bigcap t'$. Thus, if the result of replacing t by $\bigcap t'$ is a constraint p', then p was not maximal, since $p \subset p'$. Conversely, if p is not maximal, and p' is a constraint such that $p \subset p'$, there is at least one term t of p and a corresponding term t' of p' such that $t \subset t'$. Hence $\bar{t}' \subset \bar{t}$, so that p' may be described as the result of removing the conditions in $\bar{t} - \bar{t}'$ from term t of p.

7.9.5 Covers

The first step in finding the prime constraints of a system is to find a set of constraints that determine the transition set. A set R of two-place constraints, i.e. constraints of the form $a \times b$, is a *cover* if

$$\cup R = (Q \times Q) - T.$$

A cover can always be constructed from T. Note that, for any state q, $\{q\}$ is a term, since

$$\{q\} = \bigcap_{X \in A} X_{q(X)}.$$

Thus, a state pair $(q, q') \in (Q \times Q) - T$ is the element of a constraint $\{q\} \times \{q'\}$. It follows that

$$\{\{q\} \times \{q'\} \mid (q, q') \in (Q \times Q) - T\}$$

is a cover.

Covers can also be found from transition rules. For example, the next-state equation $X' = Y$ implies the constraints

$$Y_i \times X_j \qquad (i \neq j).$$

It is reasonable to try to mechanize the process of constructing a cover from a nonprocedural transition specification; the details depend on the syntax permitted for transition rules.

7.9.6 Consensus

Longer constraints can be constructed from two-place constraints by an operation called consensus. Suppose that we have the constraints $Y_0 \times X_1$ and $X_0 \times X_1$. Let X be binary; i.e. $V(X) = \{0, 1\}$. Then $Y_0 \times Q \times X_1$ is a constraint. For, suppose (q_0, q_1, q_2) is a state sequence such that $q_0 \in Y_0$ and $q_2 \in X_1$. Since X is binary, we must have either $q_1 \in X_0$ or $q_1 \in X_1$. If $q_1 \in X_1$ then $(q_0, q_1) \in Y_0 \times X_1$ and is not a simulation. If $q_1 \in X_0$ then $(q_1, q_2) \in X_0 \times X_1$ and is not a simulation. In either case (q_0, q_1, q_2) is not a simulation.

Consensus is based on the observation that

$$a(b \cup c)d \subseteq ab \cup cd,$$

where concatenation denotes set intersection. In this situation we say that $a(b \cup c)d$ is the consensus of the operands ab and cd.

Consensus can be extended to cartesian products as suggested below:

$$X_1 \times X_0 Y_1 \times Z_1 Y_1$$
$$Z_0 Y_0 \times Z_1 X_0$$
$$\overline{}$$
$$X_1 \times X_0 Z_0 (Y_1 \cup Y_0) \times Z_1 X_0 Y_1$$

Intersections are indicated by juxtaposition.

Because the consensus of constraints is a subset of the union of the operands, the consensus of constraints contains no simulations. The consensus will be a constraint, as we have defined them, only when it turns out to be a Cartesian product of terms. In the example above, if Y is binary, then $Y_1 \cup Y_0 = Q$ and the consensus is the constraint $X_1 \times X_0 Z_0 \times Z_1 X_0 Y_1$.

It can be shown that every prime constraint can be generated by starting with a cover and performing consensus. This result is beyond the scope of these notes. However, the reader acquainted with switching theory may be interested in the fact that, if all variables in the system are binary, it follows directly from an old result about prime implicants, in McCluskey [10].

7.9.7 An infinity of prime constraints

Finite systems, even very small systems, can have an infinite number of prime constraints. Consider the system the cover of which is $\{X_0 \times X_1\}$, where X is binary. By successive consensus,

$$X_0 \times X_1$$
$$\qquad X_0 \times X_1$$
$$\overline{\qquad\qquad\qquad}$$
$$X_0 \times Q \times X_1$$
$$\qquad\qquad X_0 \times X_1$$
$$\overline{\qquad\qquad\qquad}$$
$$X_0 \times Q \times Q \times X_1$$
$$\cdots$$

we can generate arbitrarily long constraints of the form

$$X_0 \times Q \times \cdots \times Q \times X_1,$$

all of which are prime. All of these prime constraints, however, can be expressed by the graph in Figure 7.7, since every path from $\longrightarrow\bigcirc$ to $\circledcirc$ has a label sequence $(X_0, Q, \cdots, Q, X_1)$ which

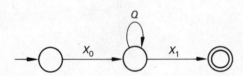

Fig. 7.7

corresponds in an obvious way to a prime constraint. We will prove below that for every system, there is a graph that generates all of its prime constraints.

7.9.8 The prime constraint graph theorem

Some technical lemmas are needed in connection with the notion of forward and backward images of a Cartesian product of state sets. Let S be the set of simulations of the system.

Definition $p^+ = \{q \mid (\exists s \in p)(s, q) \in S\}$ *is the forward image of* p. $p^- = \{q \mid (\exists s \in p)(q, s) \in S\}$ *is the backward image of* p.

Here, we regard $(\cdot, \cdot)$ as an operation that can combine a state sequence and a state into a longer state sequence.

Image lemma (1) $(p \times t)^+ = (p^+ t)^+$, (2) $(t \times p)^- = (tp^-)^-$, *where* $t \subseteq Q$.

Proof We prove $(p \times t)^+ \subseteq (p^+ t)^+$ and leave the rest for the reader. Let $q \in (p \times t)^+$. Then there exist $s \in p$ and $q' \in t$ such that $(s, q', q) \in S$. Since $(s, q') \in S$, $q' \in p^+ t$. Since $(q', q) \in S$, $q \in (p^+ t)^+$. ∎

Exclusion lemma *Let* p *and* p' *be Cartesian products of terms, and let* t *be a term. Then* $p \times t \times p'$ *is a constraint if and only if* $t \subseteq Q - p^+ p'^-$.

Proof If: Suppose $t \subseteq Q - p^+ p'^-$, and let $s \in p$, $q \in t$, and $s' \in p'$. It suffices to show that (s, q, s') is not a simulation. Since $q \in t$, we must have either $q \notin p^+$ or $q \notin p^-$. By symmetry, assume $q \notin p^+$. Then (s, q) is not a simulation, and (s, q, s') cannot be a simulation.

Only if: By contraposition. Let $q \in tp^+ p'^-$. Since $q \in p^+$, there exists $s \in p$ such that (s, q) is a simulation. Since $q \in p'^-$, there exists $s' \in p'$ such that (q, s') is a simulation. But then (s, q, s') is a simulation, and $p \times t \times p'$ is not a constraint. ∎

The proofs to follow are made smoother by using a convention about null products. We introduce a symbol e such that $e \times t = t \times e = t$. The symbol e may be used where a Cartesian product is expected. If we define

$$e^+ = Q = e^-,$$

the image lemma and the exclusion lemma remain true when e is used in place of p or p'. Also, let $t_1 \times \cdots \times t_n = e$ when $n = 0$.

The *prime constraint graph* has *nodes* and *arcs*. The nodes are pairs (u, v) of state sets. There is an arc labeled with a term t from a node (u, v) to a node (u', v'), written

$$t : (u, v) \rightarrow (u', v'),$$

if and only if these three properties are satisfied:

A1. $v' = (vt)^+$;
A2. $u = (tu')^-$;
A3. t is maximal among terms such that $t \subseteq Q - vu'$.

Theorem (F. C. Furtek) $t_1 \times \cdots \times t_n$ *is a prime constraint if and only if there exist* (u_i, v_i) *for* $i = 0, \ldots, n$, *such that*

1. $(u_0, v_0) = (\emptyset, Q)$,
2. $(u_n, v_n) = (Q, \emptyset)$,
3. $t_i : (u_{i-1}, v_{i-1}) \rightarrow (u_i, v_1)$ for $i = 1, \ldots, n$.

Proof The general idea of the proof is that the local properties A1 and A2 for a path are equivalent to the global properties $v_i = (t_1 \times \cdots \times t_i)^+$ and $u_i = (t_{i+1} \times \cdots \times t_n)^-$. With this fact plus the exclusion lemma, (A3) is then seen to be the local equivalent of the global property that the path defines a prime constraint.

Only if. Assume that $t_1 \times \cdots \times t_n$ is a prime constraint. For $i = 0, \ldots, n$, let

$$v_i = (t_1 \times \cdots \times t_i)^+,$$

where $v_0 = e^+ = Q$. Note that $v_n = (t_1 \times \cdots \times t_n)^+ = \emptyset$ since $t_1 \times \cdots \times t_n$ is a constraint.

Symmetrically, let

$$u_i = (t_{i+1} \times \cdots \times t_n)^-,$$

where $u_n = e^- = Q$. Note that $u_0 = (t_1 \times \cdots \times t_n)^- = \emptyset$.

With this definition of (u_i, v_i), we wish to show that $t_i : (u_{i-1}, v_{i-1}) \rightarrow (u_i, v_i)$. To do so, we must check A1–A3. Properties A1 and A2 are immediate from the image lemma. As for A3, the fact that $t_i \subseteq Q - v_{i-1} u_i$ is immediate from the exclusion lemma. If t_i were not maximal, we could find a term t such that $t_i \subset t \subseteq Q - v_{i-1} u_i$. By the exclusion lemma, the result of replacing t_i by t in $t_1 \times \cdots \times t_n$ would be a larger constraint, contradicting primeness of $t_1 \times \cdots \times t_n$.

If. Assume that $t_i : (u_{i-1}, v_{i-1}) \rightarrow (u_i, v_i)$ for $i = 1, \ldots, n$, where $(u_0, v_0) = (\emptyset, Q)$ and $(u_n, v_n) = (Q, \emptyset)$. We will show, first, that $v_i = (t_1 \times \cdots \times t_i)^+$ by induction on i.

For $i = 1$, we must show that $v_1 = t_1^+$. But, by A1, $v_1 = (v_0 t_1)^+$, and $v_0 = Q$ by hypothesis.

Now, assume that $v_{i-1} = (t_1 \times \cdots \times t_{i-1})^+$. By A1,

$$v_i = (v_{i-1} t_i)^+ = ((t_1 \times \cdots \times t_{i-1})^+ t_i)^+$$

$$= (t_1 \times \cdots \times t_i)^+$$

by the image lemma.

The proof that $u_i = (t_{i+1} \times \cdots \times t_n)^-$ is similar, and is omitted.

The fact that $t_1 \times \cdots \times t_n$ is a constraint now follows from A3 and the exclusion lemma. It is prime, i.e. maximal, because, if $t_1' \times \cdots \times t_n'$ is a larger constraint, there is at least one index i such that $t_i \subset t_i'$, and then the result of replacing t_i by t_i' in $t_1 \times \cdots \times t_n$ will be a constraint (it is included in $t_1' \times \cdots \times t_n'$). Hence, by the exclusion lemma, $t_i' \subseteq Q - v_{i-1} u_i$, contradicting maximality of t_i for this property. ∎

7.9.9 The construction of the prime constraint graph

Since a system has only a finite number of variables and a finite number of values per variable, it can have only a finite number of states. It follows that the prime constraint graph can have only a finite number of nodes and arcs.

For the purpose of analyzing the deductions possible in a system, it is not necessary to construct the whole prime constraint graph. One needs only those arcs belonging to paths from $(\emptyset, Q)$ to $(Q, \emptyset)$, and sometimes only a portion of those are necessary. Some work is in progress to develop an algorithm for building up the graph in such a way that few unnecessary arcs are constructed. Its details are beyond the scope of these notes, but the general approach can be described briefly [5].

Each two-place constraint in a cover produces a two-arc path. The constraint $a \times b$ produces the path

$$(\emptyset, Q) \xrightarrow{a} (Q - a, Q - b) \xrightarrow{b} (Q, \emptyset).$$

Note that $a = (Q - (Q(Q - a))$, so (A3) is satisfied. The fact that $a \times b$ is a constraint means that $a^+ b = 0$, so $Qa^+ = a^+ \subseteq Q - b$. Thus, the arcs almost satisfy A1 and, by symmetry, A2. (Why not exactly?) The algorithm starts out with these almost-right paths, and generates new paths by consensus, using a procedure sufficient to generate all prime constraints, throwing away the nonprime ones. By constructing and remembering the nodes associated with each new arc, the algorithm can recognize loops in the graph, and thus avoid infinite regressions for sets of constraints like $X_0 \times Q \times \cdots \times Q \times X_1$.

The set of relevant arcs can still be too large to construct this way if some variables have a large value set. The transition rule $X' = Y$, for example, generates prime constraints

$$Y_i \times X_j \qquad (i \neq j);$$

and if X and Y each have N values, we have $N(N-1)$ constraints and at least that many arcs. Since all the constraints can be presented in one line, however, it is not unreasonable to expect that the prime constraint graph can be similarly encoded. In fact, the graph schema in Figure 7.8 would do.

Finding an algorithm to generate a prime constraint graph schema from a constraint schema is still a research problem, but there are cases where the previous approach can be modified to work with certain kinds of schemas.

If $u \subseteq V(X)$ and $v \subseteq V(Y)$, let us interpret the constraint schema

$$Y_v \times X_u$$

as the set of $Y_i \times X_j$ such that $i \in v$ and $j \in u$. If $Y_i \times X_j$ is a constraint for all $i \neq j$, then

$$Y_u \times X_{V(X)-u}$$

is a set of constraints for all $u \subseteq V(Y)$. Furthermore, if $X_u \times X_{V(X)-u}$ also happens to be a constraint schema for all $u \subset V(X)$, then we can perform a consensus-like operation

$$
\begin{array}{ll}
Y_u \times X_{V(X)-u} & \\
X_u & \times X_{V(X)-u} \\
\hline
Y_u \times Q & \times X_{V(X)-u}
\end{array}
$$

which results in a constraint schema valid for all $u \subseteq V(Y)$.

Fig. 7.8

Symbolically, we are doing the same thing as if Y were a binary variable with value set $\{u, V(Y)-u\}$, and X a binary variable with the value set $\{u, V(X)-u\}$. This leads to the conjecture that, for some systems and covers, at least a partial valid graph schema can be constructed by reinterpreting the arcs of a graph produced under the assumption that certain variables are binary, when in fact they may have large, or even infinite, value sets.

7.9.10 Consequences for flow analysis

Both explicit and implicit flows can be recognized as cases of the same situation, in this context. If $X' = Y$, we have the constraints

$$Y_i \times X_j \qquad (i \neq j)$$

and if we have a transition rule

if $Y = 0$ then $X' = 0$,

we have the constraints

$$Y_0 \times X_j \qquad (j \neq 0).$$

In both cases, there is flow from the variable on the left of a two-place constraint to the variable on the right.

Conditional flow, as in

if $Y = 0$ then $X' = Z$,

is also evident from the two-place constraints

$$Y_0 Z_i \times X_j \qquad (i \neq j).$$

By taking any variable on the left as the 'from' variable, the remaining conditions are flow conditions. Thus, we have the conditional flows

$$Y_0 \Rightarrow Z \rightarrow X,$$
$$Z_i \Rightarrow Y \rightarrow X \qquad (\text{all } i).$$

The second group of flows is really unconditional, since Z always has some value.

It has been shown (in [12]) that the flow policy is sufficient to prevent compromise via any deduction, if the flows are identified from a covering set of two-place constraints as suggested above, under the condition that authorization levels are constant. It is undoubtedly true, but it has not yet been proved, that the result still holds when authorization levels are state-dependent.

References

1 Denning, D. Secure information flow in computer systems, Ph.D. Thesis, Purdue University, 1975.

2 Denning, D. A lattice model of secure information flow, *Comm. ACM*, **19,** 236–242, 1976.

3 DeMillo, R. A., Dobkin, D. P., Jones, A. K., and Lipton, R. J. (eds) *Foundations of Secure Computation*, Academic Press, New York, 1978.

4 Furtek, F. C. Constraints and Compromise, in *Foundations of Secure Computation*, (R. A. DeMillo *et al.*, eds), Academic Press, New York, 1978, pp. 189–204.

5 Furtek, F. C. A validation technique for computer security based on the theory of constraints, MITRE Corporation ESD-TR-78-182, Dec. 1978.

6 Graham, R. M. and Denning, P. J. Protection – principles and practice, *SJCC*, **40,** 417–429, 1972.

7 Harrison, M. A., Ruzzo, W. L., and Ullman, J. D. Protection in operating systems, *Comm. ACM*, **19,** 461–471, 1976.

8 Lampson, B. W. Protection, in *Proceedings of the 5th Annual Conference on Information Science and Systems*, Princeton, March 1971, 437–443.

9 Lampson, B. W. A note on the confinement problem, *Comm. ACM*, **16,** 613–615, 1973.

10 McCluskey, E. J. *Introduction to the Theory of Switching Circuits*, McGraw-Hill, New York, 1965, p. 68ff.

11 Millen, J. K. Security kernel validation in practice, *Comm. ACM*, **19,** 243–250, 1976.

12 Millen, J. K. Constraints and multilevel security, in *Foundations of Secure Computation* (R. A. DeMillo *et al.*, eds), Academic Press, New York, 1978, pp. 205–222.

13 Neumann, P. G., Feiertag, R. J., Levitt, K. N., and Robinson, L. Software development and proofs of multi-level security, in *Proceedings of the 2nd International Conference on Software Engineering*, IEEE Publications, New York, 1976.

14 Parnas, D. L. A technique for software module specification with examples, *Comm. ACM*, **15,** 330–336, 1972.

15 Rivest, R., Shamir, A., and Adleman, L. A method for obtaining digital signatures and public-key crypto systems, *Comm. ACM*, **21,** 120–126, 1978.

16 Weissman, C. Security controls in the ADEPT-50 time-sharing system, *Proc. AFIPS 1969 FJCC*, 119–133.

Appendix: Solution of elevator problem

Variables

FLOOR   1 to N
DOOR   o (open), c (closed)
DIR   u (up), d (down), o (off)
ELB (f) elevator inside buttons, true/false ⎫
WBU (f) wall buttons, 'up' request, true/false   ⎬ inputs
WBD (f) wall buttons, 'down' request, true/false ⎭

Timing

```
Inputs    Examine
change    inputs
  ↓    ↓    ↓  ⌒Transition
                  ↓
├──────────┤├──────────┤
   FLOOR──→ FLOOR'──→
   DOOR──→  DOOR'──→
   DIR ───→ DIR'────→
```

Changes in variables (informal analysis)

DOOR: o → c   always
        c → o   if valid request for FLOOR', or if DIR = d
                and Floor' = 1
FLOOR: +1   if DOOR = c and DIR = u
        −1   if DOOR = c and DIR = d
DIR: u → o   if no request for floor > FLOOR'
        d → o   if FLOOR' = 1
        o → u   if request for floor > FLOOR
        o → d   if no request for floor > FLOOR and
                FLOOR ≠ 1.

Typical simulation

FLOOR	1	1	2	3	3	4	4	3	2	1	1	1
DOOR	c	c	c	o	c	o	c	c	c	o	c	c
DIR	o	u	u	o	u	o	d	d	d	o	o	o
REQ	WU3	WU3	WU3	EL4	EL4	—	—	—	—	—	—	WU1

FLOOR	1	1	2	3	3	2	2	1
DOOR	o	c	c	o	c	o	c	o
DIR	o	u	u	o	d	d	d	o
REQ	EL3	EL3	EL3	WD2	WD2	EL1	EL1	—
		WD2	WD2					

Abbreviation

URQ (*f*) for (∃g > *f*)(ELB (g) or WBU (g) or WBD (g)).

Specification

ELEVATOR: if DOOR = o then DOOR′ = c
　　　　　　else if ELB (FLOOR)′ or
　　　　　　　　　　(DIR = d and WBD (FLOOR′)) or
　　　　　　　　　　(DIR = u and WBU (FLOOR′)) or
　　　　　　　　　　(DIR = d and FLOOR′ = 1)
　　　　　　then DOOR′ = o
　　　　if DOOR = c
　　　　then if DIR = u then FLOOR′ − FLOOR + 1
　　　　else if DIR = d then FLOOR′ = FLOOR − 1
　　　　if DIR = u and not URQ (FLOOR′) then DIR′ = o
　　　　if DIR = d and FLOOR′ = 1 then DIR′ = o
　　　　if DIR = o then if URQ (FLOOR) then DIR′ = u
　　　　　　　　　　　else if FLOOR ≠ 1 then DIR′ = d.